LEARNING TARGETS
for Numeracy

Shape, Space and Measures

Key Stage 2

David Clemson
Wendy Clemson

Stanley Thornes (Publishers) Ltd

First published in 1998 by
Stanley Thornes Publishers Ltd
Ellenborough House
Wellington Street
Cheltenham GL50 1YW

00 01 02 / 10 9 8 7 6 5 4 3 2

A catalogue record for this book is available from the British Library.

ISBN 0-7487-3594-1

Printed and bound in Great Britain by Redwood Books, Trowbridge, Wiltshire.

CONTENTS

Welcome to LEARNING TARGETS

Learning Targets is a series of practical teacher's resource books written to help you to plan and deliver well-structured, professional lessons in line with all the relevant curriculum documents.

Each Learning Target book provides exceptionally clear lesson plans that cover the whole of its stated curriculum plus a large bank of carefully structured copymasters. Links to the key curriculum documents are provided throughout to enable you to plan effectively.

The Learning Targets series has been written in response to the challenge confronting teachers not just to come up with teaching ideas that cover the curriculum but to ensure that they deliver high quality lessons every lesson with the emphasis on raising standards of pupil achievement.

The recent thinking from OFSTED, and the National Literacy and Numeracy Strategies on the key factors in effective teaching has been built into the structure of Learning Targets. These might be briefly summarised as follows:

- that effective teaching is active teaching directed to very clear objectives
- that good lessons are delivered with pace, rigour and purpose
- that good teaching requires a range of strategies – including interactive whole class sessions
- that ongoing formative assessment is essential to plan children's learning
- that differentiation is necessary but that it must be realistic.

The emphasis in Learning Targets is on absolute clarity. We have written and designed the books to enable you to access and deliver effective lessons as easily as possible, with the following aims:

- to plan and deliver rigorous, well-structured lessons
- to set explicit targets for achievement in every lesson that you teach
- to make the children aware of what they are going to learn
- to put the emphasis on direct, active teaching every time
- to make effective use of time and resources
- to employ the full range of recommended strategies whole-class, group and individual work
- to differentiate for ability groups realistically
- to use ongoing formative assessment to plan your next step
- to have ready access to usable pupil copymasters to support your teaching.

The page opposite provides an at-a-glance guide to the key features of the Learning Targets lessons and explains how they will enable you deliver effective lessons. The key to symbols on the lesson plans is set out here. ➔

How to deliver structured lessons with pace, rigour and purpose

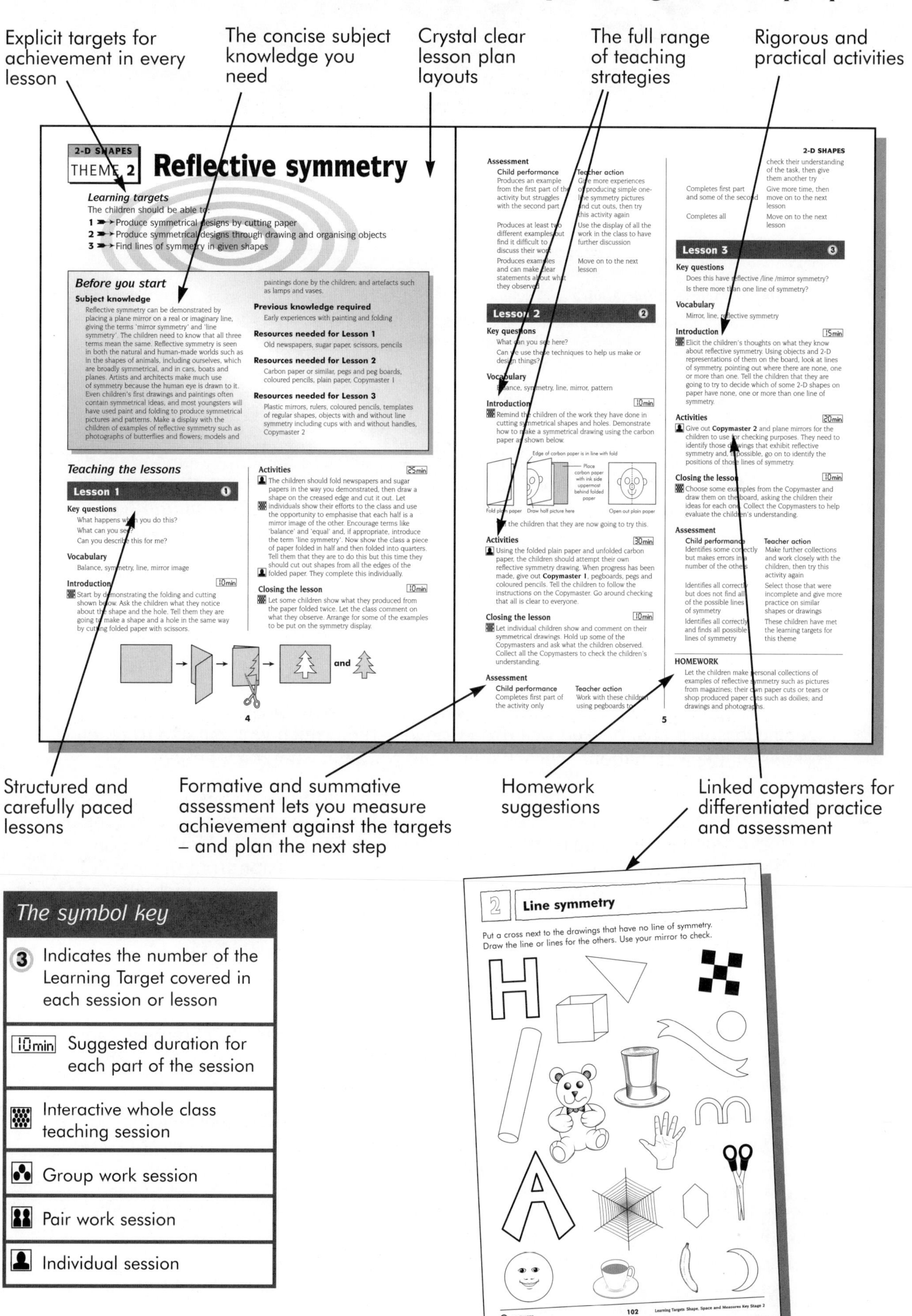

2-D SHAPES
THEME 2

Reflective symmetry

Learning targets

The children should be able to:

1 Produce symmetrical designs by cutting paper
2 Produce symmetrical designs through drawing and organising objects
3 Find lines of symmetry in given shapes

Before you start

Subject knowledge

Reflective symmetry can be demonstrated by placing a plane mirror on a real or imaginary line, giving the terms 'mirror symmetry' and 'line symmetry'. The children need to know that all three terms mean the same. Reflective symmetry is seen in both the natural and human-made worlds such as in the shapes of animals, including ourselves, which are broadly symmetrical, and in cars, boats and planes. Artists and architects make much use of symmetry because the human eye is drawn to it. Even children's first drawings and paintings often contain symmetrical ideas, and most youngsters will have used paint and folding to produce symmetrical pictures and patterns. Make a display with the children of examples of reflective symmetry such as photographs of butterflies and flowers; models and paintings done by the children; and artefacts such as lamps and vases.

Previous knowledge required

Early experiences with painting and folding

Resources needed for Lesson 1

Old newspapers, sugar paper, scissors, pencils

Resources needed for Lesson 2

Carbon paper or similar, pegs and peg boards, coloured pencils, plain paper, Copymaster 1

Resources needed for Lesson 3

Plastic mirrors, rulers, coloured pencils, templates of regular shapes, objects with and without line symmetry including cups with and without handles, Copymaster 2

Teaching the lessons

Lesson 1

Key questions
What happens when you do this?
What can you see?
Can you describe this for me?

Vocabulary
Balance, symmetry, line, mirror image

Introduction 10min
Start by demonstrating the folding and cutting shown below. Ask the children what they notice about the shape and the hole. Tell them they are going to make a shape and a hole in the same way by cutting folded paper with scissors.

Activities 25min
The children should fold newspapers and sugar papers in the way you demonstrated, then draw a shape on the creased edge and cut it out. Let individuals show their efforts to the class and use the opportunity to emphasise that each half is a mirror image of the other. Encourage terms like 'balance' and 'equal' and, if appropriate, introduce the term 'line symmetry'. Now show the class a piece of paper folded in half and then folded into quarters. Tell them that they are to do this but this time they should cut out shapes from all the edges of the folded paper. They complete this individually.

Closing the lesson 10min
Let some children show what they produced from the paper folded twice. Let the class comment on what they observe. Arrange for some of the examples to be put on the symmetry display.

and

4

Assessment

Child performance	Teacher action
Produces an example from the first part of the activity but struggles with the second part	Give more experiences of producing simple one-line symmetry pictures and cut outs, then try this activity again
Produces at least two different examples but find it difficult to discuss their work	Use the display of all the work in the class to have further discussion
Produces examples and can make clear statements about what they observed	Move on to the next lesson

Lesson 2

Key questions
What can you see here?
Can we use these techniques to help us make or design things?

Vocabulary
Balance, symmetry, line, mirror, pattern

Introduction 10min
Remind the children of the work they have done in cutting symmetrical shapes and holes. Demonstrate how to make a symmetrical drawing using the carbon paper as shown below.

Edge of carbon paper is in line with fold
Place carbon paper with ink side uppermost behind folded paper
Fold plain paper Draw half picture here Open out plain paper

Tell the children that they are now going to try this.

Activities 30min
Using the folded plain paper and unfolded carbon paper, the children should attempt their own reflective symmetry drawing. When progress has been made, give out **Copymaster 1**, pegboards, pegs and coloured pencils. Tell the children to follow the instructions on the Copymaster. Go around checking that all is clear to everyone.

Closing the lesson 10min
Let individual children show and comment on their symmetrical drawings. Hold up some of the Copymasters and ask what the children observed. Collect all the Copymasters to check the children's understanding.

Assessment

Child performance	Teacher action
Completes first part of the activity only	Work with these children using pegboards to check their understanding of the task, then give them another try
Completes first part and some of the second	Give more time, then move on to the next lesson
Completes all	Move on to the next lesson

2-D SHAPES

Lesson 3

Key questions
Does this have reflective /line /mirror symmetry?
Is there more than one line of symmetry?

Vocabulary
Mirror, line, reflective symmetry

Introduction 15min
Elicit the children's thoughts on what they know about reflective symmetry. Using objects and 2-D representations of them on the board, look at lines of symmetry, pointing out where there are none, one or more than one. Tell the children that they are going to try to decide which of some 2-D shapes on paper have none, one or more than one line of symmetry.

Activities 20min
Give out **Copymaster 2** and plane mirrors for the children to use for checking purposes. They need to identify those drawings that exhibit reflective symmetry and, if possible, go on to identify the positions of those lines of symmetry.

Closing the lesson 10min
Choose some examples from the Copymaster and draw them on the board, asking the children their ideas for each one. Collect the Copymasters to help evaluate the children's understanding.

Assessment

Child performance	Teacher action
Identifies some correctly but makes errors in a number of the others	Make further collections and work closely with the children, then try this activity again
Identifies all correctly but does not find all of the possible lines of symmetry	Select those that were incomplete and give more practice on similar shapes or drawings
Identifies all correctly and finds all possible lines of symmetry	These children have met the learning targets for this theme

HOMEWORK

Let the children make personal collections of examples of reflective symmetry such as pictures from magazines; their own paper cuts or tears or shop produced paper cuts such as doilies; and drawings and photographs.

5

2 **Line symmetry**

Put a cross next to the drawings that have no line of symmetry. Draw the line or lines for the others. Use your mirror to check.

2-D SHAPES 102 Learning Targets Shape, Space and Measures Key Stage 2

The symbol key

3	Indicates the number of the Learning Target covered in each session or lesson
10min	Suggested duration for each part of the session
(interactive icon)	Interactive whole class teaching session
(group icon)	Group work session
(pair icon)	Pair work session
(individual icon)	Individual session

INTRODUCTION

Learning Targets: Shape, Space and Measures Key Stage 2 includes lessons on all of the main ideas in shape, space and measures for children aged 7–11 (Years 3–6/P4–7). Together with its companion book *Learning Targets: Number Key Stage* 2, it offers support for the teaching of all the key features of mathematics suitable for children of this age group. In planning and writing this book the authors have not only sought to meet the requirements of the National Curriculum (England and Wales), and Curriculum and Assessment in Scotland: National Guidelines: Mathematics 5–14, but have also borne in mind the fact that there are currently demands for teachers to use direct and whole class teaching as a regular part of their teaching repertoire, and that teachers need to be aware of and address the imperatives highlighted in the National Numeracy Project.

This book and its companion volume do not, of course, constitute a complete scheme. They cannot provide you with all the resources needed for every mathematics session. As they cover all of the main ideas in mathematics work, however, these books are a backbone resource for mathematics teaching. There are some lessons at each level of work appropriate for the Key Stages. These texts can, therefore, be seen as an extremely valuable and effective aid to the delivery of directly taught lessons. They contain a series of well-structured, detailed and specific lesson plans, backed by linked Copymasters, which you can use to teach lessons in line with national curricula and the National Numeracy Project.

As each of the four mathematics books in the series addresses work at a whole Key Stage (either Years R–2/P1–3 or Years 3–6/P4–7), it is necessary to select lessons at the appropriate level. To help you do this, the books are organised into sections which each contain a number of themes. There is a progression from the start of each section to its end. Within each theme there are three lessons which also offer a progression, and the lessons should, therefore, be taught in order.

How this book is organised

Sections

This book is organised into seven sections, being: 2-D Shapes; 3-D Shapes; Angles and Co-ordinates; Length, Area and Perimeter; Capacity and Volume; Mass and Weight; and Time.

At the start of each section you will find a short overview of the mathematics ideas which we see as important in offering the children appropriate learning opportunities. A section is divided into a number of themes, each with its own set of clear learning targets. There is a progression within each section. To conclude each section there is a set of extension ideas. These can be used in any mathematics session where the key ideas related to this section are being worked on. They may be incorporated within a programme of lessons, used in sessions that immediately follow learning target lessons, used in sessions designated as mathematical investigation sessions or used as additional homework activities.

Themes

The order of the themes within each section has been arranged to offer progression. Thus, in the first section, 2-D Shapes, there are six themes. The first theme, 'Name, make and sort 2-D shapes', may be seen as more appropriate for children at an earlier stage in their mathematical education than the next theme, 'Reflective symmetry'. Thus, 'Name, make and sort 2-D shapes' might be the theme tackled in Year 3/P4, while the theme on reflective symmetry may form part of the course for a Year 4/P5 class of children. The themes which follow place an increasing demand on children's mathematical skills and knowledge, and might therefore be taught to children in successive years.

Within each theme, the lessons are also sequenced to provide more demand as the children move on from the first, to second and then third. The learning targets state explicitly what the children should know or be able to do by the end of each lesson. The learning targets provide you with a clear set of assessable objectives.

The themes in a section altogether form an overall set of lesson plans for a mathematics topic. The themes are free-standing. It is also possible for you to choose lessons from within a theme as free-standing lessons. At the end of each lesson there are descriptions of children's performance and suggested teacher actions. At the end of each theme there are suggestions for homework activities.

The lesson plans with each theme are very specific and detailed in their teaching suggestions, written to allow you to undertake direct teaching to clear objectives. Some lessons have accompanying Copymasters which are completely integrated into the teaching activities.

National curricula and numeracy

The lessons in this book have been written to meet the time demands of the 'numeracy hour' and the mathematical ideas match the required range of work in national curricula and those seen as important in the National Numeracy Project.

The need to revisit mathematics topics as children progress through Key Stage 2 (Year 3–6/P4–7) has meant that the book is organised into sections which, as already indicated, can be used flexibly across the whole age range. The lessons are written so that the teacher can differentiate between children's learning by the outcomes of their work.

Each theme can provide the material for a string of numeracy hours. Every teacher will interpret the demands of the numeracy hour in the light of their own situation and the structure of the book allows for this. To plan your number work it is suggested that you consult the appropriate section and theme title to locate the lesson you want when you wish to offer a direct teaching session to your class.

The learning targets for each theme have been mapped against the Programme of Study in the National Curriculum for England and Wales, Levels 3–5 and areas in the National Numeracy Project Recommendations. This chart is presented on pages viii–ix.

The learning targets for each theme have also been mapped against the statements in the attainment targets in Curriculum and Assessment in Scotland: National Guidelines: Mathematics 5–14 at Levels B, C and D. This chart is presented on page x. Teachers in Scotland can therefore be confident that the lessons in this book meet the requirements to which they are working.

Curriculum planners
National Numeracy Project Recommendations

Theme No.	Problems involving measures	Data handling/ Probability	Vocabulary	3-D shape	2-D shape	Reflective symmetry (line and plane)	Position and direction	Rotation, angle, point symmetry								
1			●		●											
2						●										
3			●		●											
4			●		●											
5			●		●											
6			●		●											
7			●	●												
8			●	●												
9			●	●												
10			●	●												
11								●								
12							●									
13								●								
14								●								
15							●	●								
16					●		●	●								
17							●	●								
18	●															
19	●															
20	●				●											
21	●			●	●											
22	●				●											
23	●															
24	●	●														
25	●															
26	●			●												
27	●	●		●												
28	●			●												
29	●			●												
30	●	●														
31	●	●														
32	●	●														
33	●	●														
34	●	●														
35	●	●														
36	●	●														

Curriculum planners
Programmes of study in the National Curriculum (England and Wales)

Shape, Space and Measures

Theme No.	2a	2b	2c	3a	3b	3c	4a	4b	4c
1	●	●	●	●					
2	●		●						
3	●	●							
4	●	●	●	●					
5	●	●	●	●					
6	●	●	●	●					
7		●							
8		●							
9		●							
10		●	●						
11	●					●			
12	●				●				
13	●					●			
14	●	●				●			
15					●				
16	●		●	●					
17	●					●		●	
18							●	●	
19							●	●	
20							●		●
21	●	●							
22									●
23				●		●	●		
24							●	●	
25	●							●	
26		●					●		●
27							●	●	●
28							●		
29							●	●	
30							●	●	
31							●	●	
32							●		
33							●	●	
34							●		
35							●	●	
36							●		

Handling Data

Theme No.	2a	2b	2c	2d	3a	3b	3c
1							
2							
3							
4							
5							
6							
7							
8							
9							
10							
11							
12							
13							
14							
15							
16							
17							
18							
19							
20							
21							
22							
23							
24		●					
25							
26							
27		●		●			
28							
29							
30		●					
31		●	●				
32		●		●			
33	●	●		●			
34	●						
35							
36	●	●		●			

Curriculum planners

Scottish guidelines planner

LEVEL B	LEVEL C	LEVEL D
INFORMATION HANDLING ATTAINMENT TARGET		
Organise		
	Use a database Theme 32	Use diagrams and tables Theme 34
Display		
Use labels, charts or diagrams Theme 24	Construct table or chart Theme 24 Construct a bar graph with multiple units Theme 32	Construct graphs Themes 30, 31
Interpret		
From displays, asking specific questions Theme 33		From a range of displays and databases Theme 34
NUMBER*, MONEY* AND MEASUREMENT ATTAINMENT TARGET		
Measure and estimate		
Length: m, $\frac{1}{2}$ m, $\frac{1}{4}$ m, cm Themes 18, 19 Weight: kg, $\frac{1}{2}$ kg Theme 28 Place objects in order of length and weight Themes 18, 24, 28 Use abbreviations: m, cm and equivalences Theme 19 Length conservation when shapes change Themes 20, 24 Read scales Themes 19, 25	Volume: litre, $\frac{1}{2}$ litre, $\frac{1}{4}$ litre Theme 26 Area: shapes composed of different shapes or grids Themes 20, 22 Estimate length and weight in standard units Themes 23, 29 Read scales Themes 19, 25, 26, 29 Weight and area conservation when shapes change Theme 29	Length: small/large Theme 23 Weight: extended range of articles Themes 30, 31 Volume: accuracy extended to small units Themes 26, 27 Area: right-angled triangles Themes 22, 27 Estimate small weights, areas and volumes Themes 27, 31 Imperial units of measurement Theme 30
Time		
Place events in time Theme 33	Conventions for recording time Theme 35 Work with hours, minutes Theme 33 Use calendars Theme 32	Use 24-hour times and equate with 12-hour times Theme 34 Calculate duration in hours/minutes Themes 34, 35, 36 Calculate speeds Theme 36
Perimeter, formulae, scales		
		Calculate perimeters Theme 22
SHAPE, POSITION AND MOVEMENT ATTAINMENT TARGET		
Range of shapes		
Respond to written/oral descriptions of shapes Themes 1, 3, 4, 7 Shapes that will tile Themes 5, 6 Make 3D shapes Themes 8, 9, 10	Identify 2D shapes wthin 3D shapes Themes 8, 9, 10 Draw circles Theme 21 Recognise 3D shapes within 2D drawings Themes 7, 8, 9, 10	Discuss 3D/2D shapes Themes 1, 3 Recognise pentagon, hexagon Theme 1 Identify and name equilateral and isosceles triangles Theme 3 Make 3D models: cube and cuboid. Rigidity properties of triangles Themes 8, 9, 10
Position and movement		
Recognise and name the four compass points Theme 12 Grid references Theme 12	Create paths on squared paper Theme 12	Use an 8-point compass rose Themes 13, 17 Use a co-ordinate system to locate a point on a grid Themes 15, 16 Create patterns by rotating a shape Themes 6, 10
Symmetry		
Recognise symmetrical shapes Themes 2, 5	Find lines of symmetry Theme 2	Create symmetrical shapes Theme 16
Angles		
Draw right angle Themes 11, 21	Know that a right angle = 90° Themes 11, 14, 21 Use 'right, acute, obtuse' to describe angles Themes 13, 21 Know that a straight line = 180° Theme 14	Draw, copy and measure angles accurately within 5° Theme 14 Use standard notation 060, 150, 300, to express bearings Theme 17

*For coverage of number and money see the companion book: *Learning Targets: Number Key Stage 2*.

2-D SHAPES

It was, as with so many things, the Ancient Greeks who located an understanding of the characteristics of 2-D shapes as a central part of mathematics. The term 'geometry' means earth measuring and through initially intensely practical concerns to do with building, the Greeks developed a whole field of study concerned with shapes. Most of us know the names of two of the ancient Greek mathematicians, Pythagoras and Euclid. Pythagoras is best remembered for his work on right-angled triangles though he achieved much more than this. Euclid's great textbook entitled *Elements*, on the theories and theorems of geometry formed the basis of the study of geometry in schools until recent times. In studying 2-D shapes in primary schools today the idea that geometry is rooted in practical matters is still important. Whereas much of the work we do in arithmetic is linear in its development and more constrained by the defined content, work with shapes can and should be much more holistic, intensely practical, and open-ended. The variety of skills needed to understand and manipulate 2-D shapes includes cognitive, tactile and aesthetic skills.

In a three-dimensional world it is important that we all know, recognise and can work with 2-D shapes. Subjects such as mathematics, science, and art and design need an understanding of the characteristics of a range of 2-D shapes and the ways in which those shapes can be used together. For children coming to an understanding of 2-D shapes, there are key ideas to acquire. Children must learn the names of the common 2-D shapes and their basic characteristics, that is the numbers of sides and corners and the kinds of angles formed at those corners. In addition, children need to know about the symmetrical properties of shapes, and whether they tessellate.

When looking at characteristics we have to handle several ideas at once, so children need a rich variety of experiences which involve angle, orientation and dimension. It is, therefore, understandable that we try to contain the demands by repeatedly offering particular examples of 2-D shapes. However, in our attempts to reduce the variables that children need to handle, we sometimes run the risk of giving erroneous messages. For example, if we always represent triangles with horizontal bases and pentagons as regular then it should be no surprise when some children think that these are basic characteristics of the shapes.

Finally, it is the case that some people equate mathematics only with number. To do so is not only to impoverish mathematics but also to reduce children's ability to be involved positively in key aspects of modern life. There has been a growing appreciation in recent years that the built environment has real effects on how we live, work and play. To understand this environment we all need a good grounding in geometry.

Name, make and sort 2-D shapes

Learning targets

The children should be able to:

1 ➤ Make a range of 2-D shapes using triangles
2 ➤ Make larger or smaller versions of some 2-D shapes
3 ➤ Sort common 2-D shapes using consistent criteria

Before you start

Subject knowledge

The children should have had a variety of encounters with 2-D shapes. They should know the names and broad characteristics of squares, circles, triangles and rectangles. They will also know the names of some other 2-D shapes because of their popular use, for example, a star. Here, our aims are to further develop this knowledge of named 2-D shapes and to set the foundations for later work on symmetry, enlargement, reduction and congruence. By making, discussing and naming the 2-D shapes, we can support children's understanding of the characteristics of particular shapes and help them to make important connections within shape work and, particularly, 3-D shape and the built environment. In sorting 2-D shapes at this stage, the children's attention needs to be drawn to the number of corners, the number of sides and the sizes of angle at the corners. The term 'similar' should be introduced to their vocabulary. By similar, here, we mean shapes that have the same relationship between the corners and the sides but have different dimensions. The names of 2-D shapes are important and sometimes difficult. You need to be consistent in your use of terms, such as 'quadrilateral, 'square' and 'rectangle' and, if some books use it, 'oblong'. At this stage, we should emphasise that shapes with three straight sides are triangles, those with four are quadrilaterals, those with five are pentagons and hexagons have six straight sides.

Previous knowledge required

Familiarity with squares, rectangles, circles and triangles

Resources needed for Lesson 1

As many plastic or card triangles as you can gather together including right angled, isosceles and equilateral triangles

Resources needed for Lesson 2

Geoboards, elastic bands, Copymaster A, Copymaster B

Resources needed for Lesson 3

A large quantity of a variety of 2-D shapes including some with curved edges such as circles and ovals and a variety of triangles, quadrilaterals and other polygons

Teaching the lessons

Lesson 1 ①

Key questions

What is that shape called?

Can you make a…?

Vocabulary

Square, rectangle, triangle, quadrilateral, pentagon, hexagon, other names of shapes that may arise

Introduction — 10 min

Draw, on the board, the common 2-D shapes that you would expect the children to know and ask them to name them. Ask what characteristics these shapes have. Tell the children they are going to make as many of these shapes as possible using triangles. They will go on to use triangles to make as many other shapes as they can.

Activities — 25 min

The children work collaboratively to produce 2-D shapes using the triangles you have given them. Ask them to record their discoveries by sketching what they find. They should name the shapes if they can. Make a note of examples you encounter, as you go around the class, to use in the closing session.

Closing the lesson — 10 min

Using the examples collected, review all the shapes that have been made. Put the names of each on the board, making sure that pentagons and hexagons appear. Finish by reinforcing that triangles have three straight sides, quadrilaterals four and so on.

Assessment

Child performance	Teacher action
Constructs a limited number of shapes	Work with these children on the making and naming of a chosen set of 2-D shapes, then extend this to include more shapes
Constructs and names a limited number of shapes	Give an opportunity to look at and discuss the shapes that others found
Constructs and names a wide selection of shapes	Move on to the next lesson

Lesson 2

Key questions

What shape is that?

Are these two similar?

Does it have the same shaped corners?

How did you work out how to make bigger (or smaller) versions?

Vocabulary

The shape names, larger, smaller, similar

Introduction

15min

Draw a square on the board. Then measure and draw two more: one with sides half the length of the original and the second with sides twice the length of the original. Talk about what you have done, getting ideas from the children. The key idea is to retain the same shape but change the lengths of the sides by the same factor. If necessary, do this exercise again for an equilateral triangle. Introduce the term 'similar'. Tell the children that they are going to make shapes using elastic bands and geo-boards, then record these shapes on dotted paper.

Activities

25min

Using the geoboards and recording on the appropriate dotted paper, the children make 2-D shapes of their choice and then attempt to make larger and smaller versions of each of them. In some cases, the dotted paper will allow only an approximation of the shapes to be recorded. Let the children name the shapes as they record them. As they work, make a note of examples of the shapes to use at the end of the lesson.

Closing the lesson

10min

Using examples of the shapes the children have produced, talk about characteristics including the idea of similarity. Recap the names of shapes.

Assessment

Child performance	Teacher action
Makes and records original shapes but has problems in making similar shapes	Do some more work on the characteristics of a limited range of common 2-D shapes
Makes and records correctly a limited number of common 2-D shapes	Give further opportunities and support the children in extending their making of 2-D shapes
Makes and records correctly a wide range of 2-D shapes	Move on to the next lesson

Lesson 3

Key questions

Why have you put these together?

What are you using to make your choices?

Vocabulary

The common shape names, choice, decision, characteristic

Introduction

10min

Tell the children that now they know a lot of the names for 2-D shapes, they are going to use this knowledge to group a range of 2-D shapes. They have to be able to explain why they have grouped the shapes in the ways they have chosen.

Activities

20min

The groups have to work collaboratively to sort the wide range of shapes you have provided. Encourage them to discuss their choices and the reasons for making them.

Closing the lesson

15min

Using what you observed and, through eliciting individual responses, review the characteristics of all of the 2-D shapes that were available. Accept that in the case of circles, for example, the naming might be sufficient for the group, but ovals and circles do need an explanation if they are separated.

Assessment

Child performance	Teacher action
Sorts most of the shapes satisfactorily but finds it difficult to explain their reasons for some of their choices	Give further practice in this sort of activity
Sorts the shapes and produces sensible reasons for most of the choices	Give further practice in relation to those shapes the children found most difficult to characterise
Sorts and names all of the shapes and justifies all of their choices	These children have met the learning targets for this theme

HOMEWORK

Let the children make a small 'I Spy 2-D Shapes' booklet to make a record of 2-D shapes they spot at home, in the street and at the school.

2-D SHAPES

THEME 2

Reflective symmetry

Learning targets

The children should be able to:

1 ➤ Produce symmetrical designs by cutting paper

2 ➤ Produce symmetrical designs through drawing and organising objects

3 ➤ Find lines of symmetry in given shapes

Before you start

Subject knowledge

Reflective symmetry can be demonstrated by placing a plane mirror on a real or imaginary line, giving the terms 'mirror symmetry' and 'line symmetry'. The children need to know that all three terms mean the same. Reflective symmetry is seen in both the natural and human-made worlds such as in the shapes of animals, including ourselves, which are broadly symmetrical, and in cars, boats and planes. Artists and architects make much use of symmetry because the human eye is drawn to it. Even children's first drawings and paintings often contain symmetrical ideas, and most youngsters will have used paint and folding to produce symmetrical pictures and patterns. Make a display with the children of examples of reflective symmetry such as photographs of butterflies and flowers; models and paintings done by the children; and artefacts such as lamps and vases.

Previous knowledge required

Early experiences with painting and folding

Resources needed for Lesson 1

Old newspapers, sugar paper, scissors, pencils

Resources needed for Lesson 2

Carbon paper or similar, pegs and peg boards, coloured pencils, plain paper, Copymaster 1

Resources needed for Lesson 3

Plastic mirrors, rulers, coloured pencils, templates of regular shapes, objects with and without line symmetry including cups with and without handles, Copymaster 2

Teaching the lessons

Lesson 1 ①

Key questions

What happens when you do this?

What can you see?

Can you describe this for me?

Vocabulary

Balance, symmetry, line, mirror image

Introduction (10 min)

Start by demonstrating the folding and cutting shown below. Ask the children what they notice about the shape and the hole. Tell them they are going to make a shape and a hole in the same way by cutting folded paper with scissors.

Activities (25 min)

The children should fold newspapers and sugar papers in the way you demonstrated, then draw a shape on the creased edge and cut it out. Let individuals show their efforts to the class and use the opportunity to emphasise that each half is a mirror image of the other. Encourage terms like 'balance' and 'equal' and, if appropriate, introduce the term 'line symmetry'. Now show the class a piece of paper folded in half and then folded into quarters. Tell them that they are to do this but this time they should cut out shapes from all the edges of the folded paper. They complete this individually.

Closing the lesson (10 min)

Let some children show what they produced from the paper folded twice. Let the class comment on what they observe. Arrange for some of the examples to be put on the symmetry display.

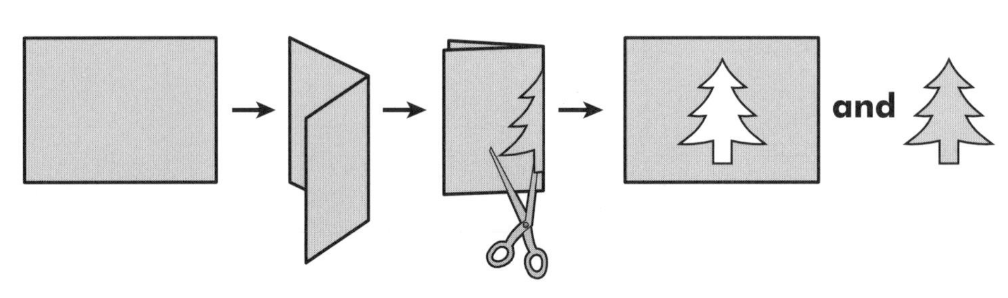

Assessment

Child performance	Teacher action
Produces an example from the first part of the activity but struggles with the second part	Give more experiences of producing simple one-line symmetry pictures and cut outs, then try this activity again
Produces at least two different examples but find it difficult to discuss their work	Use the display of all the work in the class to have further discussion
Produces examples and can make clear statements about what they observed	Move on to the next lesson

Lesson 2 ❷

Key questions

What can you see here?

Can we use these techniques to help us make or design things?

Vocabulary

Balance, symmetry, line, mirror, pattern

Introduction

10 min

Remind the children of the work they have done in cutting symmetrical shapes and holes. Demonstrate how to make a symmetrical drawing using the carbon paper as shown below.

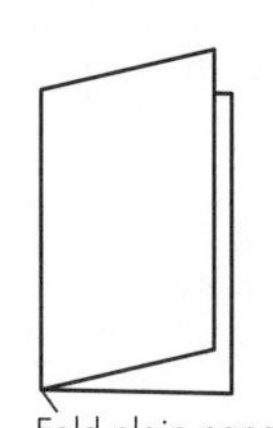

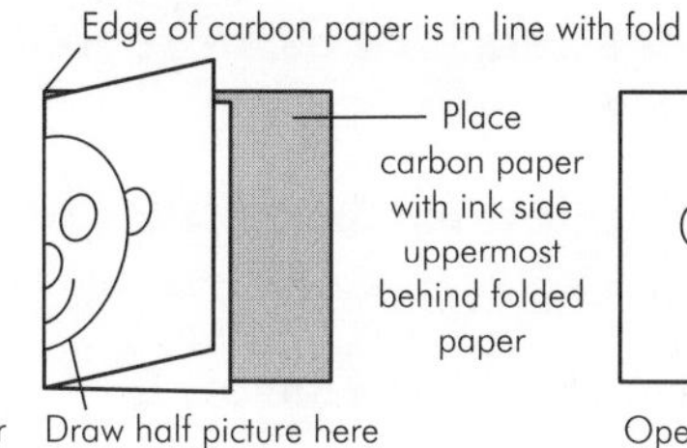

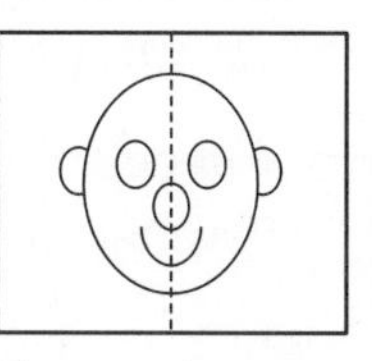

Tell the children that they are now going to try this.

Activities

30 min

Using the folded plain paper and unfolded carbon paper, the children should attempt their own reflective symmetry drawing. When progress has been made, give out **Copymaster 1**, pegboards, pegs and coloured pencils. Tell the children to follow the instructions on the Copymaster. Go around checking that all is clear to everyone.

Closing the lesson

10 min

Let individual children show and comment on their symmetrical drawings. Hold up some of the Copymasters and ask what the children observed. Collect all the Copymasters to check the children's understanding.

Assessment

Child performance	Teacher action
Completes first part of the activity only	Work with these children using pegboards to check their understanding of the task, then give them another try
Completes first part and some of the second	Give more time, then move on to the next lesson
Completes all	Move on to the next lesson

Lesson 3 ❸

Key questions

Does this have reflective /line /mirror symmetry?

Is there more than one line of symmetry?

Vocabulary

Mirror, line, reflective symmetry

Introduction

15 min

Elicit the children's thoughts on what they know about reflective symmetry. Using objects and 2-D representations of them on the board, look at lines of symmetry, pointing out where there are none, one or more than one. Tell the children that they are going to try to decide which of some 2-D shapes on paper have none, one or more than one line of symmetry.

Activities

20 min

Give out **Copymaster 2** and plane mirrors for the children to use for checking purposes. They need to identify those drawings that exhibit reflective symmetry and, if possible, go on to identify the positions of those lines of symmetry.

Closing the lesson

10 min

Choose some examples from the Copymaster and draw them on the board, asking the children their ideas for each one. Collect the Copymasters to help evaluate the children's understanding.

Assessment

Child performance	Teacher action
Identifies some correctly but makes errors in a number of the others	Make further collections and work closely with the children, then try this activity again
Identifies all correctly but does not find all of the possible lines of symmetry	Select those that were incomplete and give more practice on similar shapes or drawings
Identifies all correctly and finds all possible lines of symmetry	These children have met the learning targets for this theme

HOMEWORK

Let the children make personal collections of examples of reflective symmetry such as pictures from magazines; their own paper cuts or tears or shop produced paper cuts such as doilies; and drawings and photographs.

2-D SHAPES

THEME 3

Shape families and their names

Learning targets

The children should be able to:

1 ➤➤ See differences between given triangles and know the names of different triangles

2 ➤➤ See differences between different quadrilaterals and know the names of different quadrilaterals

3 ➤➤ Name a given variety of 2-D shapes

Before you start

Subject knowledge

The children should by now be able to recognise and name the common 2-D shapes. This is important, as such shapes are common to the arts and many technologies. We have to continue to add to the recognition and naming of 2-D shapes as the children progress through their shape work. In making decisions about the nature of 2-D shapes, they need to focus on sides, corners and orientation. They need to consider the number of sides, their length and their shape – curved lines are a challenge and the mathematics of circles, ellipses and particular curved lines is demanding. Children should learn to recognise the corners, or vertices, as acute, obtuse or reflex angles. Orientation is an issue because we commonly present shapes such as triangles with a horizontal base but must not allow children to believe that a 'flat bottom' is a characteristic of a triangle. We need to present the named 2-D shapes in many possible orientations. Also in this theme the foundations for a sound understanding of similarity and congruence are being laid. Children need to recognise equilateral, isosceles, scalene and right-angled triangles. It should be noted that a right-angled triangle is also either scalene or isosceles but never equilateral. The lessons in this theme concentrate on triangles and quadrilaterals but they can be readily adapted to deal with other polygons.

Previous knowledge required

The names of common 2-D shapes such as triangle, square and rectangle, some experience of 'angle'

Resources needed for Lesson 1

Copymaster 3

Resources needed for Lesson 2

Copymaster 4

Resources needed for Lesson 3

Copymaster 5

Teaching the lessons

Lesson 1 ①

Key questions

What do these triangles have in common?

How are these triangles different?

Vocabulary

Triangle, equilateral, right-angled, isosceles, scalene

Introduction 15min

Draw a triangle of your own choosing on the board. Ask the children its name and to tell you what makes it a triangle. Now draw a different triangle next to the first. Ask what it is and how it differs from the first triangle. Repeat this with a third triangle. Then tell the children that there are four main triangles that they need to know – equilateral, isosceles, scalene and the right-angled triangle. Make sure examples of all these are on the board and then talk through their characteristics.

Activities 20min

Give out **Copymaster 3**, telling the children that they need to try and name the different triangles on the Copymaster. As the children work through this, keep reminding them of the characteristics of the different triangles and that right-angled triangles can also be either scalene or isosceles.

Closing the lesson 10min

Discuss the characteristics of the different triangles again, using some of the examples on the Copymasters. Collect the Copymasters for evaluation.

Assessment

Child performance	Teacher action
Identifies right-angled triangles and some of the others but makes errors	Using templates, talk through and discuss the different triangles and label them, then give the children another opportunity to do this activity
Identifies all in the first part of the Copymaster but not in the second	Make paper templates of the shapes, cut them up to see if the children can now identify them
Identifies all on the Copymaster correctly	Move on to the next lesson

Lesson 2

Key questions

What do you notice about this shape?

What is this one called?

What do you notice about the corners?

Do the sides have anything in common?

Vocabulary

Quadrilateral, square, rectangle, rhombus, parallelogram, trapezium, kite

Introduction

In this lesson, the children will be learning or confirming the names of the common quadrilaterals (see page 8) and refining their ability to focus on particular characteristics of given 2-D shapes. Draw and discuss the common quadrilaterals, one at a time. Draw them on the board in the following order: square, rectangle, rhombus, parallelogram, trapezium and kite. Discuss with the children what each is named and what is special about each one.

Activities

Give out **Copymaster 4**. The children will use the introduction to the lesson to consolidate their knowledge of the names and key characteristics of the shapes. Use the key questions as the children work through the Copymaster individually.

Closing the lesson

Revise the names and key characteristics of the shapes in the Copymaster, and then collect them to check the children's recall.

Assessment

Child performance	Teacher action
Names most of the shapes and identifies some characteristics	Concentrate on linking attributes and names using templates, then try this exercise again
Names all the shapes and identifies some characteristics	Review the Copymaster with the children and then move on to the next lesson
Names all the shapes and identifies all of the key characteristics	Move on to the next lesson

Lesson 3

Key questions

What is this sort of triangle called?

What is this quadrilateral called?

Vocabulary

The triangle and quadrilateral names

Introduction

10min

Recap the triangles and quadrilaterals that the children should now be able to identify and name. Clean the board, as you want to see what the children can recall during the activity.

Activities

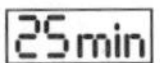

Give out **Copymaster 5**. The children have to label each of the shapes correctly.

Closing the lesson

10min

Review a sample of the shapes, getting the children to name them. Collect in the Copymasters for evaluation of the children's progress.

Assessment

Child performance	Teacher action
Can name a few	Depending on your analysis of the children's work, do more on either triangles or quadrilaterals and then try this exercise again
Can name most	Review those that are wrong or missing, to see whether more practice is needed.
Can name all	These children have met the learning targets for this theme

HOMEWORK

Using mosaics or drawing and colouring, the children should make some symmetrical patterns using triangles and quadrilaterals of different dimensions.

2-D SHAPES
THEME 4

The characteristics of some 2-D shapes

Learning targets

The children should be able to:

1 ➛ Explore 2-D shapes by partitioning them
2 ➛ Explain some of the key features of four sided shapes
3 ➛ Appreciate the difference between regular and irregular 2-D common shapes

Before you start

Subject knowledge

One of the key strategies in mathematics is simplification. Complex ideas or representations of ideas can often only be satisfactorily understood if they are simplified. One way of doing this in an exploration of 2-D shapes is to relate given shapes to other common ones. For example, an understanding that a rhombus is a 'collapsed' square helps us recall some of its key features. Drawing a diagonal in a rhombus gives us two isosceles triangles and this helps us to be clearer about what the characteristics of such triangles are – and helps us construct a rhombus. These points are illustrated below.

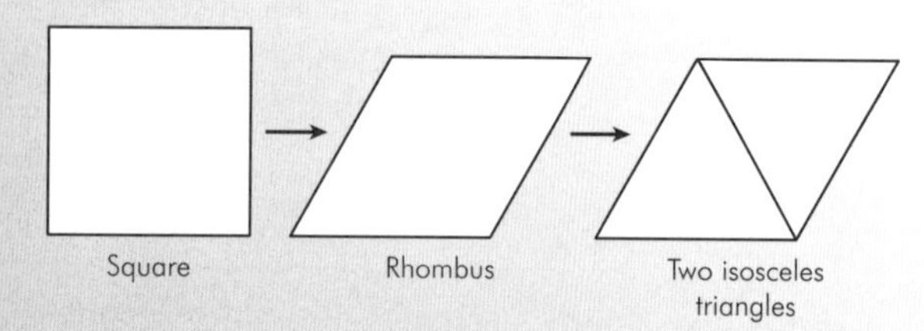

At this time, we need to be encouraging the children to be making increasingly more sophisticated judgements about 2-D shapes, their characteristics and differences. Here, this imperative is developed through some features of quadrilaterals. Quadrilaterals include all figures with four straight sides. The common quadrilaterals are shown above.

Common quadrilaterals

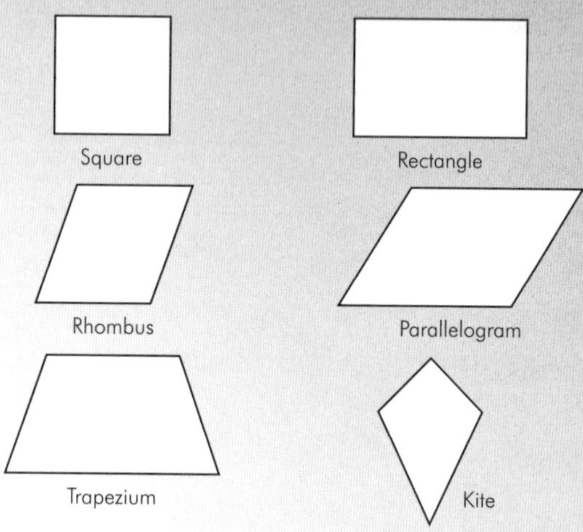

Previous knowledge required

The common named 2-D shapes such as triangle, square and rectangle

Resources needed for Lesson 1

Copymaster 6, rulers

Resources needed for Lesson 2

Plastic templates of a wide range of quadrilaterals, sufficient for the number of groups in the class

Resources needed for Lesson 3

Copymaster 7, protractors for those who know how to use them, rulers

Teaching the lessons

Lesson 1

Key questions

Can you divide this shape into triangles or squares or a mixture of both?

How many triangles/squares can you make?

What do you notice about this shape?

What is this shape called?

Vocabulary

Triangle, square, diagonal, divide

Introduction

15 min

Draw a square on the board and then divide it into two triangles by drawing a diagonal. Talk about what you have done, writing up the term 'diagonal'. Draw in a second diagonal, pointing out that you now have four triangles. Draw a rectangle on the board that can be divided into squares (a three by one or three by two rectangle). Divide it into squares and talk about this. Now draw diagonals in the squares to make triangles as before. Following this, draw another rectangle, with a diagonal to show two right-angled triangles. Tell the children that you are going to give them a Copymaster on which there are a number of shapes which they should try to divide up into triangles or squares, or triangles and squares, in as many ways as they can.

Activities

25min

Give out **Copymaster 6**. Make sure the children have rulers. Encourage them to look at different ways of dividing the shapes but remind them that they must only make triangles or squares or a combination of both. Observe the efforts of all the children and make a mental note of those you choose to make a particular contribution to the closing part of the lesson.

Closing the lesson

10min

Using chosen individuals from the whole range of aptitude and ability in the class put some of the solutions on the board and invite the rest of the class to comment. Collect the Copymasters for evaluation of the children's work.

Assessment

Child performance	Teacher action
Carries out most of the task but does not always divide into triangles and/or squares	Work closely with these children, using these 2-D shapes to consolidate what is required. Then try them again on the activity
Carries out the task but only with a given number of shapes	Either move on or arrange group work for more practice using the experiences of the children who were able to extend the activity
Carries out the task and extends the activity with a good range of additional examples	Move on to the next lesson

Lesson 2

Key questions

What is this shape called?

What does this shape have in common with that one?

What differences are there between these two shapes?

Vocabulary

Quadrilateral, square, rectangle, rhombus, parallelogram, trapezium, kite

Introduction

10min

Explain to the children that in this lesson, they are going to try different ways of sorting quadrilaterals. Explain what a quadrilateral is and tell them you want them to put similar shapes together. The key ideas for the children to understand are the meaning of quadrilateral, and that length of sides and angles of corners are the variables to look at. Encourage them to think about 'squashing' or 'tilting' shapes when they make their decisions.

Activities

20min

Working in pairs with the templates you have made available, let the children make some decisions about the relationship between the shapes. They can draw around the templates to keep a record and should write down the characteristics they noticed next to the shapes. When the time is right, put two pairs together to compare and contrast what they have detected and accomplished.

Closing the lesson

15min

Common groupings are to put the square and rectangle, rhombus and parallelogram, and trapezium and kite together. However, the rhombus might be put with the square, as it is a 'tilted' square. Discuss with your class what has been done and why. Finish by suggesting a family tree of quadrilaterals as shown below.

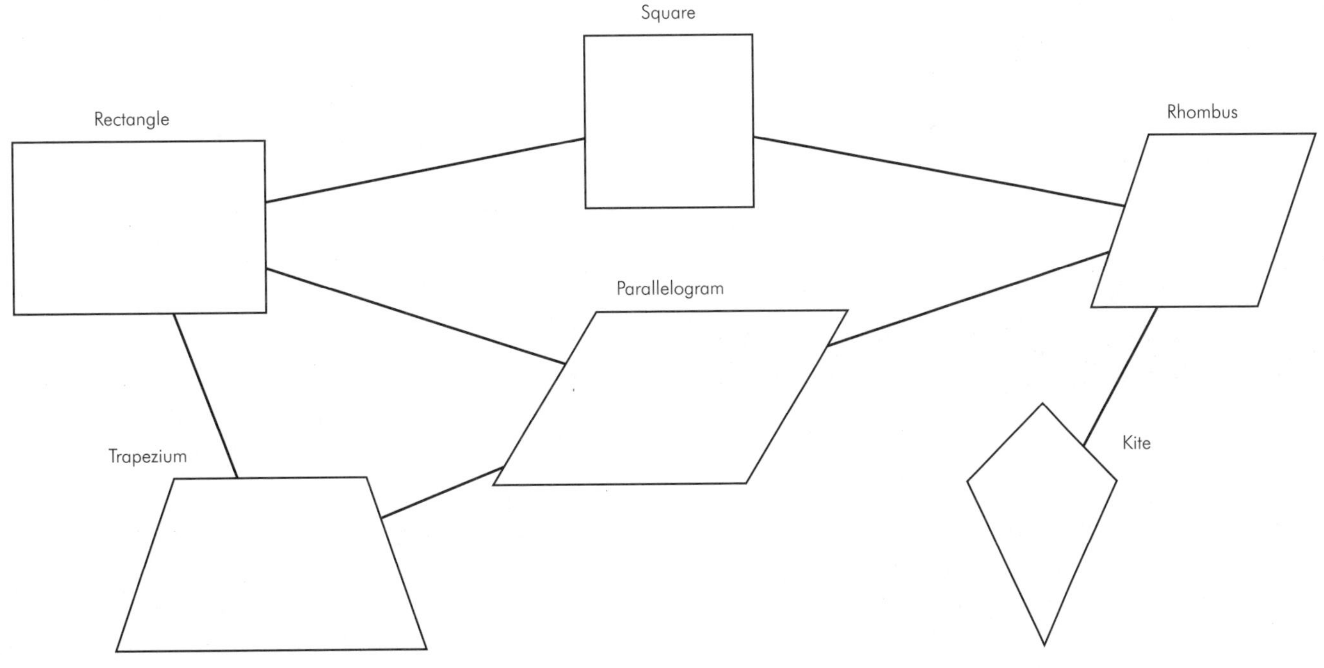

Assessment

Child performance	Teacher action
Knows the characteristics of quadrilaterals but not the names of all the examples	Give more practice with the common 2-D shapes including naming and the recall of names
Knows the shapes and produces a grouping with some explanation	Move on to next lesson
Knows the shapes and produces a variety of sorts with some explanation and statements about them	Move on to next lesson

Lesson 3

Key questions

What is different about this one?

Can you name this shape?

Vocabulary

Triangle plus the names of some from equilateral, scalene, isosceles, pentagon, hexagon, regular, irregular and angle names – acute, obtuse, reflex as appropriate

Introduction

10 min

Revise what the children know about named 2-D shapes. Encourage them to identify characteristics that support similarities and differences. Use the opportunity to reinforce the names of the common 2-D shapes. Explain that shapes which have the same length sides and internal angles are known as regular shapes. Then tell the children that in this lesson, they have to put 2-D shapes into groups and explain the difference between the shapes in each group.

Activities

25 min

Give out **Copymaster 7**. Encourage the children to look at and think about sides and corners. Ask whether they can name triangles and angles.

Closing the lesson

10 min

Review the Copymaster so that the children understand the connections you are looking for and the similarities and differences within the groups. Go over the meaning of 'regular' again and point out that the others are irregular. Collect the Copymasters for evaluation of the children's work.

Assessment

Child performance	Teacher action
Groups some of the shapes but not all	More work on the common 2-D shapes should be undertaken and this exercise attempted again
Groups the shapes but has incomplete explanations for the differences within groups	Talk through the ideas again with these children and give them another similar exercise
Completes the exercise without difficulty and clearly identifies the regular 2-D shapes	These children have met the learning targets for this theme

HOMEWORK

Let the children choose a 2-D shape they like and then produce a pocket guide to that shape which includes all they know and can find out about it.

2-D SHAPES

THEME 5

Tessellation

Learning targets

The children should be able to:

1 ➣➝ Make regular tessellations

2 ➣➝ Make semi-regular tessellations

3 ➣➝ Make other tessellating shapes

Before you start

Subject knowledge

In common with symmetry, and often as a result of a desire for symmetry, tessellation is to be found in the built environment and occasionally in the natural world. Examples include patchwork quilts, tiling on floors and the hexagons of a beehive. Tessellation means covering a plain surface continuously with the same 'shape'. This shape can be either a single one or a repeated combination. We can also transform shapes that will tessellate. There are only three regular shapes which will tessellate, these being the equilateral triangle, the square and the regular hexagon. Indeed, the regular hexagon itself can be made from equilateral triangles. Tessellations made from these basic building blocks are called regular tessellation. An example of one made from hexagons is shown here. It is a pattern that has been much used in the design of, for example, patchwork quilts. The use of colour can add interesting effects to this simple pattern.

Where more than one 2-D shape is used to create a tessellation, we commonly term this semi-regular. In Victorian and Edwardian tiling of hall floors, the square and octagon were much used. This pattern is shown below.

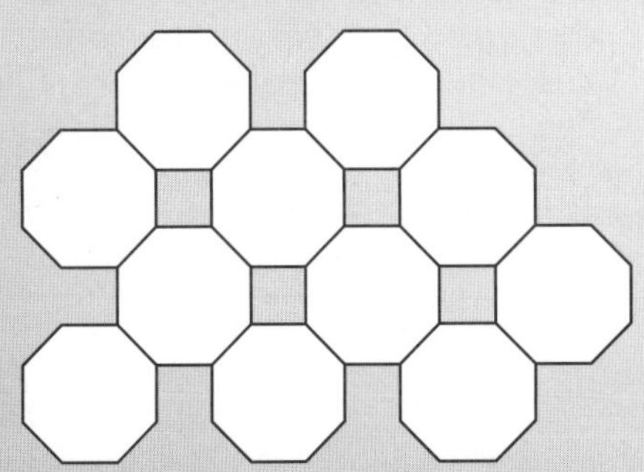

M. C. Escher (1902-1972) was an artist who made great and powerful use of many mathematical ideas. Many of his famous works were tessellations. Their development is complex but he started with the basic building blocks and, by cutting, translating and transforming shapes, made his potent designs. Children produce tessellation in a similar way. An example is shown here.

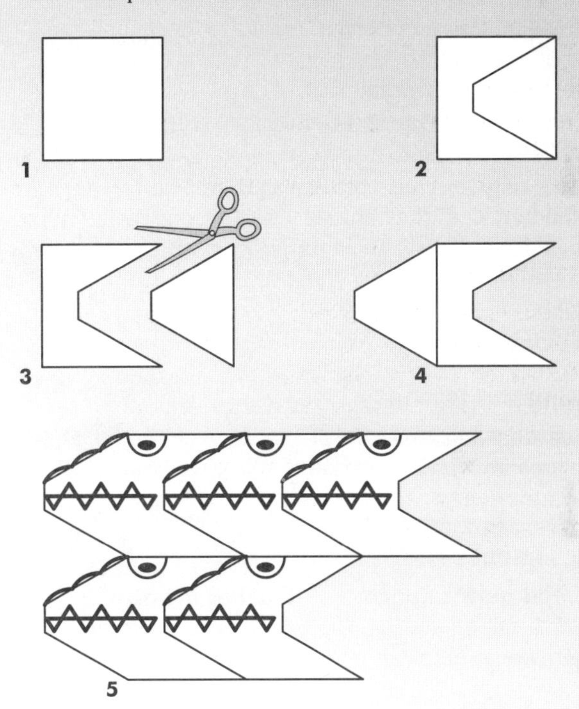

Previous knowledge required

Practical skills, symmetry, names and characteristics of 2-D shapes

Resources needed for Lesson 1

Copymaster A, Copymaster B, coloured pencils, rulers

Resources needed for Lesson 2

Templates of a range of 2-D shapes having the same length edges, coloured pencils

Resources needed for Lesson 3

If possible, some posters, postcards or books showing the works of M. C. Escher, scissors, card, sticky tape, plain paper, coloured pencils, an overhead projector, card and scissors for demonstration purposes

Teaching the lessons

Lesson 1 ❶

Key questions

What are these shapes called?

What do they have in common?

What is tessellation?

Vocabulary

Tessellation, square, equilateral triangle, regular hexagon

Introduction 10 min

Draw an equilateral triangle, square and regular hexagon on the board and label them with the help of the children. Now show how many squares can be fitted together to cover a plane surface. Tell the children that this is called tessellation. Explain that only the 2-D shapes that you have drawn can tessellate by themselves, leaving no gaps. Tell the children that they are going to have a go at making tessellation using the shapes.

Activities 25 min

Give out **Copymasters A** and **B**, reminding the children what they have to do. Give out the coloured pencils and invite them to use colour to make their tessellation designs distinctive. Encourage them to make at least two tessellations using any two of the three basic shapes.

Closing the lesson 10 min

Let individuals show what they have achieved. Finish by reminding the children of the three basic shapes that make regular tessellation.

Assessment

Child performance	Teacher action
Produces one design with some help	Give some more time
Produces one design and starts another	Let the children finish, then move on
Produces two designs confidently	Move on to the next lesson

Lesson 2 ❷

Key questions

What are these shapes?

Which of these can be used to make a tessellation?

Vocabulary

Common 2-D shape names, regular, semi-regular

Introduction 10 min

Remind the children of their work in making regular tessellation. Tell them that, in this lesson, they are going to make tessellations which need two shapes and that these are often called semi-regular tessellations. Explain that you want the children to avoid using equilateral triangles, squares or hexagons to begin with and see what happens when they attempt to tessellate, for example, pentagons and octagons.

Activities 25 min

Give out templates and let the children choose one and draw around it, trying to make it tessellate. When they have attempted this, ask the class for examples of what they have found. Now ask them to see if they can identify pairs of templates that will fit together to tessellate, then try them out. They should write down the names of the shapes that go together. Invite the children to use coloured pencils to add variation to their semi-regular tessellation.

Closing the lesson 10 min

Put two examples on the board and support the children in coming to realise that, in order to tessellate, the corners should make one whole rotation (360°) where they meet. Collect the children's efforts to see how they have developed the ideas.

Assessment

Child performance	Teacher action
Produces one example with some help	Give more practice with regular tessellation; then try this activity again
Produces two different examples	Discuss the children's efforts, looking at the corners where the shapes meet
Produces two different examples and can explain how the tessellation works	Move on to the next lesson

Lesson 3 ❸

Key questions

What happens if you move that piece to there?

What if you 'flip' and/or 'rotate' this piece?

Vocabulary

Escher, translate, rotate, flip, tessellate

Introduction 15 min

Briskly recap what the children know about tessellation and tessellating shapes. If possible, show them some of Escher's work (it is possible to make an overhead transparency of part of a poster) and talk about how he might have made some of his tessellating shapes. Now, using a card square, make a simple tessellating shape as shown on page 23. Tell the children they are going to work together to make a tessellating shape of this kind.

Activities 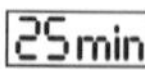

Give out card, sticky tape, scissors, plain paper and coloured pencils. Go around helping, advising and questioning the children. Encourage them to try

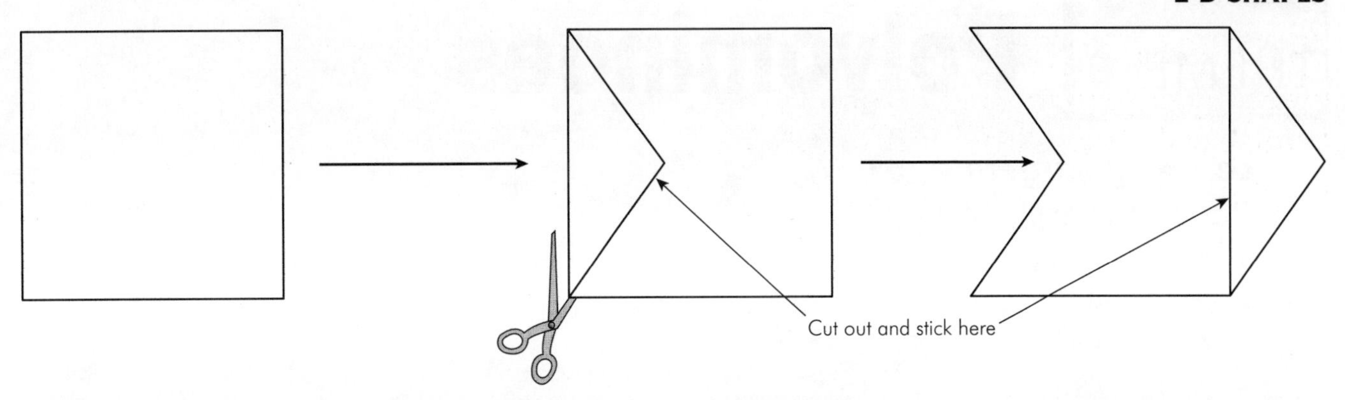

things out but they must test the card shapes they make to see if they really do tessellate. When they have a tessellation, they can draw on the shapes, as Escher did, to make them even more striking. The drawing has to be the same on each shape, though it can be a different colour.

Closing the lesson

10min

Hold up some examples for the children to see. Remind them of the rules for tessellations. Collect the work and put it on display.

Assessment

Child performance	Teacher action
Makes a tessellating shape like the demonstration but has difficulty in creating one of their own	Work with these children in extending their appreciation and confidence
Makes a simple tessellating shape	Give more opportunities following their evaluation of the work of others in the class
Makes a tessellating shape which has a number of features	These children have met the learning targets for this theme

HOMEWORK

The children can look for, list or collect places, pictures or packages, which have tessellations in them. Examples could be brought to school and displayed.

Polyominoes

Learning targets

The children should be able to:

1 ➤➤ Identify and investigate tetrominoes
2 ➤➤ Identify and investigate pentominoes
3 ➤➤ Tessellate given polyominoes

Before you start

Subject knowledge

It is as important in shape and space work as in number, to extend understanding through the application of known facts to new situations. At this stage, the children should know the names and characteristics of the common 2-D shapes and be experienced in manipulating those shapes in a variety of ways. Here, we are illustrating the kinds of investigation and application work that can be undertaken in studying shape, space and measures through looking at polyominoes. Polyominoes are made up of squares. Two squares together make a domino – a familiar term to many.

Tromino: made from three squares it has two possible arrangements

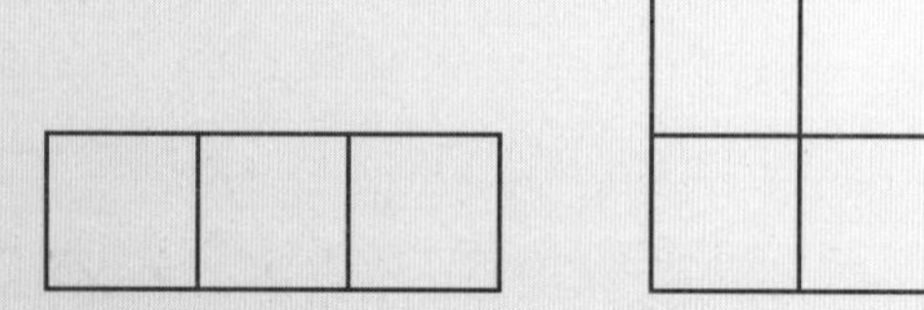

Any other arrangements are reflections or rotations of these.

The polyominoes, made up from two to six squares are domino (2), tromino (3), tetromino (4),pentomino (5), and hexomino (6). A domino has only one possible arrangement, as one of the rules in constructing polyominoes is that the squares touch on at least one side. Trominoes can be formed in two different ways, as shown below left.

In tackling the investigations in this theme, the children will exploit their experience and knowledge of symmetry and tessellation. The lessons in the theme are closely connected and it will help if all of the work is kept and re-used in each lesson.

Previous knowledge required

Symmetry, tessellation work, practical skills

Resources needed for Lesson 1

Plastic squares of the same size, General Copymaster A

Resources needed for Lesson 2

Plastic squares of the same size, General Copymaster A

Resources needed for Lesson 3

Plastic squares of the same size, Copymaster A, card, glue, scissors, plain paper, coloured pencils, work from previous lessons

Teaching the lessons

Lesson 1 

Key questions

How many ways can we arrange this number of squares?

What do you think this arrangement might be called?

Vocabulary

Domino, tromino, tetromino, arrangement, rotation, reflection, tessellate, duplicate

Introduction 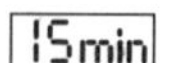

Draw a square on the board, then another edge-to-edge with it. Explain that in this lesson the children are going to investigate how many ways they can arrange different numbers of squares with the rule that they must be placed edge-to-edge. Ask the children if two squares can be arranged in any other way than the one you have drawn on the board. If other suggestions are made, use them to talk about rotation and the edge-to-edge rule. Now ask the children to tell you how to arrange three squares. When they have found the two possibilities and are content with the solution, move them on to their activities.

Activities 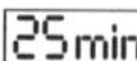

Give out **Copymaster A** and the plastic squares. Working collaboratively, the children need to work out all the possible arrangements of four squares. There are five of these, as shown on page 25, and they can be reviewed at the end of the lesson.

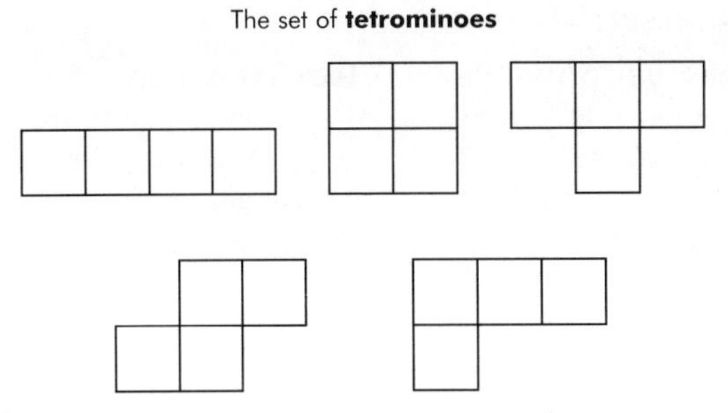

When the children have arranged their squares and recorded them on Copymaster A, stop the class and write the term on the board. Ask if they could use any of the tetrominoes they have made to tessellate or make a tessellating pattern. In pairs, they can now investigate this.

Closing the lesson

10min

Put the five tetrominoes on the board and discuss them. If the children have alternatives, use the opportunity to talk about duplicates and use reflection, rotation and flip to demonstrate these. Make sure that the recorded work is kept safely as it will help in the next lesson.

Assessment

Child performance	Teacher action
Finds some but not all of the arrangements	Work through the ideas again, starting with the domino. Then try this activity once more
Finds all the arrangements though has some duplicates	Discuss what has been happening to make sure the children are clear about why some of the arrangements are duplicates, then move on
Finds all the arrangements and makes progress with tessellation	Move on to the next lesson

Lesson 2

2

Key questions

How many ways can we arrange these without getting duplicates?

Do any of these tessellate?

Vocabulary

Tetromino, pentomino, arrangement, duplicate, tessellation

Introduction

10min

Using the work done on tetrominoes, remind the children of the rules for making such shapes. Remind them about duplicates and the need to carefully check for these. Tell them that in this lesson, they are going to move on to arranging five squares and that these are called pentominoes. Relate the first part of the term to the word 'pentagon'.

Activities

25min

Give out **Copymaster A** and plastic squares. The children need to use their previous experience to work out all the possible different arrangements of five squares. The solutions are shown here and they should be reviewed at the end of the lesson.

As you go around and the children start to complete the task, invite them again to think about whether any of their solutions would tessellate.

Closing the lesson

10min

Elicit arrangements from the class until you have all of them on the board. If there is uncertainty, then talk about reflection, rotation and flip. Keep the recorded work safe for support in the next lesson.

Assessment

Child performance	Teacher action
Does not find all the arrangements	Give more time and then check through them with the children before moving on
Finds all the arrangements	Give an opportunity to talk about any features the children notice. For example, one of these solutions clearly makes an open-topped box
Finds all the arrangements and connects with nets (see Theme 8) and tessellation	Move on to the next lesson

Lesson 3

3

Key questions

Will all these shapes tessellate? If not, which ones will tessellate?

Vocabulary

Polyominoes, domino, tromino, tetromino, pentomino, hexomino, tessellation

Introduction

10min

The opportunity to tessellate may have been present in previous lessons, but time may well have constrained the activity. Tell the children that they are going to use their earlier work to explore tessellating polyominoes. Give out their work from a previous lesson. Select one of tetrominoes and show that it tessellates. Ask the children to choose another tetromino and try it to see whether it will tessellate.

Activities

25min

Give out the plastic squares, **Copymaster A**, card, scissors and coloured pencils. Remind the children they need to choose one of the tetrominoes you have not used and see whether it tessellates. When the children have worked through this, tell the class you now want to see what they can do about tessellating pentominoes. Again, collaboratively, they should chose at least one pentomino and test it for tessellation.

Closing the lesson

10min

Show some of the work. Finish by telling the children that we could go on and that arrangements of six squares are known as hexominoes. Collect the work for display.

Assessment

Child performance	Teacher action
Tessellates with one tetromino but struggles with the remainder of the activity	Consider giving more practice with earlier polyominoes and then try this activity again
Tessellates one tetromino and one pentomino	Give further challenges using tetrominoes and then pentominoes
Sees that all the tetrominoes will tessellate and develops some tessellations also with pentominoes	These children have met the learning targets for this theme.

HOMEWORK

Equilateral triangles can be used instead of squares. These are called polyiamonds with the diamond being made up of two equilateral triangles. We often call this a rhombus. The children could investigate polyiamonds up to pentiamonds (of which there are 4), or hexiamonds (of which there are 12).

Investigations

- Explore and make tangrams (seven piece puzzle squares).
- Fold a piece of paper twice to make quarters. Cut across the folded corner. What shape do you make? By varying the angle of the cut what shapes can you make? Are there any common 2-D shapes you cannot make?
- Design and make a booklet on 2-D shapes for young children. Look at a range of designs, thinking about the fact that the booklet is a 3-D object about 2-D matters. Think about the target audience, and gain inspiration from other authors who have used shapes as characters in stories. Bear in mind that the information in the booklet has to be accurate, consistent and correct.
- Do more work on the art of M. C. Escher. There are some computer packages that support the design and production of tessellations.
- Using commercial sets of mats, make designs and repeat patterns.
- Acquire old wallpaper and border pattern books, or have an old wallpaper collection scheme. Explore the wallpapers and borders for patterns.
- The secret society of the followers of Pythagoras, the Pythagoreans, used the pentagram as their club logo. There are many aspects of the pentagram that can be investigated. For example, joining all of the corners in the central pentagon makes a new small pentagram, with another pentagon at its centre! Joining the points on the outside makes a large pentagon on which triangles can be placed to make a larger pentagram. Finally, the lengths of parts of the pentagram are in the golden ratio which is about 1.618 to 1.

a **pentagram** is a 5-pointed star formed by extending the sides of a **pentagon**

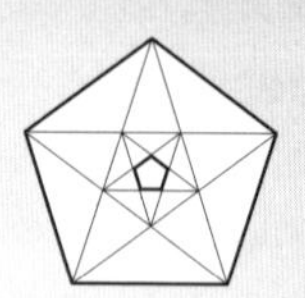

- Explore ways of drawing or printing pentagrams. Explore the pentagram in the ways suggested and others you can think of.

Assessment

- Divide a picture or drawing into its constituent common 2-D shapes.
- Make, draw and name all the common 2-D shapes in different sizes and orientations. Make connections between related shapes.
- Name the different quadrilaterals and list their similarities and differences.
- Make different triangles using practical apparatus (for example, geostrips) or on paper, name them and give their similarities and differences.
- Construct named triangles using drawing instruments.
- Enlarge and reduce squares, hexagons and triangles using two different methods.
- Given a range of 2-D templates find which of them tessellate.
- Create a design exhibiting reflective symmetry.

3-D SHAPES

In order to make sense of our 3-D world of length, depth and breadth, we break down complex shapes into simpler ones, and we learn to represent three dimensions in two dimensions. This learning needs to take account of both the whole object and its constituent parts, including its representation. This means that children need to handle, turn around and view from different angles as many 3-D shapes as possible. Working with 2-D representations is important but can become confusing if the children do not appreciate what the real thing looks like. As well as inspecting, examining and pictorially representing we also need to be able to discuss 3-D objects. Tall, short, long, high and so on are often to be heard in a 3-D discussion along with wide, narrow, broad and so on. What is happening here is the isolation of a noticeable 2-D feature of the 3-D shape. In talking widely about 3-D shapes we reinforce an understanding of 2-D and allow youngsters to get a clear picture of what the characteristics of 3-D shapes are and how they might be represented on paper. Representations of 3-D objects as 2-D drawings, paintings or photographs are something with which we are all familiar. However, we do not have to go far back in art history to see that representations have changed over time. There is a wealth of mathematics in the whole area of perspective and the development of drawing based on vanishing points, horizons, and what the 'hidden side' might look like.

Broadly, there are three categories of 3-D shapes, having some attributes of a sphere, prism or a pyramid. In the built and natural environment we find these three sorts of shape or parts of these three shapes. Some examples are shown below.

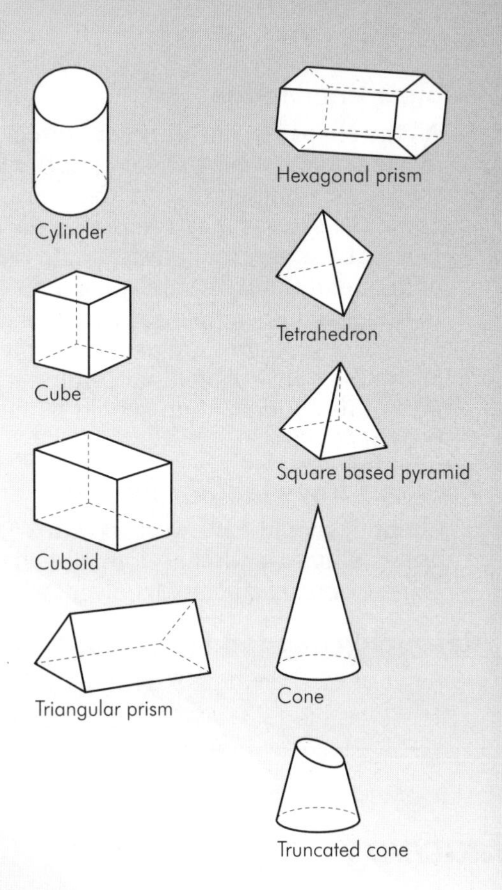

The characteristics of 3-D shapes that we come to discuss first are to do with surfaces, edges, and corners. Taking a cube as an example we can note its six faces, twelve edges, the fact that three edges in each case meet at a corner or vertex; and there are eight vertices. Once faces, edges and vertices are understood we can go beyond these physical attributes to explore planes of symmetry, and whether 3-D objects pack together or not. This serves to emphasise the fact that working with 3-D shapes and objects is part and 'parcel' of our everyday lives.

3-D SHAPES
THEME 7

Name and sort 3-D shapes

Learning targets

The children should be able to:

1 ➤➤ Name 3-D shapes
2 ➤➤ Sort 3-D shapes
3 ➤➤ Identify shapes in the built environment

Before you start

Subject knowledge

All the shapes in our world are three-dimensional – even a sheet of paper has thickness. Children should, therefore, be able to name the shapes they see in everyday life, as part of their general knowledge. In order to understand the properties of shapes they need to observe and compare similarities and differences. Shapes are assigned different roles in the built environment, according to their properties, and children should be helped to recognise this.

Previous knowledge required

Children should have worked with 3-D shapes at Key Stage 1 and, therefore, already know some of the vocabulary involved.

Resources needed for Lesson 1

A set of mathematical 3-D shapes, including a cube, a cuboid, a cylinder, a sphere, prisms with triangular and hexagonal bases, a square based pyramid; name cards for these shapes; objects from everyday life including two cubes, two cuboids, two cylinders, a sphere, a triangular prism; Copymaster 8

Resources needed for Lesson 2

A large collection of empty food packs and cartons in as large a range of shapes as possible. Invite the children to bring junk packaging into school before the lesson, so that there are enough cartons for every group to have a collection of at least ten

Resources needed for Lesson 3

Opportunities to look around the school; a Polaroid camera and film or photographs of the school buildings

Teaching the lessons

Lesson 1 

Key questions

What is the name of this shape?
Show me a triangular prism.
Which shape is the odd one out?

Vocabulary

Cube, cuboid, cylinder, sphere, prism, pyramid, face, surface, base

Introduction

15min

There is much to pack into this lesson, and the assumption is that the children will have had some experience of mathematical work with 3-D shapes beforehand. Show the children a drawing of a square and a solid shape such as a wooden block or cube from a mathematical set. Point out that the 'flat shape' is called '2-D' because it has 'two Ds or dimensions' which are length and breadth (it has no thickness). A '3-D' shape, by contrast has 'three Ds or dimensions'. These are length, breadth and thickness. Point out these dimensions on the shapes. Take up a cube shape from a set of mathematical shapes and ask the children what it is called. Write the word 'cube' on the board. Then hold up the cuboid and ask them to name it. Now do the same with a cylinder.

Activities

30min

Set out, at random, around the room, two cubes (for example a stock cube and a giant dice) two cuboids (for example, a cereal box and a pencil tin) and two cylinders (for example, a drum of kitchen cleaning powder and a coin). Label each with a number and allow the children a few minutes to inspect each one.

Ask the children to name the shapes set out in the

room. Then show them, from the set of mathematical shapes, the cube, cuboid, cylinder, sphere, prisms with triangular, rectangular and hexagonal bases and square based pyramid. They should readily name the cube, cuboid and cylinder. Tell the children the names of the other shapes. Place the shapes in a long row and put name cards in front of them. Write the names of the prisms and the pyramid on the board, pointing to the details of how they are spelt.

Ask the children to complete **Copymaster 8**.

Closing the lesson

15min

Ask individual children to assign names to shapes from the mathematical set as you hold them up.

Assessment

Child performance	Teacher action
Cannot name common 3-D shapes	Give the children the chance to handle the shapes, from the set of mathematical shapes, from construction block sets and from a collection of empty packaging. Give the children name labels to attach to these. Give quick fire questions on naming shapes, over several sessions.
Names cube and cuboid but not sure of other names	Show the children the shapes they are not sure of. Allow them to do rough sketches and write in the names. Then go on to the next lesson where they will get more practice.
Names common 3-D shapes	Go on to the next lesson

Lesson 2

2

Key questions

What is this group a set of?

How have I sorted these?

Which of these shall we put together?

Vocabulary

Cube, cuboid, cylinder, sphere, prism, pyramid, face, surface, base

Introduction

10min

While the children look on, take a collection of ten packs and sort them. You may, for example, take cubes, cuboids, cylinders and prisms, and place all the shapes together except for the cylinders. The children may respond by saying these are sets of cylinders and 'not cylinders'. They could also be a set of shapes with a curved surface and those with 'not curved' (that is plane faces). Try more sorts using these shapes.

Activities

30min

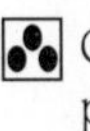

Give each group a large collection of empty food packs and cartons, and invite the children to have a turn at sorting each according to different criteria. Ask each group to recall the characteristics used for each sort. Set these out on the board, down one side. When all the sorts are listed, ask the children how the resultant sets of shapes looked and to complete the table. Here are some example entries:

How the shapes were sorted	What happened to the shapes
six or fewer corners	cylinder, pyramid, triangular prism
more than six corners	cube, cuboid
all faces square	cube
not all square faces	cylinder, pyramid, triangular prism, cuboid

Closing the lesson

10min

Describe a shape to the children giving a clue at a time, and see how quickly they can say which shape you are thinking of. Allow individual children to describe shapes in this way, too.

Assessment

Child performance	Teacher action
Cannot sort 3-D shapes	Give the children plenty of opportunities to do practical sorting with shapes, allowing them to talk about what they are doing and asking key questions as they work.
Sorts shapes but lacks confidence	Give the children more opportunities to do activities like those set out in this lesson
Can sort shapes with confidence.	Go on to the next lesson.

Lesson 3

3

Key questions

What shapes can you see here?

Where do we find triangular prisms in buildings? Why is this shape used?

Vocabulary

Some or all of these may be appropriate, according to the points made in discussion with the children: elevation, bird's eye view, construction, cube, cuboid, cylinder, sphere, prisms with triangular and hexagonal bases, a square based pyramid.

Introduction

10min

Point out that there are 3-D shapes to be seen all around us. The world is made of 3-D shapes, and everything actually has thickness as well as length and breadth. Ask the children to identify common

3-D shapes again and ask them what shapes they think are in use in the school buildings.

Activities

35min

With an accompanying adult, ask the children to look around the school and spot as many shapes as they can. They should keep a record of the locations of these. Take Polaroid photographs if such a camera is available.

Ask the children to make a shape drawing of the school and its environs. Results may look something like this:

Shape drawing of the school

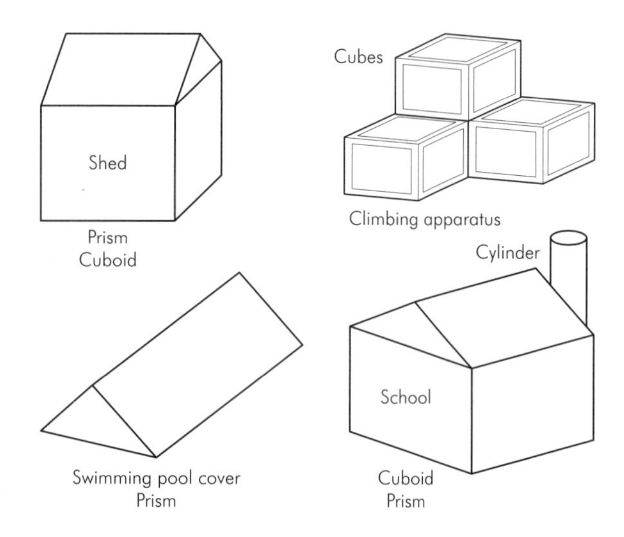

Closing the lesson

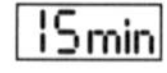

Pin up Polaroid or other photographs of the school buildings for the children to look at.

Assessment

Child performance	Teacher action
Cannot identify shapes in the built environment	Show the children a set of construction blocks and shapes and invite them to 'build' model buildings. Recap the names of the shapes they have used. Then allow them to look again at real buildings and match block shapes to these.
Can identify some shapes	Invite the children to handle some model blocks that are less common shapes. Check that the children can recognise and name these. Then allow them to seek these shapes in photographs and buildings.
Identifies shapes and seeks out shapes in complex structures.	The learning targets for this theme have been met.

HOMEWORK

Ask the children to do a shape drawing of their own house.

Ask the children to conduct a shape survey in their home to find at least two of the following shapes in every room in the house. Ask them to do drawings and make a record of this work:

Cuboid

Cylinder

Triangular prism

Hexagonal prism

3-D SHAPES

THEME 8

Nets and constructing shapes

Learning targets

The children should be able to:

1 ➔ Identify and draw nets for cubes and cuboids

2 ➔ Identify and draw nets for cylinders, pyramids and triangular prisms

3 ➔ Construct 3-D shapes

Before you start

Subject knowledge

Knowledge of how shapes would look if they were opened out serves to support children's ideas about the characteristics of shapes. Indeed the use of two-dimensional nets to produce three-dimensional objects is a major element in much of our manufacturing industry.

Previous knowledge required

Names of common 3-D shapes, vocabulary of shape including face, edge, corner, base

Resources needed for Lesson 1

Solid cuboid and cube; empty food boxes, which are cuboid and cube shapes; Copymaster C; card templates of squares, and rectangles of compatible measurements, as shown below

Resources needed for Lesson 2

Solid pyramid and triangular prism; card pyramids and triangular prisms that can be opened out; set squares; card templates of rectangles, squares, circles and triangles of compatible measurements, as shown below right; Copymaster 9

Suggested measures for squares, rectangles, circles and triangles

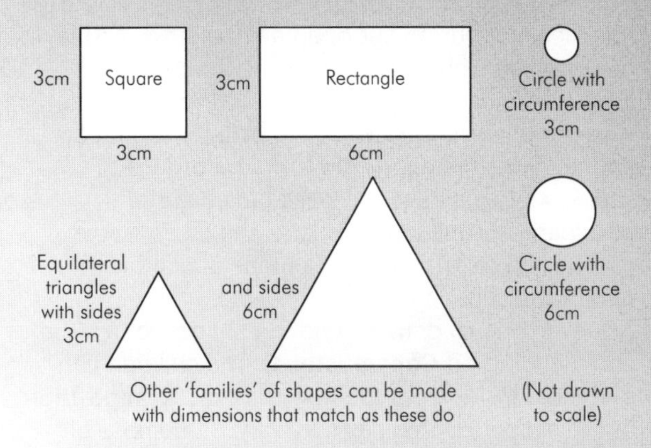

Resources needed for Lesson 3

Artstraws®, Plasticine® or other soft modelling material, sticky tape, pipe cleaners; thin card, set squares, scissors and glue

Suggested measures for squares and rectangles

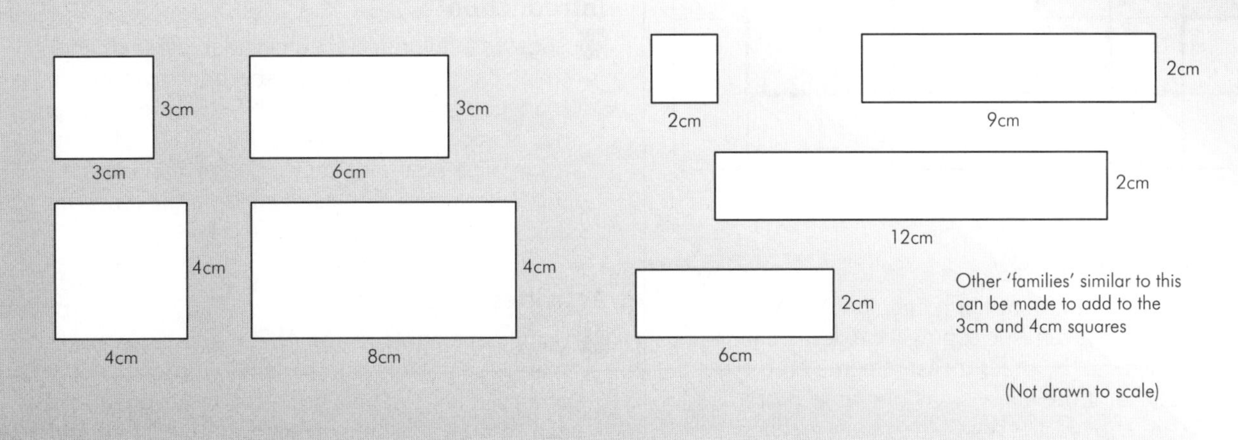

Teaching the lessons

Lesson 1 

Key questions

What do you think this shape would look like if we opened it out?

What shape could we make from this net?

Vocabulary

Cube, cuboid, face, square, rectangle, net

Introduction 

Place a solid cube alongside a cube shaped box and a solid cuboid alongside a cuboid box. Give the children rough paper and ask them to imagine what these shapes would look like if they could be opened out and laid flat. They should draw rough pictures and then hand them in. Carefully open out the cuboid box and show the children that it has six faces, three pairs of matching rectangles. Then open out the cube and point to the six square faces.

Activities 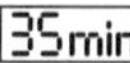

Allow each group to cut open a cuboid box and lay it out on a large sheet of paper and draw around it. Each child can do a part of the job (here is a suggested list: 1) cut open box, 2) lay box out flat and anchor to paper, 3) draw around outline of shape, 4) with a ruler and pencil mark in the boundaries of the faces, 5) label the faces. Allow each group to hold up their outline and show the rest of the class.

Ask everyone to draw around net shapes for a cube and a cuboid on **Copymaster C**. The children can then colour the faces to show the exact composition of the shapes. Outcomes may vary. Some possible outcomes are given below.

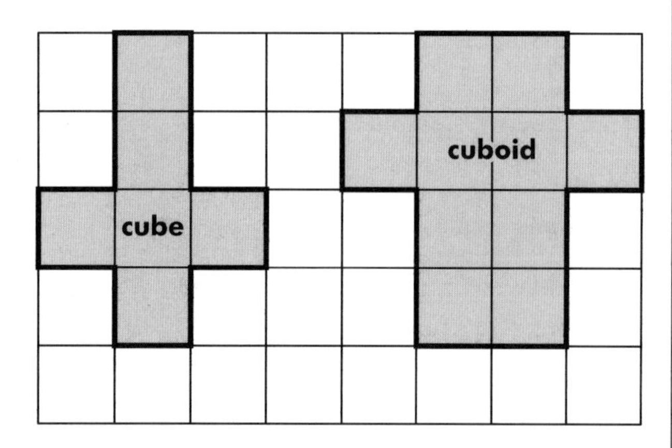

Closing the lesson 5min

On the board, draw a net of a cuboid with the measurements given (see top right). Ask the children to determine all the other measurements on the net. Point out that if the dimensions of one face of a cuboid are known, it is possible to draw an accurate net for the shape. Allow the children to review their rough sketches of nets, from the beginning of the lesson.

Net for a **cuboid**

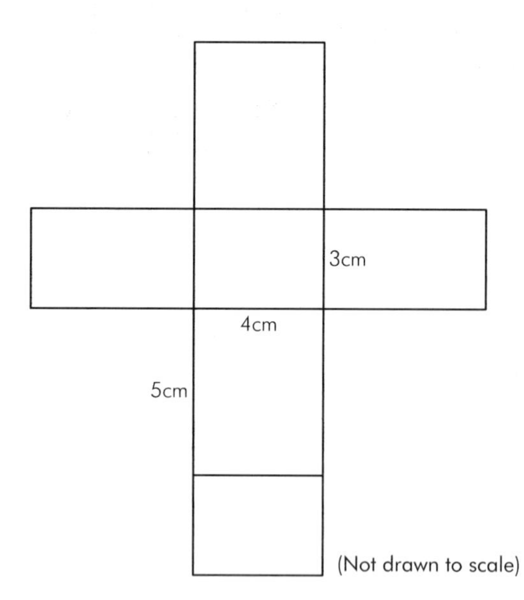

Assessment

Child performance	Teacher action
Cannot identify nets for cubes and cuboids	Allow the children to open out a number of boxes, and name and count the faces
Cannot draw nets for cubes and cuboids	Allow the children to open out some boxes, draw around them and glue both them and the resultant nets back together
Can label and make nets	Move on to the next lesson.

Lesson 2 

Key questions

Of what shape is this the net?

Which is the net of this shape?

Vocabulary

Net, cylinder, pyramid, prism

Introduction 15min

Show the children a solid cylinder, pyramid and triangular prism, and a card cylinder, pyramid and a triangular prism. Invite the children to draw a rough net of each of these shapes. Put the rough drawings aside. Open out a card cylinder, pyramid and a triangular prism. Show the children the resultant nets and point out the shapes of the faces.

Activities 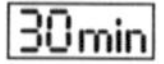

Using compatible rectangle, square, circle and triangle templates ask the children to produce nets of a cylinder, pyramid and a triangular prism. They can then swap with another pair of children and draw nets of the shapes using different dimensions.

Ask the children to work on the net puzzles on **Copymaster 9**.

Closing the lesson 5min

Invite the children to look at and evaluate their rough drawings of the nets made at the beginning of the lesson.

Assessment

Child performance	Teacher action
Cannot identify and draw nets for pyramids and triangular prisms	Allow the children to open out a pyramid and a triangular prism box and name and count the faces
Lacks confidence, or makes errors in work on nets.	Give the children some of the card templates and allow them to draw around them making nets of a set of pyramids and of triangular prisms of increasing size.
Can work on nets for pyramids and triangular prisms	Move on to the next lesson.

Lesson 3 

Key questions

What shape is this model?

Can you build this shape using the net as a plan?

Vocabulary

Cube, cuboid, face, square, rectangle, circle, net, pyramid, prism

Introduction 

Show the children the equipment they are going to be using and join together two Artstraws®, using Plasticine® and then two pipe cleaners as shown below.

Artstraws®, Plasticine® and pipe cleaner joints

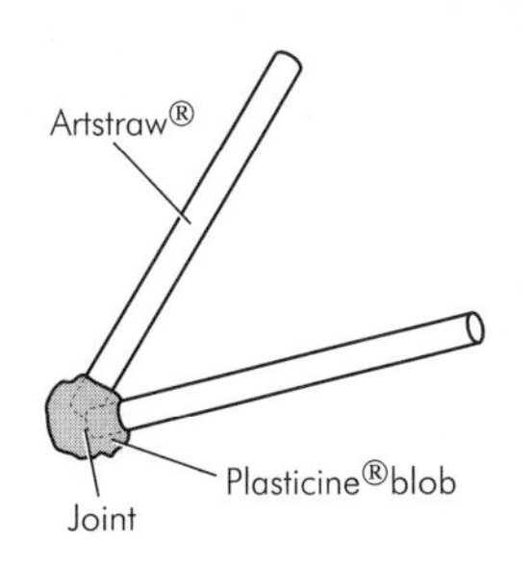

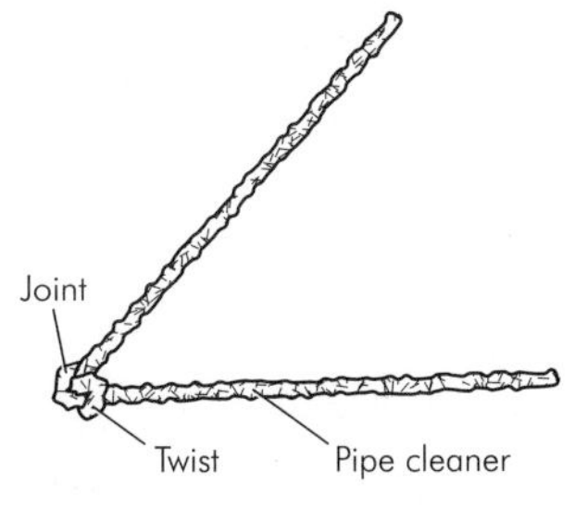

Activities 35min

Ask the children to construct a shape using Artstraws®, Plasticine® or other soft modelling material, pipe cleaners and sticky tape if joins will not hold. Divide the room into five areas, and assign each a shape to make (cube, cuboid, cylinder, pyramid, and triangular prism). The resulting shapes can be evaluated and displayed. This activity can be repeated, asking the children to create a different shape, or the children can be asked to try the activity that follows.

Using thin card, a set square, scissors and glue, invite the children to try making a cube or cuboid box. Remind them of the need for right-angled corners and accurate measurements. They should cut small flaps on some faces so that the box can be glued together.

Closing the lesson 10min

Discuss with the children, some of the problems they experienced in making straw/pipe cleaner and/or card models. Ask them to suggest ways of overcoming problems.

Assessment

Child performance	Teacher action
Cannot construct 3-D shapes	Return to a discussion about 3-D shapes. Allow the children to handle, play with and name the shapes before beginning the work on nets again.
Constructs shapes but needs more practice	Allow the children to do again some of the activities presented in the lessons in this theme.
Constructs shapes well	Move on to another theme

HOMEWORK

Invite the children to make up a gift box by tracing or sticking the outline on Copymaster 10 onto card. This can be decorated. Ask them to try making a gift box that is like a cuboid or triangular prism.

3-D SHAPES

THEME 9

More nets and the five regular solids

Learning targets

The children should be able to:

1 ➤➤ Construct shapes using given nets

2 ➤➤ Identify a tetrahedron and its net

3 ➤➤ Name and construct regular polyhedra

Before you start

Subject knowledge

There are only five regular shapes and in this theme the children are introduced to them. They are called 'regular' because their faces are all equal regular polygons. The shapes are:

- cube – six faces; each face is a square; three faces meet at each corner or vertex.
- tetrahedron – four faces; each face is an equilateral triangle; three faces meet at each vertex.
- octahedron – eight faces; each face is an equilateral triangle; four faces meet at each vertex.
- icosahedron – 20 faces; each face is an equilateral triangle; five faces meet at each vertex.
- dodecahedron – 12 faces; each face is a pentagon; three faces meet at each vertex.

Previous knowledge required

2-D and 3-D shapes and shape vocabulary

Resources needed for Lesson 1

Copymaster 10, Copymaster 11, glue, scissors, thin card, made up examples of a cube and a square based pyramid for demonstration purposes – not glued

Resources needed for Lesson 2

Copymaster E, protractors, thin card, scissors, glue

Resources needed for Lesson 3

Copymaster E, protractors, thin card, scissors, glue, Copymaster 12

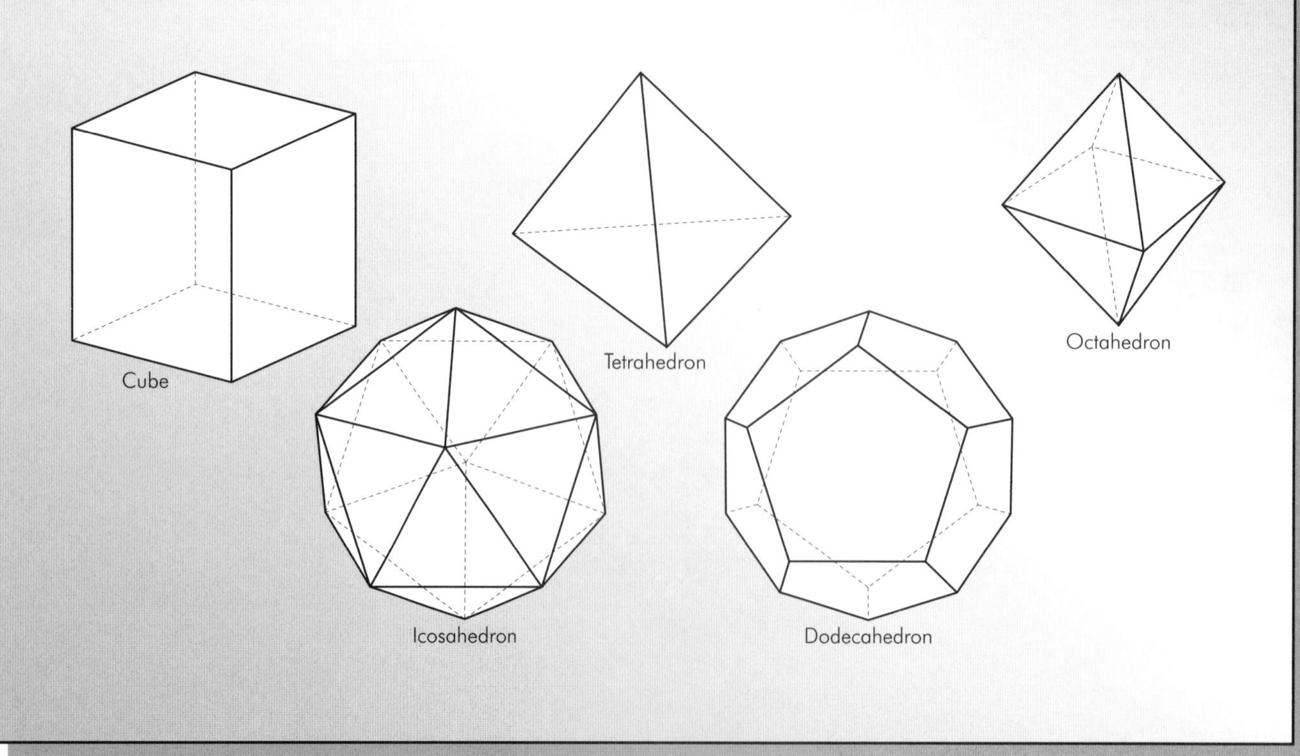

Teaching the lessons

Lesson 1 

Key questions

What do you notice about the square face on the pyramid and on the cube?

How many pyramids are needed?

Vocabulary

Net, cube, square based pyramid

Introduction 

Remind the children how to make a cube. Show them your example and then fold it flat to show the net. Now do the same for the square based pyramid. Tell the children that they are going to work in teams to produce a 3-D shape made from one cube and six square based pyramids.

Activities 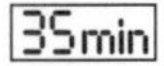

Give each group one copy of **Copymaster 10** and six copies of **Copymaster 11**, glue, scissors and card. The children, between them, have to produce one well made cube and six well made square based pyramids. As they complete these, tell them that you want them to glue the square based pyramids to the cube to make a star. Demonstrate with one pyramid on one face of the cube.

Closing the lesson 

Hold up some of the finished stars to show the children and collect all the stars for display.

Assessment

Child performance	Teacher action
Cannot begin to construct using the nets	Revise the characteristics of cubes before looking at and talking through the nets of these. Then help the children to make up some nets including those for square based pyramids.
Constructs components but does not manage a complete star	Give more time, then discuss what the children have done
Makes up a star	Move on to the next lesson

Lesson 2 

Key questions

What patterns of triangles will form nets of shapes?

Vocabulary

Isometric, equilateral triangle, tetrahedron, face

Introduction 10min

Remind the children of the work they have done using squared paper, and making nets. Show them paper with triangles on it and point out that nets can be made from these.

Activities 30min

Allow the children to each have a sheet of isometric paper **(Copymaster E)** and experiment in drawing around and looking at linked chains of triangles. Ask them whether they can see any nets for shapes among the patterns.

Show the children a solid shape that is a tetrahedron. Tell them what it is called and show them that it has four faces, each of which is an equilateral triangle.

Ask the children to try drawing a net for this shape on their isometric paper. Draw the net for the tetrahedron on the board. Allow the children to compare their nets with this drawing.

Net for a **tetrahedron**

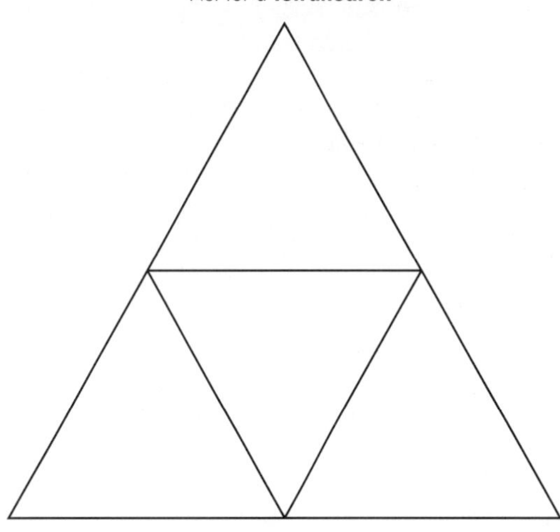

If there is time, ask the children to draw the net on a piece of thin card, making it larger than the net on the isometric paper, and remembering to put tabs on some faces. They can cut this out and fold and glue it.

Closing the lesson 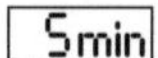

Discuss the problems the children may have had in net drawing or shape construction. Ask them how many faces, edges and corners (vertices) the tetrahedron has. Also check that they know that an equilateral triangle has all internal angles equal at 60°.

Assessment

Child performance	Teacher action
Cannot use isometric paper or identify a tetrahedron and its net	Invite the children to 'play' with isometric and triangular dotted paper. Also allow the children to mark and then draw around each of the faces of a tetrahedron
Not yet confident about the attributes of a tetrahedron.	Allow the children to handle tetrahedra and make some of varying sizes
Can demonstrate knowledge of the tetrahedron	Go on to the next lesson

Lesson 3

③

Key questions

What is this shape called?

What is a polyhedron?

What is a regular polyhedron?

Can you name some regular polyhedra?

Vocabulary

Regular, polyhedron, cube, tetrahedron, octahedron, icosahedron, dodecahedron

Introduction

15min

Tell the children that a polyhedron is a solid shape with plane faces and a regular polyhedron has faces that are all regular polygons (that is, plane shapes with all sides the same). There are only five such shapes. Tell the children that they have already worked with two of them. Draw a cube and a tetrahedron on the board and check that the children can name them and talk about their attributes. Then tell them the next shape is an octahedron. It is like two square based pyramids with equilateral triangle faces stuck together. If there are solid shapes that fit like this amongst the mathematics equipment in the classroom, show them to the children.

Activities

35min

Give each child a sheet of isometric paper **(Copymaster E)**, and give them a few minutes to try drawing the net for an octahedron.

Draw the net for an octahedron on the board. Allow the children to compare their nets with this drawing.

Ask the children to try to draw a net for an icosahedron on their isometric paper. Then on rough paper, using a protractor, they should try one for a dodecahedron. They can check their efforts against **Copymaster 12**.

Ask the children to try making an octahedron, icosahedron or dodecahedron, using protractors, thin card, scissors and glue. If one third of the class try each shape, and they are made in different colours of card, they can be used for a mathematical display.

Closing the lesson

10min

Ask the children to evaluate their own efforts at nets and constructions

Assessment

Child performance	Teacher action
Cannot name regular polyhedra	Allow the children to work at attaching name labels to solid polyhedra from a mathematics set. They should also be given the chance to talk about the faces, and angles of these shapes. Then ask them to repeat some of the activities from this theme
Cannot construct nets and shapes of regular polyhedra	Allow the children to draw around card shapes to match all the faces of the shapes, and to unfold and open out card models of the shapes, before having more goes at making nets
Can name and make regular polyhedra	The learning targets for this theme have been met

HOMEWORK

Make some of the set of regular solids from thin card.

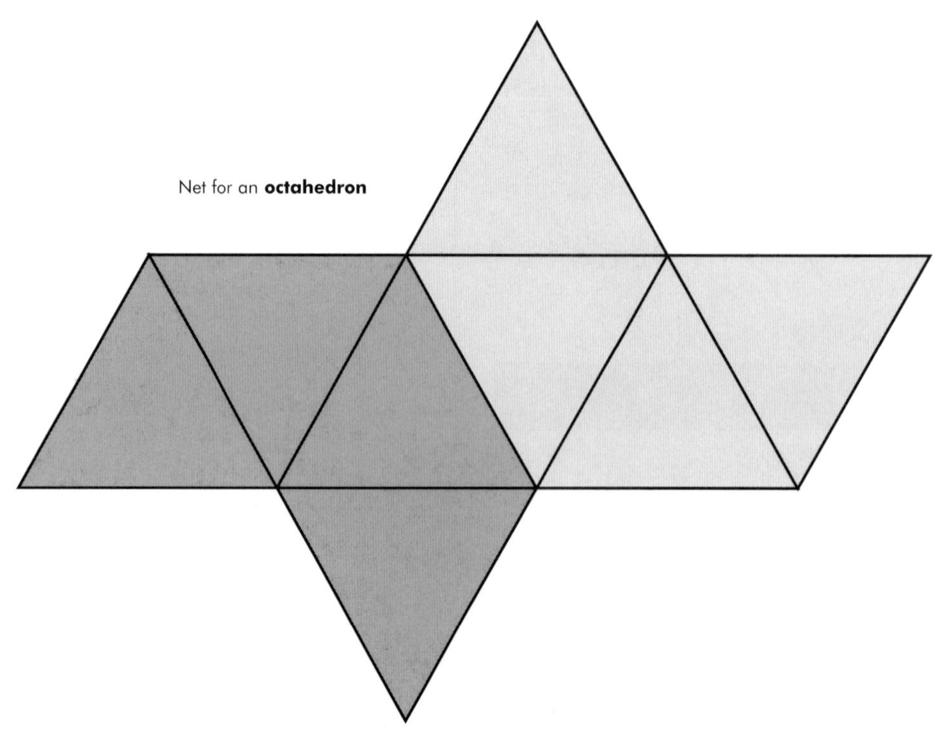

3-D SHAPES

THEME 10

Faces, edges and planes

Learning targets

The children should be able to:

1 ➤ Use modelling material to make 3-D shapes and observe what happens when they are cut up

2 ➤ Name the shapes of the cut faces when a solid shape is sliced up

3 ➤ Demonstrate Euler's relation

Before you start

Subject knowledge

This theme gives children the chance to build on their knowledge of 3-D shapes and their attributes. They will learn that for shapes with plane faces there is a formula. This was discovered by Leonhard Euler 1707-83, a Swiss mathematician, who wrote more than 800 books and papers about pure and applied mathematics, physics and astronomy. The formula applies to all the polyhedra that children at Key Stage 2 are likely to have experience of, whether regular or not.

Previous knowledge required

Shape vocabulary, nets, and regular polyhedra

Resources needed for Lesson 1

Plasticine® or similar modelling material, modelling boards and tools, rough paper

Resources needed for Lesson 2

Copymaster 13

Resources needed for Lesson 3

Sets of 3-D mathematical shapes and a collection of other solid shapes with plane faces, including non-regular solids.

These should include the following for each work group in the class: a cube, a cuboid, a triangular prism, a hexagonal prism, a pyramid, a tetrahedron, an octahedron, a cone, and a truncated cone

Teaching the lessons

Lesson 1 

Key questions

What is this shape called?

Can you make a … (name of shape) in Plasticine®?

Cut the shape in half. What shapes are the cut faces?

Vocabulary

Cube, cuboid, triangular prism, hexagonal prism, pyramid, tetrahedron, octahedron, cone, plane face

Introduction

10min

Write a list of the following names for shapes on the board: cube, cuboid, triangular prism, hexagonal prism, pyramids, tetrahedron, octahedron, and cone. Tell the children they are going to have the opportunity to make these shapes in turn from one piece of modelling material.

Activities

40min

Give each child a blob of modelling material and ask them to make the first shape shown on the board. Ask them to try cutting carefully through the shape. Each child in the group should cut in a different direction. They should then look at the cut surfaces and compile, as a group, a rough diagram of the shape, the direction of the cuts, and the resulting cut surfaces. They then do the same with the second and so on. An example of how a rough may look is shown below.

Rough of **triangular prism**

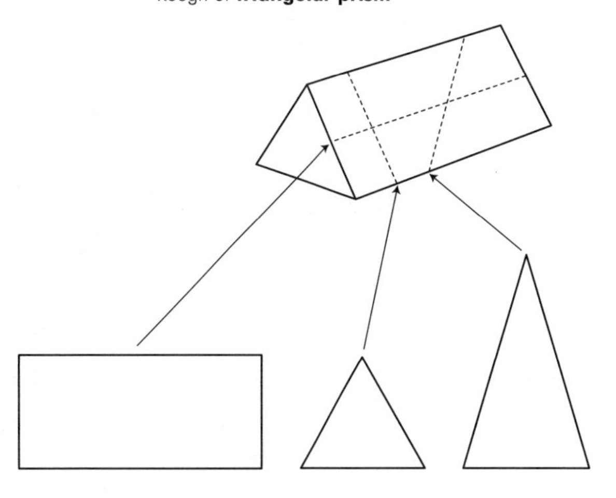

Closing the lesson

5min

Compare the rough work the groups have produced, looking for similarities and differences.

Assessment

Child performance	Teacher action
Lacks the skills or vocabulary to make 3-D shapes and talk about what happens when they are cut up	Give the children more practical experience in handling and naming shapes, before repeating the activities set out in this lesson
Uncertain of shape vocabulary	Talk about, label and discuss shapes and their attributes, over several sessions, giving the children the chance to create a picture glossary of shape words. Then move on to next lesson
Can make shapes, cut them, and talk about them	Move on to the next lesson

Lesson 2

Key questions

What shape is this?

What other plane shapes can you name?

Vocabulary

Cube, cuboid, triangular prism, hexagonal prism, pyramid, tetrahedron, octahedron, cone, plane face and names of plane faces as required

Introduction

5min

Quickly hold up each of the solid shapes the children will be working on, and ask them to name them. Place the shapes at different locations in the room.

Activities

35min

Either give each group a complete set of solid shapes to handle or ask the groups to visit each shape in the room in turn, and talk about the cut faces made if the shapes were sliced up. The group should choose one child to write their record on a chart:

Name of shape	Shapes of cut faces
cube	square rectangle
cone	circle ellipse

Ask the children to complete **Copymaster 13.**

Closing the lesson

10min

Pin up all the group charts and allow the children time to look at and evaluate them.

Assessment

Child performance	Teacher action
Cannot predict and name the shapes of the cut faces when a solid shape is sliced up	Return to lesson 1 in this theme and ask the children to model and cut shapes. Then repeat this lesson
Lacks confidence in predicting and naming these shapes	Give the children many opportunities to solve puzzles such as 'What shape is made if I cut this shape here?
Can predict the results of cuts and name shapes	Move on to the next lesson

Lesson 3

Key questions

How many faces?

How many edges?

How many corners (vertices)?

Can you see how these might be connected?

Vocabulary

Euler, face, edge, corner, equation, relation, cube, cuboid, triangular prism, hexagonal prism, pyramid, tetrahedron, octahedron, cone, truncated cone

Introduction

5min

Tell the children that they are going to investigate some shapes by following the work of Leonhard Euler, a famous eighteenth-century mathematician, who looked at the characteristics of solid shapes.

Activities

40min

Using a set of solid shapes with plane faces, invite the children to make a chart showing the numbers of faces, edges and corners on each shape. Each child should make their own chart, but the counts can be done as a group, so that the children can check each other's counts. When they are nearing completion, ask the children to look very carefully at the numbers in their chart to see whether they can make up a general statement that shows that the number of faces is connected to the number of edges and vertices, for each shape.

Closing the lesson

5min

Review the children's suggestions and show them that the following relation holds good for the shapes they have looked at: Euler's relation can be expressed as $F + V = E + 2$ (number of Faces plus number of Vertices equals number of Edges plus two).

Assessment

Child performance	Teacher action
Cannot tabulate the data required	In sessions with an adult allow the children to make their own charts showing the characteristics of shapes. Then return to activities within this theme.

Does not know how to try creating an equation	Show the children some simple formulae before allowing them to test out Euler's relation
Can try to detect a relationship between the data	The learning targets for this theme have been met.

HOMEWORK

Ask the children to investigate how many planes of symmetry a cube has. How does this total relate to the number of lines of symmetry in a square?

Investigations

- Make up a 3-D quiz 'Name That Shape' and try it out with friends. The quiz should give clues to the shape that has to be named. Real examples can then be used to check.
- Undo an empty package and lay it out flat then make a drawing of a net that might have been used to create the package. Look at any printing on the package – is it all the same way up? How might a manufacturer design and produce this sort of packaging. Write to the manufacturer to find out.
- Read about the Dodecahedron in Norton Juster's story *The Phantom Tollbooth* (William Collins, Sons & Co Ltd, 1962). Discuss the jokes and puns. Make up a story about another regular polyhedron. There are other intriguing mathematical ideas in the story too.
- Make cuboids and cones from modelling clay and try slicing them in different ways to see what shape faces you can make.
- Find out about optical illusions. These are often to do with trying to see 3-D in a 2-D representation.
- Make a collection of postcards and pictures of paintings from different periods of art. How have the different artists tried to make the 2-D look 3-D – or have they ignored that? Do some measuring and see what you can find. This might also link to the golden ratio (see page 16).
- Make a model or collect some scale models and investigate them. Try taking photographs and see if you can fool someone into thinking it is the real thing.

Assessment

- Group a collection of solids and explain your grouping. Can you group them in another way?
- Using constructional apparatus/ materials make up a variety of named 3-D shapes
- Identify nets that would make given solids. Take a cylinder (there are convenient ones that hold sweets) apart and then draw a net for a cylinder. Can you now draw a net for a cone? Solutions are shown here.
- Make a container to hold a given number of objects. These objects could be coins, sugar cubes, square based pyramids or other convenient shapes.

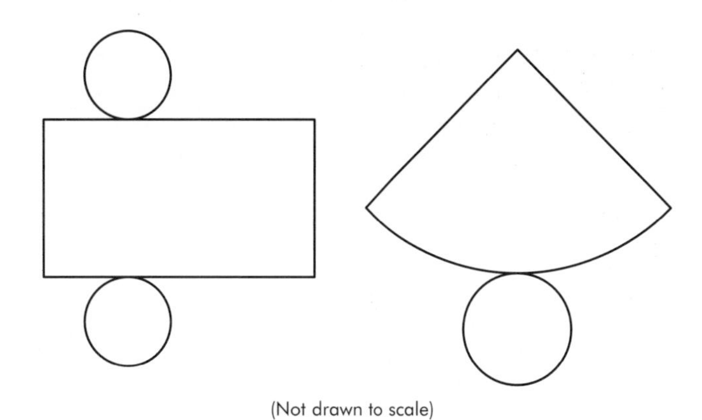

(Not drawn to scale)

ANGLES AND CO-ORDINATES

The right angle and the division of a circle into 360 degrees are ideas developed centuries ago. The use of a device for determining right angles for building purposes is of clear importance. There is evidence that Egyptian builders used ropes, knotted at equal intervals and pegs to make 'square corners'. From our knowledge of Pythagoras' theorem we can appreciate that a triangle of three knots by four knots by five knots is a right-angled triangle. The Babylonians used sixty as a base number. They gave us not only sixty seconds in a minute and sixty minutes in an hour but also six times sixty degrees in one rotation, that is 360 degrees. The Ancient Greeks developed work on angle and produced many theorems about, not only, right-angled triangles but also, for example the degrees in any triangle.

Angle needs to be viewed in two ways. It can be seen as part of a rotation or as a measure of the dimensions of a fixed corner. We can think about these as being a snapshot of a movement, a fleeting description of a dynamic event, or as the measure of a fixed and therefore static relationship. The hands on a clock represent an example of the former, the conjunction of two walls the latter. Whilst we need to know about both uses of angle, we should favour the dynamic view as it is so prevalent in everyday life. There are, however, a number of terms that children need to learn that relate clearly to static angles. The common terms with which they need to be familiar are acute, obtuse and reflex. To these we might add the right angle.

In developing a dynamic view of angle we need to have a concept of position. If we are to take a snapshot of a movement then we have to have a way of identifying the start and end of that movement. René Descartes (1596-1650) a French philosopher and mathematician gave us one important way of looking at position. He developed what we now term Cartesian co-ordinates and opened up a relationship between geometry, algebra and number. Co-ordinates in the first quadrant are in common use nowadays in everyday life, and through the medium of television many children will have encountered the use of co-ordinates in maps and mappings, both of the world and, for example, of human skulls to determine facial appearance. Ideas and insights about angles and co-ordinates will enhance any child's appreciation of football, cricket, netball, orienteering, and also their interest in the stars and the extent of the universe.

ANGLES AND CO-ORDINATES

THEME 11

Right angles

Learning targets

The children should be able to:

1 ➤ Find right angles in the built environment

2 ➤ Make and use a right angle detector

3 ➤ Identify right angles in pictures and diagrams

Before you start

Subject knowledge

The right angle is a fundamental idea in the study of shapes. It has a long history, in a practical sense. In order to build, for example, square or rectangular based buildings, the builder needs to be able to construct corners that are right-angled. One way of doing this is to use a rope knotted at regular intervals with three pegs arranged so that the rope has three, four and five knots on each side of the triangle that the pegs form. This will create a right angle. Pythagoras' theorem indicates why it works. Right angles are commonly found in the shapes of buildings and other constructions such as windows, picture-frames, books and so on. Children should come to be able to readily identify right angles.

Previous knowledge required

General observation and drawing skills. Experience with construction toys or apparatus.

Resources needed for Lesson 1

Copymaster A

Resources needed for Lesson 2

Torn pieces of paper, assistance to accompany children to different parts of the school as necessary

Resources needed for Lesson 3

Copymaster 14

Teaching the lessons

Lesson 1

Key questions

Is this a right angle?

Can you show me a right angle?

Where are the right angles here?

Vocabulary

Right angle, corner

Introduction — 15 min

Using the corner of the classroom, explain to the children that the shape the walls make when they join in the corner has a special name – a right angle. Draw a right angle on the board then, using the door to the classroom, point out places where there are right angles. Ask the children if they can tell you anywhere else in the room that they can see a right angle. If any of the suggestions are not right angles, draw an acute angle on the board and explain that this is an angle but not the special kind we are looking for.

Activities — 20 min

With the children working in small groups, ask them to find out all the right angles they can in the classroom. They should make notes to help them remember which ones they have spotted. After a few minutes of activity, ask the children to share some of their findings with you. Point out the places and the objects as they are mentioned, using this as an opportunity to reinforce their appreciation of a right angle. Draw three more right angles on the board using different orientations.

Give out **Copymaster A** and ask the children, working in pairs, to use the dots to help them draw a picture of at least one part of the classroom or one object in it that has at least one right angle.

Closing the lesson — 10 min

Let some of the pairs of children show their efforts to the class. Draw a rectangle on the board and ask where the right angles are and how many there are.

Assessment

Child performance	Teacher action
Finds a limited range of right angles	Check to see whether orientation is causing the children to dismiss some right angles as being inappropriate. Then give another opportunity to find them
Finds numbers of readily observable right angles	Encourage the children to look for a greater range. Show some examples
Finds many right angles including some that are difficult to detect	Ask the children how they were able to do this. Then move on to next lesson

Lesson 2

Key questions

Can you see that this is a right angle?

How many right angles have you found?

Where are some of your right angles?

Vocabulary

Right angle, right angle detector, total

Introduction

10min

Ask the children what they know so far about right angles. Tell them that they are all going to make right angle detectors and use them to find right angles around the school. Using a torn piece of rough paper, demonstrate to the children how to make a detector as shown below. Explain that the creases must be really sharp and that, when you fold the second time, the crease must make the edges match.

Activities

20min

Give out torn paper sheets and get the children to fold their right angle detectors. Help as necessary and recruit children to assist each other. Allocate different locations in the school to each group and tell them that they need to find as many right angles as they can and test them with their detectors. If they prove to be right angles, the children should keep a note of where the angles are.

Closing the lesson

10min

Get representatives of each group to say how many right angles they found and to give examples of them, especially any that they found surprising. Collect the lists to pin up for all the class to see. Ask the children to keep their right angle detectors to help with the next lesson.

Assessment

Child performance	Teacher action
Has problems with folding	Give a range of paper folding opportunities making such things as booklets, mirror pictures and stand up cards
Shows some uncertainty about their search for right angles	Let the children discuss the lists that were assembled and take the children, with their detectors, to look at some right angles that other children found
Completes the task satisfactorily	Move on to next lesson

Lesson 3

Key questions

Where are the right angles?

How many right angles are there in this one?

Vocabulary

Right angle, total

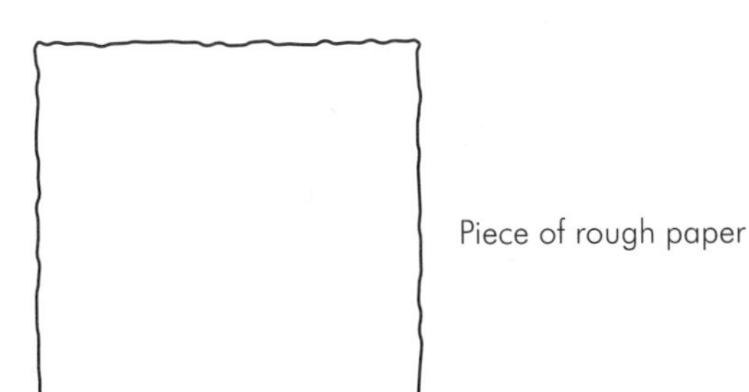

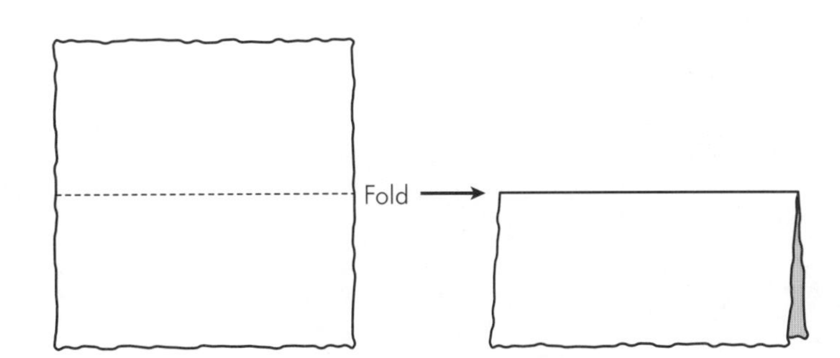

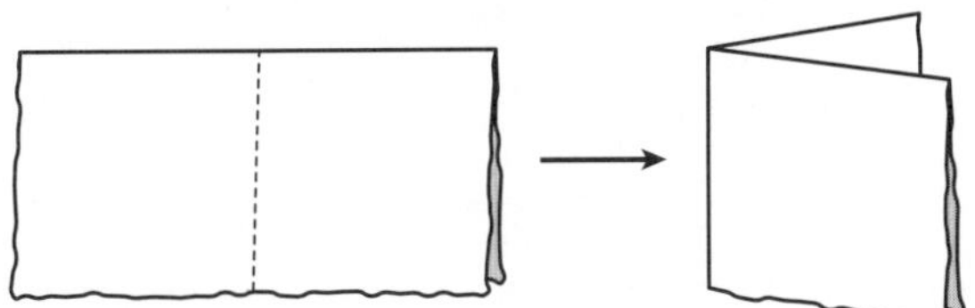

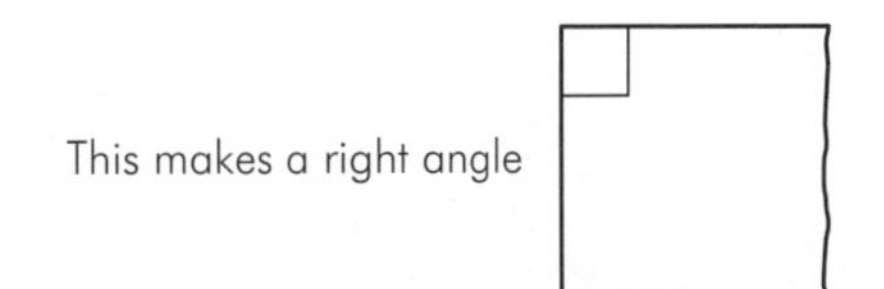

Introduction

10min

In this lesson, the children should consolidate what they have learnt and start the process of transferring observation in the built environment to drawings and diagrams. Draw a rectangle on the board. Let one of the children use their right angle detector from Lesson 2 to show the four right angles. Tell the children that they will be given a set of drawings in which there are some right angles. They have to find and mark each one and work out how many in each drawing. They can, if they wish, use their detectors to help.

Activities

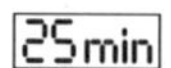

Give out **Copymaster 14** and go around the class asking the key questions and supporting children as necessary.

Closing the lesson

Look at some examples on the Copymaster with the children and identify which are the right angles and how many there are in each drawing. Discuss the difference between identifying right angles in a drawing and in a real object. Collect the children's work for assessing their understanding of right angles.

Assessment

Child performance	Teacher action
Finds easily detected examples but does not complete the task	Work with the children in a group using the Copymaster to extend their perception and appreciation
Completes the task with one or two right angles not identified	Give feedback after checking their work and, at a later date, give the Copymaster to them again
Completes all satisfactorily	The children have met the learning targets for this theme

HOMEWORK

Let the children take home, or make at home, the right angle detector and use it to find some right angles in their bedrooms. Make a collection of pictures from comics and magazines, which contain right angles.

ANGLES AND CO-ORDINATES

THEME **12**

Grids and position

Learning targets

The children should be able to:

1 ➳ Use grid references to locate features on a grid

2 ➳ Use grid references and the four main compass points to locate features on a map

3 ➳ Make a map using a grid

Before you start

Subject knowledge

Before children can move on to using co-ordinates to determine points on a grid, they need sound experience of locating and naming regions. According to convention the naming of columns and rows on a grid is a combination of letters and numbers. Many road and town maps use this convention. So, when looking for a street name or a town, the reference might be A3, G7. It is, of course, possible to use numbers for both row and column. The use of grid references is an essential foundation for later work using greater precision for describing position. Allied to the location of positions we can also use compass points to help orientate ourselves. Children learn, first, that N, S, W and E indicate the directions of north, south, east and west, and learn the other main compass points later.

Previous knowledge required

Simple, pictorial representation; early order and sequence work.

Resources needed for Lesson 1

Copymaster 15

Resources needed for Lesson 2

Copymaster D, Copymaster 16, dice, counters of two different colours

Resources needed for Lesson 3

Copymaster D

Teaching the lessons

Lesson 1 ①

Key questions

What is the label for this square?

Which did you look at first, the row or the column?

Vocabulary

Grid, row, column

Introduction 10 min

Draw a grid on the board and label it with letters for the columns and numbers for the rows. Draw a smiley face in one of the squares on the grid. Explain to the children that we can say that the smiley face is in a 'named' square. Name the square that you have used, for example, C3. Put an unhappy face on the grid and ask the children to tell you where it is. If necessary, do another one and another until you are sure that the children understand. Then ask how many squares would the first smiley face need to be moved to cover the unhappy face. Draw a trail and count the squares with the children.

Activities 25 min

Give out **Copymaster 15**. Ask the children to work through the questions. Remind them of the convention for naming squares and, when they have answered these questions, the ways in which we can calculate the distances to travel.

Closing the lesson 10 min

Go over the questions on the Copymaster, getting individuals to give their answers in order that the class can carry out self-checking.

Assessment

Child performance	Teacher action
Makes errors in naming the squares	Using Copymaster D, work with the children in labelling and placing counters in named squares, then let them do it themselves
Completes most of the work satisfactorily	Give more time for completion
Completes all the work satisfactorily	Move on to the next lesson

Lesson 2

Key questions

What is the label for this square?

Where is this object?

What direction is this object from this other object?

Vocabulary

Grid, row, column, label, location, north, south, east, west, horizontal, vertical, diagonal

Introduction — 5 min

Tell the children that they are going to play a game using squared paper, dice and coloured counters. To understand the game, they first have to know how to set up and label the grid for the game. On the board draw a grid like the one shown below.

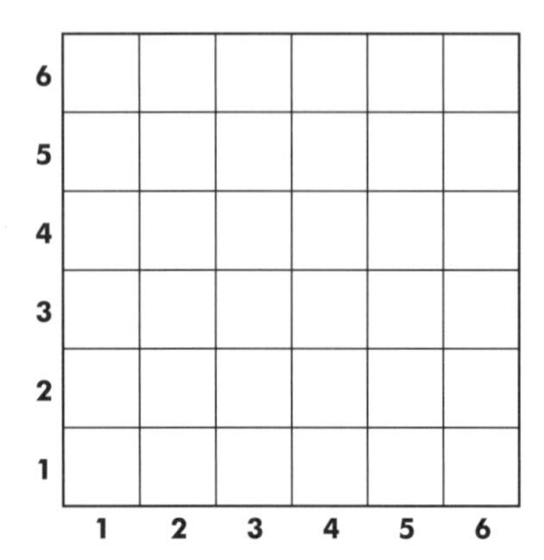

Point out that, in this case, we are using numbers for both columns and rows. Tell the children that working in pairs they are going to draw their own grid. To play the game they take turns to throw a pair of dice. The numbers that are thrown are used, in either order, to identify a square in which the player's counter is placed. The first player to get three counters in a row, vertically, horizontally or diagonally, is the winner.

Activities — 35 min

Give out **Copymaster D**, one sheet for each pair of children. Give out two dice for each pair and counters of two different colours. The children make their grid like the one on the board and play the game. Give time for this but encourage the children to play at a reasonable pace. When you feel they are ready to stop the game, tell the class that you are going to give them a task to do on their own. Give out **Copymaster 16**. Point out that on the map of this treasure island, there are the compass points N, S, W and E. Ask the children what they know about these. Do they know which way north is from the classroom? And in which direction is west? The children then attempt the questions on the Copymaster.

Closing the lesson — 10 min

With the class together, ask for the children's comments on the game. Go over the Copymaster using individual answers for self-checking. Collect the Copymaster for marking.

Assessment

Child performance	Teacher action
Makes errors in locating squares	Give further support as suggested in Lesson 1
Completes the game and part of the Copymaster	Allow more time to complete the Copymaster, check the answers
Completes both tasks satisfactorily	Move on to the next lesson

Lesson 3

Key questions

What is this called?

Why did you put that there?

What is the reference for?

Vocabulary

Grid, reference, location, map

Introduction — 10 min

With the class, go over the main things the children should have learnt about the uses of a grid and the main compass points. Tell them that, in this lesson, they are going to make up their own treasure maps. Remind them of the one they used in Lesson 2.

Activities — 30 min

Give out **Copymaster D**. The children have to draw their own treasure island and put features on the map. Go around, asking them to tell you the grid labels for some of the features they have included. Ask those who make good progress to write questions about their maps for others to answer.

Closing the lesson — 5 min

Ask what the children found easy or difficult about making their maps. Collect the maps for display.

Assessment

Child performance	Teacher action
Map is drawn but there is still some confusion about labelling or naming squares	Give help based on earlier lessons. Help to prepare questions to pin on the display
Map is drawn and evidence from questions that labelling is understood	Give time for some questions to be written and pinned up on the display
Map completed and some appropriate questions prepared	Children can help with the display and add further questions

HOMEWORK

Ask the children to look at maps that use a grid system. Allow them to take home Copymaster 16. They can give directions and grid references for a tour around the island and mention the sights to be seen en route.

Angle and rotation

Learning targets

The children should be able to:

1 ➤ Identify and discuss examples of turning in activities and situations
2 ➤ Investigate rotations and part-rotations
3 ➤ Draw and name particular kinds of angle

Before you start

Subject knowledge

There are two circumstances in which children encounter angles – angles as corners (static) and as rotation (dynamic). Here, emphasis is given to angle as rotation, though what is learnt can readily be applied to a consideration of static angles. The key idea is that children should come to recognise that turning is an important part of everyday life and that it is possible to make precise statements about that turning. In viewing angle as rotation, we can appreciate that there can be more than one complete rotation. So, for example, the number of rotations made in turning a screwdriver to drive home a screw is related to the screw thread and the length of the screw. Static angles can be accommodated only within the idea of one whole rotation being all that is possible.

Previous knowledge required

Right angles, common fractions

Resources needed for Lesson 1

A PE lesson in which turning and holding new positions is the focus, constructional apparatus which involves nuts and bolts

Resources needed for Lesson 2

A large clock face, a compass with eight points made from an overhead transparency or carefully drawn on the board, Copymaster 17

Resources needed for Lesson 3

Copymaster 18

Teaching the lessons

Lesson 1 ①

Key questions

What is turning?

How much of a turn is this?

How many turns have you made?

Vocabulary

Turning, turn, rotate, rotation, objects, activity

Introduction 10 min

This lesson should follow or be linked with a PE lesson in which the children have been moving, turning and making shapes with different angles. Use this sort of experience to discuss with the children their ideas about turning. Get them to try and define both 'a turn' and 'turning'. Tell them that, in this lesson, they are to think of as many ideas as possible about where, in everyday life, they use things that turn or where they themselves turn. Give an example of each – the turning of the hands of a clock or the turns they make in coming to school or going home. Put these on the board under the headings 'Objects' (the clock) and 'Activities' (walking home).

Activities 25 min

Working in small groups the children have to identify activities and objects that involve or use turning. They should agree these and list them. Allow them to look around the classroom if they wish. After about 15 minutes, put out the constructional apparatus and ask them if this gives them any more ideas.

Closing the lesson 10 min

Using the two categories on the board, get examples from the children and put them under their correct headings. Discuss those where the children may disagree or are clearly uncertain. Add some of your own if more stimulus is needed. Finish the lesson while walking around a table, pointing out that at each corner you are making a quarter turn and that when you get back to where you have started, you have made four quarter turns, that is one whole rotation. Then walk quickly around the table a few more times to illustrate the idea that you can have more than one rotation.

Assessment

Child performance	Teacher action
Produces a restricted list, mainly of one type of turn	Following the lesson, discuss the ideas again. See whether the stimulus of other people's ideas has helped these children to see more possibilities.
Produces examples of both situations and objects	Move on to the next lesson
Produces a lot of examples and ideas on turning	Move on to the next lesson

Lesson 2 ②

Key questions

What part of a rotation is this?

What fraction of a whole turn is there?

Vocabulary

Rotation, fraction, turn

Introduction 15 min

Remind the children of what they know about the right angle. Draw a circle on the board and draw in a quarter turn. Link the right angle with this quarter turn and ask how many quarter turns are in one complete rotation. Now divide the right angle in half and ask what fraction this makes. The children should appreciate that each segment is now one eighth of a whole rotation. Either on the board or using an overhead transparency, put up a compass rose with N, S, W, E, NE, SE, SW and NW on it. Link it to what they have just done with the circle. Now show a large clock face and point out that the quarter turns on this are right angles and the face is divided into twelfths.

Activities 25 min

Give out **Copymaster 17**. Working individually, the children need to undertake the core activities. There are some additional challenges, but these should be attempted only when the main tasks are completed.

Closing the lesson 10 min

Using the Copymaster and a range of the children's responses, recap the main points of the lesson in respect of fractions of a whole rotation. Point out that there are more possibilities than the ones covered by the Copymaster. The children, especially those who attempted the additional challenges, could make suggestions about these.

Assessment

Child performance	Teacher action
Completes most of the core activities	Give some more time but with close support
Completes all the core activities	Give some more time
Completes all the core activities and attempts the additional challenges	Move on to the next lesson

Lesson 3 ③

Key questions

What sort of angle is this?

Vocabulary

Right, acute, obtuse, reflex, straight and whole turn

Introduction

15 min

All the angles that need to be covered in this lesson are shown here.

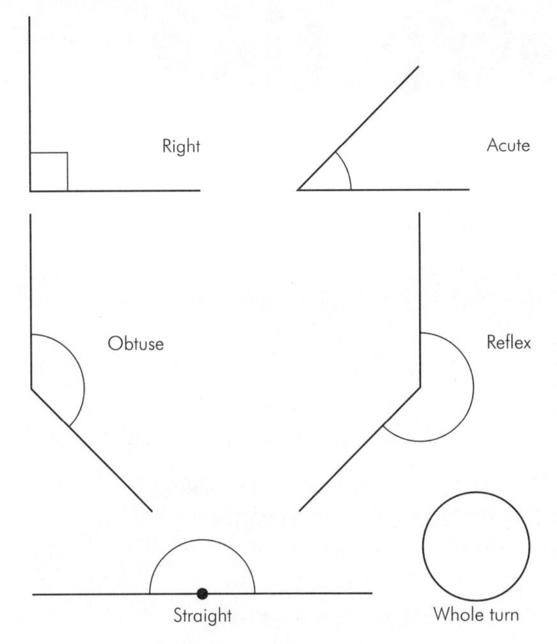

The use of the arcs for making angles can be related to being part of a whole turn.

Put a circle on the board. Ask children where to draw the lines to make right angles. Tell them that the term 'right' is an important one but that there are others that are important too. Rub out the circle leaving the right angle and remind them of the symbol we use with such angles. Now draw an acute angle, putting in the symbol and writing up the name. Ask the children what they notice. They need to appreciate that it is a smaller angle than a right angle. Now do the same exercise for obtuse angles, reflex angles and straight angles.

Activities

20 min

Give out **Copymaster 18**. This gives the children lots of practice in identifying types of angles.

Closing the lesson

10 min

Select examples from the Copymaster that cover all of the main angle types. Put them on the board and ask the children to tell you what they are. Collect the Copymasters to check the children's accuracy and understanding.

Assessment

Child performance	Teacher action
Identifies some angles but confuses at least two of the types	Go over the characteristics and then let the children try the Copymaster once more
Identifies most angles correctly	Talk over the answers given to check they are mistakes rather than a lack of understanding
Gets all correct	The children have met the learning targets for this theme

HOMEWORK

The children could look for turns and angles at home and around the community and present their ideas on a display. Encourage them to look at doors opening, hinges, wind-up toys, folding doors, box lids, the shape of shower heads, taps and so on. There is a vast array of places where they will see rotation and part-rotation as well as angles as corners.

ANGLES AND CO-ORDINATES

THEME **14**

Measuring and constructing angles

Learning targets

The children should be able to:

1 ➤➤ Relate particular angles to each other
2 ➤➤ Use degrees in measuring angles
3 ➤➤ Construct two dimensional shapes

Before you start

Subject knowledge

In developing children's understanding of the use of degrees for measuring angles, it is important to build on what is known about right angles, straight angles and their relationship to a full circle. This knowledge can then be employed in looking at ways in which different two-dimensional shapes fit together. All these experiences can be combined in discussing the use of the 360° system for one rotation. The protractors and drawing instruments we are going to need for this sort of work require careful and precise use. Skills may need to be practised. While protractors are often semi-circular, the use of circular protractors is recommended as these support the transfer of ideas readily from the earlier work.

Previous knowledge required

Two-dimensional shapes, some work on tessellation is desirable but not essential, skills in using drawing instruments and careful measurement, division

Resources needed for Lesson 1

Plastic or card templates of squares, right angled triangles, equilateral triangles, rectangles and hexagons; scissors, small sheets of sugar paper

Resources needed for Lesson 2

Protractors, an overhead projector is essential, a transparent protractor for use on the overhead, a transparency with some angles drawn which you can measure, for example, 60°, 45° and 15°, Copymaster 19

Resources needed for Lesson 3

Protractors, pairs of compasses, rulers, sharp pencils, paper

Teaching the lessons

Lesson 1

Key questions

How many straight or right angles are there here?
What angles can you make with these?
How many straight angles make a whole rotation?

Vocabulary

Right angle, straight angle, whole rotation, shape names

Introduction

15min

Get the children to look at a circle cut by a straight angle into semi-circles and then quartered using two straight angles to make four right angles. Talk about the relationships, that is, one rotation has two straight angles, one for each semi-circle, and four right angles. Two right angles make one straight angle. Tell the children that they are going to explore these and other relationships further. First, they are going to use some shapes to see whether they can make one rotation, a straight angle or a right angle. Draw a square, then two, and then four on the board, as shown below.

One square
for a right angle

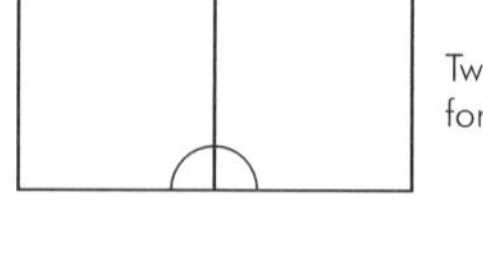

Two squares
for a straight angle

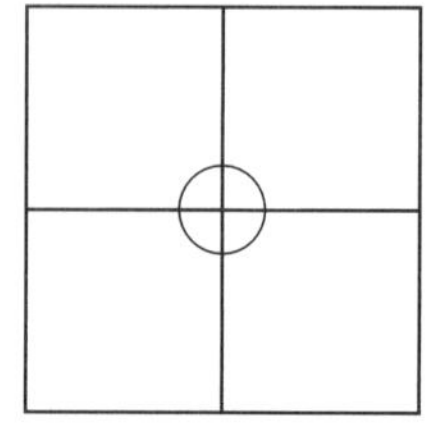

Four squares
for one complete rotation

Activities

The children have to see how many ways they can arrange shapes together to make right angles, straight angles, and complete rotations. They need to record carefully what they find. Go around the class, encouraging them and supporting them in this.

Closing the lesson

10min

Make all the angles by drawing appropriate shapes on the board, for example, three equilateral triangles to make a straight angle; then six to make a rotation. Ask which of the angles is easiest to make. Get some examples from the children.

Assessment

Child performance	Teacher action
Produces a limited range of examples	Work with the children, manipulating shapes and observing what angles they can make
Produces at least one example of each type of angle	Give more time to explore the ideas further
Produces a number of examples of each type of angle	Move on to the next lesson

Lesson 2

Key questions

How do you place the protractor?

How do you read the protractor?

How many degrees in a circle, straight angle or right angle?

How many degrees in this angle?

Vocabulary

Angle, right angle, straight angle, protractor, degrees

Introduction

15min

Let the children tell you how to make rotations from right angles and straight angles. Tell them that we need to be able to measure smaller angles so we need a new measure. Draw a circle on the board and tell the children that we use the measure called 'degrees' and that there are 360 of them in one whole rotation. Show them the symbol for degrees. Divide the circle into half and ask how many degrees a straight angle has. Then divide it into quarters and ask how many degrees there are in each right angle. Now put a 360° transparent protractor on the overhead projector and show the children how it is used, measuring the angles on your prepared transparency. Tell them that, in this lesson, they are going to use protractors to measure angles for themselves.

Activities

20min

Give out protractors and **Copymaster 19**. Move around the class, reminding the children of where to place the protractor and the need to be careful in measuring the angle. Remind them of terms like 'acute', 'obtuse' and 'reflex'.

Closing the lesson

10min

Review the process again and check the children's results for each of the angles on the Copymaster. Explain where the symbol for degrees is written and how we might write 45 degrees, for example.

Assessment

Child performance	Teacher action
Has difficulty in using a protractor	Give more general skills practice as well as close support in working through the Copymaster again at a later date
Does most of the task satisfactorily	Give some time using a protractor
Completes the task with a good level of accuracy	Move on to the next lesson

Lesson 3

Key questions

How many sides does a ... have?

What is 360° divided by ...?

Vocabulary

Shape names, pairs of compasses, protractor, and degrees.

Introduction

15min

Show the children a pair of compasses, name them and explain what they are used for. If necessary, show how to insert the pencil, ensuring its point coincides with the point of the compasses. If you have a pair of board compasses, demonstrate the drawing of some circles. Using a circle on the board, mark its centre and explain that you are going to use this to help draw a square. Ask how many sides there are in a square, how many degrees in a circle and what is the number of degrees divided by the number of sides. When you get to 90°, mark off 90° segments from the centre of the circle.

Using a circle to draw a square

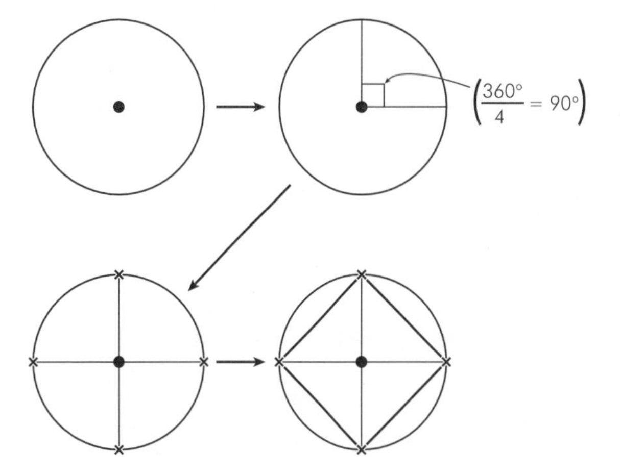

The line from the centre should reach the perimeter of the circle. The points on the perimeter can then be used to draw the desired shape.

Using a circle to draw an equilateral triangle

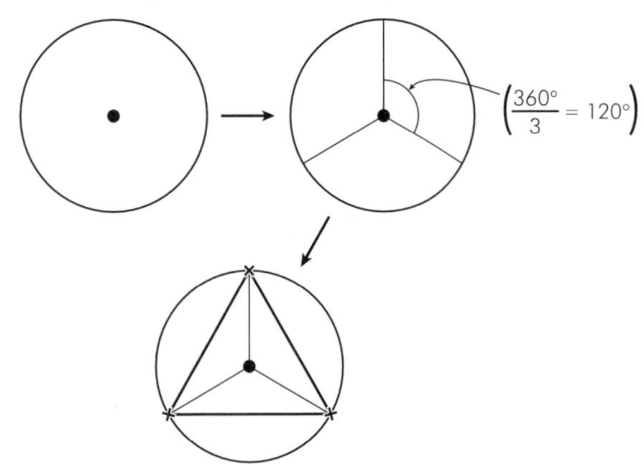

Now demonstrate how to draw an equilateral triangle within a circle. Reinforce the calculation law, that is, 360° divided by the number of sides produces the angles you need to divide the circle into.

Activities

Give out the resources with suitable warnings about the care needed when using a pair of compasses. Write a list of shapes on the board. Ask the children to make as many of them as they can. The suggested list is: square, equilateral triangle, hexagon, pentagon, octagon – but any regular polygon can be drawn using this method.

Closing the lesson

Show some examples of what individual children have achieved. Tell the children that they now know a method for drawing any regular, two-dimensional shape.

Assessment

Child performance	Teacher action
Can do the square and triangle following your work but finds it hard to do the other shapes	Check whether the problem is in the calculation or use of protractor or both and then give the necessary practice
Completes some of the challenges on the list	Give more time to further develop the children's skills
Completes challenges with confidence and accuracy	Invite the children to complete the list and, if time is available, add some of their own

HOMEWORK

Give further exercises which involve the use of a protractor. Ask the children to find reproductions of famous paintings and measure the angles that they can see in them with a protractor.

ANGLES AND CO-ORDINATES

THEME **15**

Co-ordinates

Learning targets

The children should be able to:

1 ➤ Use co-ordinates with simple maps

2 ➤ Draw shapes from given co-ordinates

3 ➤ Develop their own drawings using co-ordinates to describe them

Before you start

Subject knowledge

Co-ordinates have three main areas of use: graphs, the reading of maps and the construction of diagrams and shapes. At this stage, the children are generally working in the first quadrant, with positive numbers on both axes, though it is quite easy to move them to all four quadrants if you wish. The convention that needs to be adopted when working with co-ordinates is that there is an order to reading and writing them, placing the co-ordinate by using the x axis first then the y axis. Co-ordinates are a very powerful tool for a variety of mathematical purposes.

Previous knowledge required

Pictorial representation, straight line graphs, grids

Resources needed for Lesson 1

Copymaster 20

Resources needed for Lesson 2

Copymaster 21, rulers, sharp pencils or coloured pencils

Resources needed for Lesson 3

Copymaster C, rulers, sharp pencils or coloured pencils

Teaching the lessons

Lesson 1

Key questions

Which axis do we use first?

Where is this point?

What can we see here?

Vocabulary

Co-ordinates, axis, axes, point, key, order

Introduction

15min

Ask the children what they can tell you about using and making graphs. Focus on how you put points on a graph, the order and the fact that we are using ordered pairs of numbers to identify a point. Remind them of work they have done on identifying regions using grids (naming the squares) on maps. Reiterate that, in the exercise they are going to do, they must remember that the first number in each pair relates to the numbers on the x-axis and the second to the y-axis. Tell them that they are going to be working with a map that has a key. Discuss what a key means and why maps have them.

Activities

20min

Give out **Copymaster 20**. The children have to attempt to interpret the map in order to answer the questions. Give continuing support on the order in which to read co-ordinates and the use of the simple key.

Closing the lesson

10min

Review the questions with the children using the opportunity to reinforce the fact that the co-ordinates are read in a particular order and are used to identify points, not regions.

Assessment

Child performance	Teacher action
Makes some mistakes on ordering	Give more time, using a variety of co-ordinate representations to practise the reading of co-ordinates
Completes the task	Move on to the next lesson
Completes the task and suggests further ideas or asks further questions	Move on to the next lesson

Lesson 2

Key questions

What shape do these co-ordinates make?

What is the missing co-ordinate?

Vocabulary

Co-ordinates, shape names

Introduction

10 min

In this lesson, the children are going to construct a number of shapes using co-ordinates. Explain this to them, using the opportunity to revise what they know about co-ordinates already. Put a grid on the board, as shown below and make the rectangle using the appropriate co-ordinates.

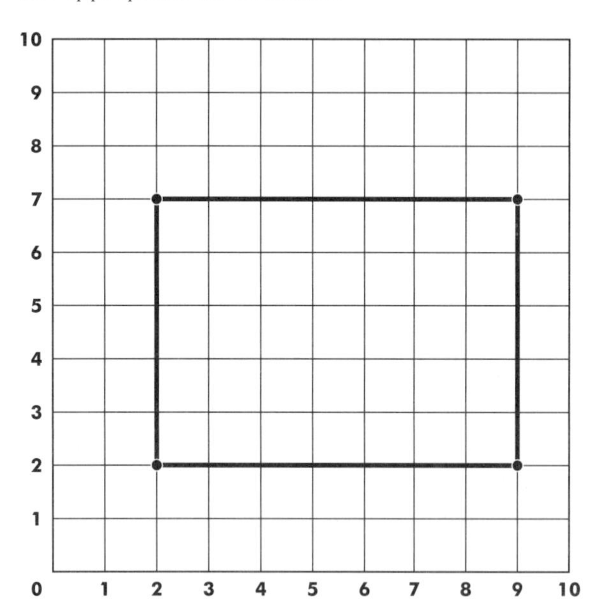

Co-ordinates are: (2, 2), (9, 2), (2, 7) and (9, 7)

Activities

25 min

Give out **Copymaster 21**, telling the children that they should work through each grid carefully, taking care with locating points, then drawing in the lines to make the shapes. Some of the later challenges require them to put in missing points to produce named shapes.

Closing the lesson

10 min

Review examples from the Copymaster on the board to help the children check their understanding. Collect the Copymasters for an evaluation of the children's progress.

Assessment

Child performance	Teacher action
Completes most of the shapes but with some errors	Check whether the errors are mistakes or misunder-standings about the order of co-ordinates
Completes all the given shapes but lacks confidence	Move on to the next lesson but come back to this if difficulty is experienced in progressing
Completes all the challenges	Move on to the next lesson

Lesson 3

Key questions

What instructions must you give?

Can your partner make your picture?

Vocabulary

Co-ordinates, x-axis, y-axis

Introduction

10 min

Remind the children of what they now know about co-ordinates, especially how to construct shapes. Tell them that they are going to invent two pictures on grids and make a list of co-ordinates for each which will allow a partner to draw the pictures.

Activities

30 min

Give out two copies of **Copymaster C** to each child. They have to draw two shapes or pictures and work out the co-ordinates so that their partner can draw the shapes or pictures using only the list of co-ordinates. When they have compiled their instructions, they give them to a partner to follow whilst following their partner's instructions. Drawings should be compared.

Closing the lesson

10 min

Ask the children if all went to plan. If not, what caused the difficulty? Consider giving the class a repeat opportunity in order to refine their lists of instructions.

Assessment

Child performance	Teacher action
Manages one set of instructions with difficulty	Give more time and practice and repeat earlier work on co-ordinates if it seems appropriate
Manages both sets of instructions but with some errors	Give more time and practice
Manages both sets with little difficulty	The children have met the learning targets for this theme

HOMEWORK

Using squared paper, the children should attempt to produce co-ordinate instructions for the common 2-D shapes, including square, rectangle, triangle, pentagon, hexagon, octagon and decagon.

ANGLES AND CO-ORDINATES

THEME **16**

Translation and transformation

Learning targets

The children should be able to:

1 ➤➤ Translate a shape
2 ➤➤ Enlarge or reduce a shape
3 ➤➤ Modify a shape

Before you start

Subject knowledge

Using a co-ordinate system gives children important opportunities to control shapes and manipulate them. Indeed, with the advent of new technologies, children will encounter the use of co-ordinates in the mapping of many different surfaces. Co-ordinates are about locating points and they can be used in many settings, not just for graphing. Here, the children will be using co-ordinates to translate shapes, that is, to draw congruent shapes, starting with a given shape and its co-ordinates. Congruency means that a shape can be identical in respect of size of angle and in length of sides to another but it can be in a different location. The children will also enlarge and reduce shapes. You can do all four operations (+, −, ×, ÷) with co-ordinates. There are examples below.

Finally, we will modify co-ordinate grids so that the children can transform, in particular ways, given shapes and pictures.

Previous knowledge required

Use of co-ordinates in pictorial representation, symmetry, tessellation, area, perimeter, congruence, similarity

Resources needed for Lesson 1

Copymaster 22

Resources needed for Lesson 2

Copymaster 23

Resources needed for Lesson 3

Copymaster 24, Copymaster F

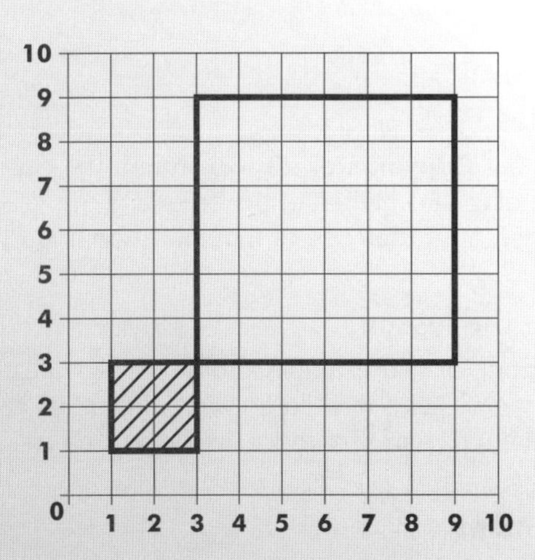

Here, the square with co-ordinates:
× **3**
(1, 1) ⟶ (3, 3)
(3, 1) ⟶ (9, 3)
(1, 3) ⟶ (3, 9)
(3, 3) ⟶ (9, 9)
has been enlarged by a factor of 3

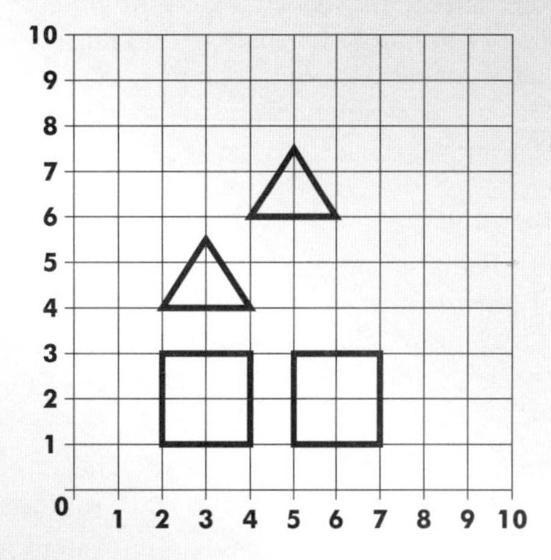

The square is translated by adding 3 to the x values:
+ **3** to $\mathbf{x}$

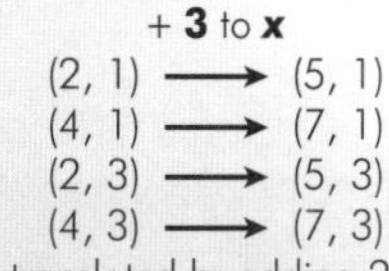
(2, 1) ⟶ (5, 1)
(4, 1) ⟶ (7, 1)
(2, 3) ⟶ (5, 3)
(4, 3) ⟶ (7, 3)

The triangle is translated by adding 2 to both x and y:
+ **2** to both
(2, 4) ⟶ (4, 6)
(4, 4) ⟶ (6, 6)
(3, 5.5) ⟶ (5, 7.5)

Teaching the lessons

Lesson 1 

Key questions

What do you have to add?

What happens if you add…?

What happens if you subtract…?

Vocabulary

Translation, symmetry, congruent, similar, co-ordinates.

Introduction 

Put a grid on the board and remind the children of what they already know about using co-ordinates to identify points. Draw a square on the board and ask the children to give you its co-ordinates. Now explain that, if we add the same number to, for example, all points on the x-axis, then we can translate the square to a new position. The new square is congruent with the first square. Now show them what happens if you add the same number for both x and y values. Tell them that they are going to translate some shapes.

Activities 

Give out **Copymaster 22**. Go around the class, reminding the children of the need to be consistent with the addition and subtraction, and that they should keep checking that they are reading the co-ordinates in the conventional manner.

Closing the lesson 

Ask the children what they found most difficult to do and why. As necessary, quickly go over, for example, the rule for reading and writing co-ordinates. Emphasise the term 'translation' and finish by drawing a repeat pattern of congruent shapes on the board, like a wallpaper border, and point out that translation can be used to produce a symmetrical pattern.

Assessment

Child performance	Teacher action
Has problems with basic use of co-ordinates	Move on to other work, for example, more pictorial representation
Manages the task with close support	Give more challenges and time to do them
Demonstrates clear understanding of the task	Move on to the next aspect of co-ordinate work.

Lesson 2 

Key questions

What happens when we multiply by…?

What happens when we divide by…?

How much bigger or smaller is this one?

Vocabulary

Factor, enlargement, reduction, co-ordinates, similar

Introduction 10 min

Remind the children of the work they have done on translation using co-ordinates. Tell them that, in this lesson, they are going to use co-ordinates to enlarge and reduce shapes. Draw a grid on the board and demonstrate enlargement as in the previous lesson, then reduction, as shown here.

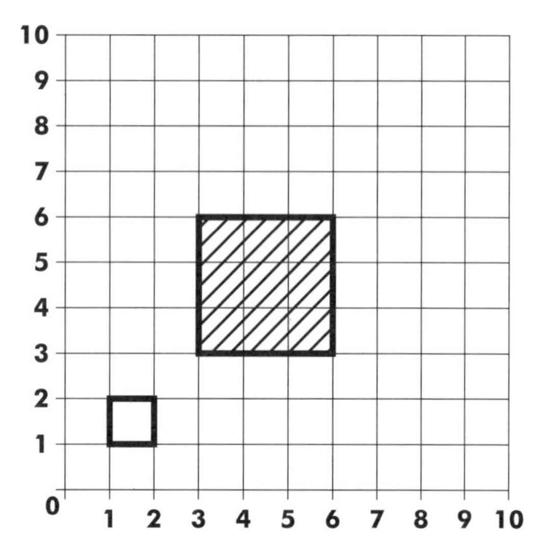

The larger square has co-ordinates which have been divided by 3 to make the smaller square:

(3, 3) ⟶ (1, 1)
(6, 3) ⟶ (2, 1)
(3, 6) ⟶ (1, 2)
(6, 6) ⟶ (2, 2)

Activities 30 min

Give out **Copymaster 23**. Go around the class, reminding the children of the order and the need to be consistent in their use of multiplication and division.

Closing the lesson 10 min

Work one or two examples from the Copymaster on the board. Ask the children what difficulties can be experienced and respond to what they tell you.

Assessment

Child performance	Teacher action
Completes most of the work with a few errors	Work with the children on similar tasks and move on to the next lesson
Completes most of the work accurately	Give more time, check work and move on to the next lesson
Completes all the work accurately	Ask the children to prepare some challenges to share, then move on to the next lesson

Lesson 3

Key questions

What do you think of the effect?

Why does this happen?

What would happen if you tried to enlarge or reduce this?

Have you seen co-ordinates being used like this on TV or computer?

Vocabulary

Co-ordinates, transformation, modification

Introduction

10min

The children should be fully familiar with conventions for co-ordinate use by now. Put on the board a grid and plot a square (see below left). Now put a grid in which the lines are not parallel and plot a shape of the same co-ordinates (see below right).

Tell the children that they are going to transform shapes like this and then have a go at designing some transformations of their own.

Activities

25min

Give out **Copymaster 24**. Go around the class eliciting their responses to what is produced. Use the key questions in support of this. The children can work on the Copymaster but also give them **Copymaster F** so that they can develop their ideas or practise what they are going to do.

Closing the lesson

10min

Ask whether the children have seen co-ordinates being used to map surfaces in a way that could be used for transformations. There is computer software often used on television programmes that uses co-ordinates to reconstruct features such as the human face from a skull and the appearance of land before weathering, and so on.

Assessment

Child performance	Teacher action
Copes with the tasks but needs close support	Give further opportunities
Copes with the tasks without much help	Encourage the children to use what they now know, to develop their own ideas
Copes with the tasks and develops the ideas further	Involve the children in an investigation of the uses of co-ordinates

HOMEWORK

All the lessons here can be followed up by giving graph paper (Copymaster G) and inviting the children to translate and enlarge or reduce shapes and pictures. Transformation possibilities abound, and the children making curved grids and transposing from pictures can generate all kinds of 'distortions'.

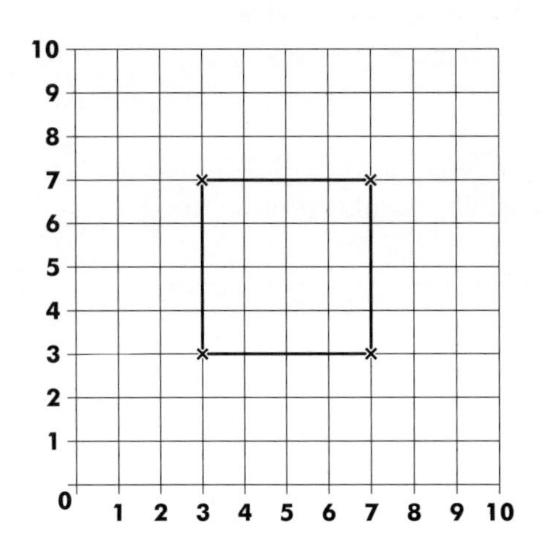

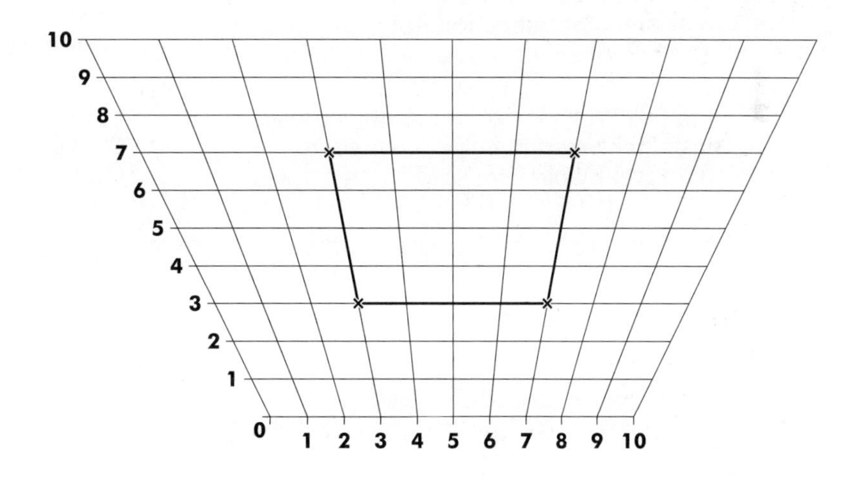

Compass points and bearings

Learning targets

The children should be able to:

1 ➤ Discuss local features using compass points
2 ➤ Locate major towns and cities in the British Isles and discuss their relative locations
3 ➤ Work out simple bearings

Before you start

Subject knowledge

Navigation is an important strategy developed through the power of human thought. From the earliest times to the present, people have desired to find where they are and where they want to travel. Over the centuries, increasingly sophisticated systems have evolved. The children should, by now, be familiar with the use of co-ordinates for locating position and the dynamic nature of angle. Here, they consolidate their understanding of how to describe direction and relative position. A key concept in this is that north, for example, is not a region and that we can point to the north or south or any other direction from wherever we are. The use of bearings is a development of the use of a compass rose giving, as it does, more precision in navigation. Common uses of bearings include sports, like orienteering, as well as travel by plane or ship.

Previous knowledge required

Co-ordinates, angle as rotation, the common eight compass points, use of a protractor

Resources needed for Lesson 1

Photocopies of a local town scale map with the direction of north marked in with N (if necessary by you), magnetic compasses – at least one in transparent plastic which you can use on the overhead projector but as many as possible for groups of children to work with, eight cards with pieces of Blu-Tack® – on the cards should be marked north, south, west, east, north-west, north-east, south-west, south-east.

Resources needed for Lesson 2

Copymaster 25, atlases

Resources needed for Lesson 3

Copymaster 26, compasses with degrees marked, if possible, circular protractors.

Teaching the lessons

Lesson 1 ①

Key questions

Where is this landmark?

What direction is this place from here?

Vocabulary

Compass point names, location, direction.

Introduction 15min

Put a transparent plastic magnetic compass on the overhead projector. Line it up so that the needle and north are aligned. Give out some Blu-Tack® and one of the eight compass point cards to eight of the children. Agree with the children that the needle is pointing north and then get the child with 'north' on their card to Blu-Tack® it to the north wall or window of the classroom. Then do the same for 'south', 'west' and 'east' before moving on to the other four. This will give eight compass points around the room. Ask the children to say in what direction are different features in the room; for example, the sink, Helen's table, the notice-board, and so on.

Activities 25min

Give out the photocopies of the local town scale maps to pairs of children. They have to identify at least eight features and write down their direction in respect to north, north-east and so on, from an agreed town centre.

Closing the lesson 10min

Using discussion or a transparency if possible, talk through some of the features and their compass directions. Finish by going over the compass points and their directions once more.

Assessment

Child performance	Teacher action
Confuses some of the compass points in use	Spend some time going over them again and check children's left/right understanding
Completes the task satisfactorily	Move on to the next lesson
Completes the task satisfactorily and raises ideas about more compass points	Move on to the next lesson

Lesson 2

Key questions

Where is...?

What direction do we need to take?

Vocabulary

Compass point names

Introduction

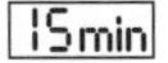

Remind the children of the eight compass points they have been working on. Explain that there are eight more that people have been using for centuries. Draw a compass rose on the board with the eight familiar points. Now add the remaining eight to finish with a compass rose like the one shown here.

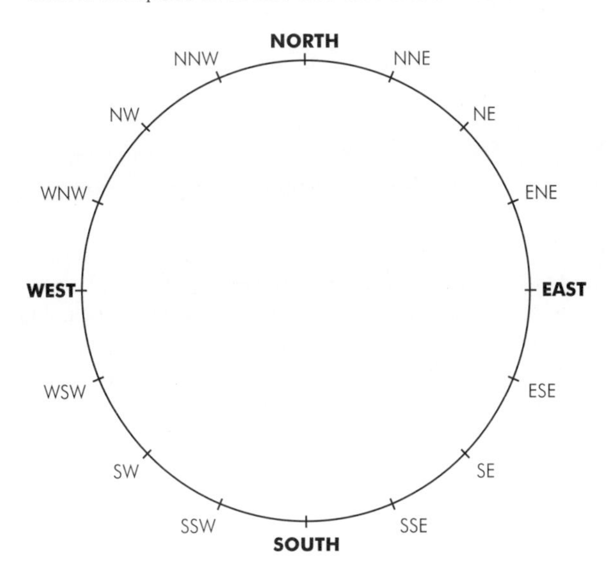

Ask the children the name of the nearest city or major town (unless they are already living in one). Tell them that you are going to ask them to work out some directions using the major cities and towns in the United Kingdom.

Activities

25min

Give out **Copymaster 25** and atlases. Help the children to locate the nearest city or town or put your own town on the map. The children have to plan a journey in which they visit England, Wales, Scotland and Northern Ireland at least once each, giving the names of places they visited and the compass directions they take.

Closing the lesson

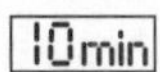

Ask for examples from some of the children. Finish by asking, briskly, questions of the type, 'What direction is Glasgow from Edinburgh?'

Assessment

Child performance	Teacher action
Comes up with a journey but clearly has problems in deciding the compass directions	Give further work on direction including getting the children to move and plan movements to instructions in PE or play-ground games and so on
Completes the task satisfactorily	Confirm the children's understanding by asking for compass directions for a route around the classroom or school
Completes the task readily	Consider extending the exercise by doing a European version and then move on to the next lesson

Lesson 3

Key questions

How many degrees in a rotation?

What is the bearing here?

Where do people use bearings?

Vocabulary

Bearings, degrees, rotation

Introduction

Ask the children when they might have difficulty in giving a precise direction when using the compass rose. Explain that, as navigation has improved, we have needed finer distinctions than the compass rose so we have adopted degrees as our measure. Ask how many degrees there are in one complete rotation. Draw the compass rose on the board and ask what the degree equivalents are from north, for south, east, west and then for finer divisions. Draw the map below on the board and explain how we get the bearings for the lighthouse and the other ship. Emphasise that we are meaning from North.

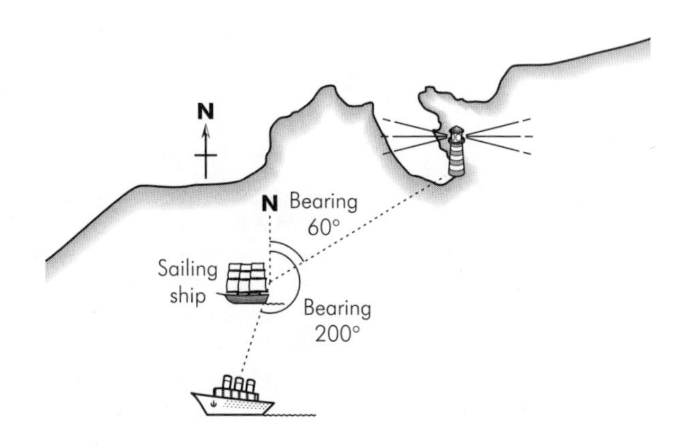

Activities

25min

Give out circular protractors and **Copymaster 26**. Tell the children that they have to work with the bearings in the way that you have just shown them.

Closing the lesson

10min

Choose an example or two from the Copymaster and do them on the board as reinforcement and for the purposes of self-checking.

Assessment

Child performance	Teacher action
Makes some errors	Check that the children understand that you need to work from north
Completes most of the work satisfactorily	Give another chance to try this or similar exercises
Completes all the work satisfactorily	The learning targets for this theme have been met

HOMEWORK

Using a compass of their own or borrowed from school the children can work out the direction of features that they can see from their home. Develop the compass and map work by using maps of the region in which they live. Using a local town or countryside map, get the children to plan a walk giving directions and bearings.

Investigations

- Find pictures in magazines that contain lines meeting at an angle. Cut them out and make an ordered sequence of the pictures beginning with the most acute angle.
- Look at some times on a clock face. What is the angle between the hands at these times? Try, for example, school start, breaks, lunch and home time.
- Use programmable robots to develop a sequence of instructions regarding angles. Relate this to the points of the compass.
- Find out about the lives and particular journeys of famous explorers. Draw their journeys on maps; then try and produce a direction manual for someone wanting to repeat their journeys.
- Artists use a variety of devices to help them in composition and scaling. These include frames, grids and the holding out of pencils (or thumbs). Find out about these sorts of strategies and how they work.
- There are many settings in everyday life where angles are important. Look at a variety of different sports and games and determine where 'angle' might be a good word to describe some of what happens. List the sports or games and give illustrated examples of angle.
- Use computer software packages that support explorations of both angle and co-ordinates
- Enlarge, reduce and 'distort' images using co-ordinates.

Assessment

- Estimate given static angles and then check their size using a protractor or angle indicator
- Given a set of drawn angles, put them in order starting with most acute
- Draw some 2D shapes, cut them out and then work out a way of finding the total of their internal angles. For example, a triangle has a total for the internal angles, which equals a straight angle, as shown below

angle **a** + angle **b** + angle **c** = 180° = a straight angle

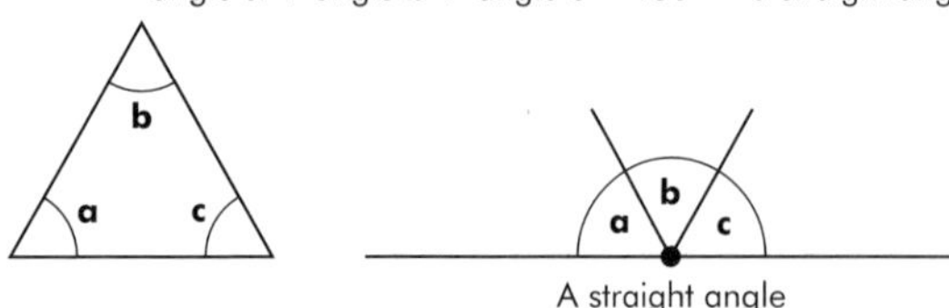

- Give and follow directions in right angles, half right angles, straight angles, and whole rotations. Do this also with the compass points.
- Make a map with directions of a known journey
- Work out the factors of 360. Choose one of these factors then draw lines radiating from a point using that factor as an angle. Connect the ends of the lines to make a 2D shape. What is the shape you have made? An example is shown below.

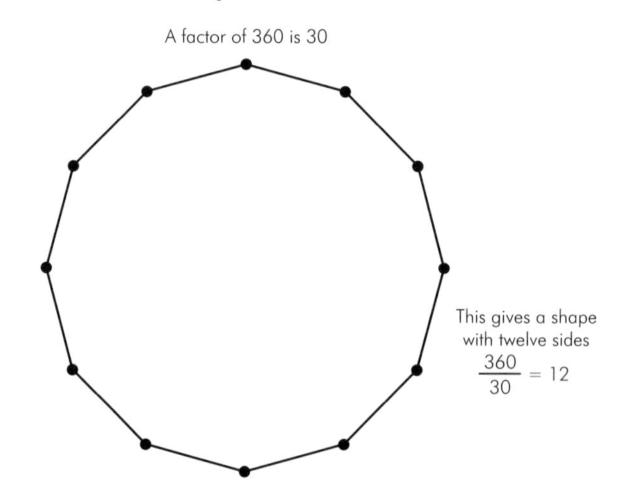

LENGTH, AREA AND PERIMETER

In developing an understanding of the concept of length it is possible to discern a sequence of ideas and relationships that most children experience. First we need to spend time on the language of length. This is often related to comparisons such as taller and shorter, high, higher, highest and so on. This foundation layer of language is vital to progression in the mathematics of dimensions. Following, and related to the comparing of lengths, is the matching of objects with similar lengths, and sorting objects on the basis of them being very different in length. In making these judgements about match, children are clearly employing some sort of measure. Often this is in the mind's eye and can be either an object in the set or another well-known object – this is about the same size as my teddy. So non-standard measures are next in our sequence. Once the use of such measures is well established it is time to introduce standard measures of length. Nowadays we are concerned primarily with metric units. However, we still make important use of some imperial measures so they too need to be progressively introduced. In using the appropriate units children also need to learn the common abbreviations for measures of length.

Perimeter is a measure of length and related to area. In looking at area, early work should emphasise the idea of coverage – how much of this is needed to cover that? Early work in area follows a similar sequence to that discussed for length. There is no need to introduce standard units until comparison, matching and ordering have been fully experienced. When we come to standard measures it is again useful to start with metric units as they are rooted in base ten, and are, therefore, much easier to use. However, as we still use measures such as acres we do need to apprise the children of some imperial units.

In developing work in area and perimeter we are moving into fields in which, eventually, equations can be developed and employed. The formulae that are used in everyday life often involve shorthand, and the real mathematics can be hidden. For example, judging the number of 'lengths' (note this word) of wallpaper to paper a particular room uses standard widths. The fact that curtains come in standard widths and lengths means that decisions are about comparison and approximation rather than the rigid application of a formula. All these things are very good vehicles for children learning about length, area, and perimeter. In this section, work on the perimeters – circumferences – or areas of circles is not featured as we see this as being at the limits of the work in most primary schools.

LENGTH, AREA & PERIMETER

THEME **18**

Comparing and ordering

Learning targets

The children should be able to:

1 ➤➤ Compare and match lengths

2 ➤➤ Order lengths

3 ➤➤ Devise approaches to measuring distances

Before you start

Subject knowledge

In earlier years the children should have engaged in work on length employing non-standard measures such as hand-spans and paces. It is important that children are not moved to standard measures and the use of scales too soon as they need to get a 'feel' for ideas of length, height, width, breadth and so on, as well as grappling with the notion of distance. To do this without being hemmed in by standard measures is vital. Allied to comparing and ordering is the skill of estimation. Estimation of length is affected by orientation. The viewpoint of the child in relation to the object to be estimated has real effects on the accuracy of those estimates. We can experience the problem for ourselves by considering whether a space is sufficient for us to lie down in. Try this for yourself and see how close you are to translating your own height into a horizontal length. In making estimates we often make reference to other objects. For example in estimating the distance across a river we might look at something on our bank to give us a 'feel' for the distance.

Previous knowledge required

Use of non-standard measures such as hand-spans and paces

Resources needed for Lesson 1

Cuisenaire® rods, Multilink®, a variety of objects of different sizes, a collection of objects that can be used as measuring aids, for example, lollipop sticks, sheets of paper, plastic pens

Resources needed for Lesson 2

Multilink®, rolls of kitchen paper

Resources needed for Lesson 3

An open area with features between which distances can be measured, trundle wheels, metre sticks

Teaching the lessons

Lesson 1 ①

Key questions

How could we use ourselves to measure this?

How could I use this object to compare these other objects?

Which is longer/ shorter, taller/ shorter?

Vocabulary

Longer, taller, shorter, height, high, breadth, width, depth, equal

Introduction 10 min

Ask the children how you might measure the length of the classroom using yourself. Demonstrate some of the suggestions and ask which seems to be the most effective. Now ask how you might measure a tabletop using yourself, then a given object. Tell the children that they are going to do a variety of measurements using themselves and given objects. Organise small groups giving each an object to measure with, and tell the class that each group should measure at least three things and keep a record of their results.

Activities 30 min

The groups should try to measure a variety of objects in the room. Employ a range of length vocabulary in discussion and encourage the children to use this vocabulary too. When they have completed the first task ask the class what they have found. Focus on what was easier to use for the given length of object. Give out sets of Cuisenaire® to the groups and tell them that you want them to find groups of rods that are equal in length to another single rod. Demonstrate this with, for example, two 3-rods and a 6-rod. Again the children should keep a note of their findings.

Closing the lesson
10min

Using examples from the groups, review the outcomes from each activity. Stress the length vocabulary in the discussion. Spend some time reviewing the comparisons using Cuisenaire®.

Assessment

Child performance	Teacher action
Needs considerable help in all aspects	Give lots more practical measuring work using non-standard measures.
Does the activities satisfactorily but finds difficulty in articulating what has been done	Spend time in discussion with these children to develop length vocabulary
Completes the work and engages in discussion satisfactorily	Move on to the next lesson

Lesson 2

Key questions

How close were you?

Vocabulary

Long, tall, short, wide, narrow, width, breadth, depth, length, height, compare, order, estimation

Introduction

Write 'length' on the board and ask for other words that the children know are used to describe length. Choose two or three children and ask them to unroll and tear off a length of kitchen paper that they think is the same length as your height. Get other children to hold it vertically and see how close they were.

Activities
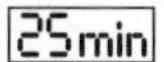

Tell the children that in pairs they have to tear off and label lengths of kitchen roll that they think are the same length as given objects in the classroom. Write these objects on the board and emphasise that the children must first estimate, and tear off a length, before they check the object. Choose objects that have different orientations i.e. some horizontal, some vertical and, if possible, some slanting. Take the opportunity to reinforce appropriate vocabulary.

Closing the lesson
10min

Use some examples and get the children to demonstrate. If you have the time and the resource let them see just how long a complete kitchen roll is. Collect in their labelled lengths of kitchen roll to display.

Assessment

Child performance	Teacher action
Makes guesses rather than estimates	Much more practice needed in general estimation of measures
Follows instructions satisfactorily but uses a limited vocabulary	Work in discussion with this group to extend vocabulary
Completes the activity confidently	Move on to next lesson

Lesson 3

Key questions

How far away do you think that is?

How can we be sure we are measuring the shortest distance?

Vocabulary

Distance, far, furthest, near, nearest

Introduction
10min

Tell the children that their challenge today is to estimate how far apart distant objects are, and to devise the best way of being certain that they have measured the shortest distance between these objects. Take the class to the field, playground or other area you have chosen and point out the particular features they are to find the distances between. Show them a trundle wheel and how far it goes for, say, five clicks – it is not important to discuss units at this stage. Do the same with, say six-metre sticks. Put a chalk line or marks on the ground as a record of these distances.

Activities
30min

Working with the features you have identified the groups need to make estimates in relation to the number of clicks or sticks. Then they measure the distance, having worked out a way of ensuring they are measuring the shortest distance. They should keep notes.

Closing the lesson
10min

Get some immediate feedback then arrange for the groups to write up their findings for you.

Assessment

Child performance	Teacher action
Has difficulty in planning, and carrying out the exercise	Analyse the practical experiences of these children and then allocate tasks that will support development
Makes some progress in solving the problems	Give further opportunities on this task
Satisfactorily estimates and measures the shortest distances	These children have met the learning targets for this theme

HOMEWORK

Make the children 'length detectives' and let them repeat the activities on estimation with family and friends.

Standard measures of length

Learning targets

The children should be able to:

1 ➤➤ Use metres and fractions of a metre
2 ➤➤ Use centimetres
3 ➤➤ Relate different units of length

Before you start

Subject knowledge

It is important to move to standard units of measurement when the children have laid a foundation of understanding of the meanings of length and distance. In the beginning this should be in relation to the metric system using the metre as the first standard unit. As children gain experience they can move to finer scaling of length. The use of abbreviations is part of the modern world and these have to be learned. At first one should use the full term before using only the abbreviations. In using rulers there are three things to think about. Children know about drawing straight lines with rulers. But drawing straight lines of a given length is another matter, not least because rulers may have been used to measure lengths of objects not drawn by the children. All these uses need to be considered when reviewing children's errors. Ruler design should also be considered. Commonly, early years' rulers are scaled from the end of the ruler. This scaling is often in colour bands as well as units. Later on children will encounter rulers that have spaces at each end and are not colour registered. Tapes can bring their own problems – it is possible to make a reading that is actually the distance from, say a metre rather than from zero. Finally, we live in a society that is operating with two different standard unit systems of length, the metric and the imperial and youngsters need to be familiar with those units that they encounter in everyday life.

Previous knowledge required

Non-standard measures, simple tables of information

Resources needed for Lesson 1

Metre rules/sticks marked in colour bands

Resources needed for Lesson 2

Centimetre rulers, metre tapes and rules marked in centimetres, Copymaster 27

Resources needed for Lesson 3

A wide variety of rulers and tapes in metres, centimetres, yards, feet and inches, trundle wheels (in both yards and metres if possible)

Teaching the lessons

Lesson 1 ①

Key questions

What do you think the length of … is?

What did you find the length of … to be?

Vocabulary

Metre, comparison, long, longer, short, shorter, length, estimation

Introduction 15min

Using a metre rule or stick talk about the fact that it is an important standard measure in the metric system. Remind the children of athletics events such as the 100m and 400m races to support your statement. Ask for examples where the children have heard metres being used. Measure something in the classroom that is more than two metres long. Ask what we might do if the object we wish to measure is not a complete number of metres. Put some common fractions on the board when this suggestion arises. Write a table on the board with three columns headed 'Object', 'Estimate', and 'Measure' and get the children to copy it.

Activities 25min

Tell the children they are to identify objects, parts of the room and other nearby areas of the school to measure. They first have to write down what they think the length is in metres and fractions of a metre then measure the chosen object to see how close they were in their estimate.

Closing the lesson
10min

Let pairs of children give you examples of what they have done and fill in the table on the board using the examples. Discuss which objects or places were easiest or hardest to estimate and measure, and probe the reasons.

Assessment

Child performance	Teacher action
Estimates are inconsistent	Lots more estimation practice is needed, in all areas of measurement
Works satisfactorily but has problems with some fractions	Check through the children's knowledge and experience of simple fractions and give some practice as appropriate
Works through with few problems	Move on to next lesson

Lesson 2
2

Key questions

What do you think the length is?

What is the measured length?

How close were you in your estimate?

Vocabulary

Estimate, metre, centimetre

Introduction
15min

Revise the children's work with metre sticks and rules. Explain the work with metres this time will involve parts of a metre called centimetres. Draw part of a ruler on the board and put in the centimetres, writing down the word. Tell them that there are one hundred centimetres in one metre. Demonstrate a measure involving metres and centimetres. Write the result on the board in metres and centimetres then again, using abbreviations. Tell the children they have to work together to measure but must make estimates first.

Activities
20min

Give out **Copymaster 27** and rulers and tapes. As the children work suggest objects that might be measured best with tapes such as around a wrist or a book. Check that children are reading the tapes from the zero end.

Closing the lesson
10min

Write a table on the board and enter some findings using example from the pairs. Use this to reinforce the correct abbreviations. Collect the Copymasters for checking.

Assessment

Child performance	Teacher action
Has problems in reading scales	Do more work using non-standard units then reintroduce standard measures
Obtains only a very few results	Discuss the work and give more time if appropriate
Carries through the activity confidently and accurately	Move on to next lesson

Lesson 3
3

Key questions

What is this in inches? What is it in centimetres?

How many metres/yards?

Vocabulary

Metre, centimetre, yard, feet, foot, inch, inches

Introduction
10min

Explain that, as well as metric, there is also an imperial measurement system that is still in use, and name some units. Explain that, in this lesson, the metric and imperial systems will be used but cannot be combined. Show the different measuring instruments.

Activities
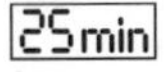

The children should be given the opportunity to measure short and long objects and distances in both metric and imperial. They should keep records of their measurements in both systems.

Closing the lesson
15min

Elicit a range of examples from different pairs and write them on the board. Discuss whether the children prefer one or other of the two systems. Finish by writing the units for each system as shown here.

Metric			Imperial		
1 kilometre	=	1000 metres	1 mile	=	1760 yards
1 metre	=	100 centimetres	1 yard	=	3 feet
			1 foot	=	12 inches

Assessment

Child performance	Teacher action
Manages a very few measurements in both systems	Give some more time then assess their understanding
Completes the task satisfactorily but finds difficulty in discussing work	Discuss the systems with them again
Completes the task satisfactorily and contributes with understanding in discussion	These children have met the learning targets for this theme

HOMEWORK

The children could ask family members for examples of where they need to measure length in their everyday lives. These examples could fuel further discussion.

LENGTH, AREA & PERIMETER

THEME **20**

Basic ideas in area and perimeter

Learning targets

The children should be able to:

1 ➤➤ Use counting squares in gauging area

2 ➤➤ Determine the perimeter of different shapes

3 ➤➤ Determine the area and perimeter of different shapes

Before you start

Subject knowledge

Young children have a range of early experiences that relate to area and perimeter. They know about covering things, for example, their face with a mask, and wrapping presents. However, these experiences have not been organised in ways that we would recognise as mathematics. Here we lay the foundations of a mathematical understanding of coverage and how far round. The use of squares for establishing area is a good place to start as it supports later appreciation of the use of, for example, square centimetres in calculating areas. The use of squares is also a good device for an early consideration of the perimeter of some shapes. Again this will help with later work on, for example, the developing of an equation for the perimeter of rectangles. In using a 'counting square' approach to area it is useful to promote discussion on what we do with partly covered squares. The convention, usually, is to count all whole squares and those that have a half or more covered. We can then ignore those squares that have less than a half covered. This gives a good approximation and is a useful vehicle for further discussion.

Previous knowledge required

Measurement of length

Resources needed for Lesson 1

Geoboards, elastic bands, Copymaster C, a variety of templates of shapes, some irregular shapes such as a leaf, a birthday card with scalloped or shaped edges, or cardboard cut-outs from packages or pictures, an overhead transparency of squares on which you can place templates and visibly count squares for demonstration purposes

Resources needed for Lesson 2

Geoboards, elastic bands, Copymaster C, an overhead transparency of square and triangular grids for demonstration purposes

Resources needed for Lesson 3

Copymaster 28

Teaching the lessons

Lesson 1 ①

Key questions

How many squares are covered here?

How can we do this one with uneven sides?

What can we do about squares that are only partly covered?

Vocabulary

Area, counting squares, total

Introduction (10 min)

Using the overhead transparency of the grid of squares, show the children two different rectangular templates. Ask them whether these shapes would cover different sized surfaces. Put each shape in turn on the grid and explain that one way of comparing their coverage – known as their area – is to count the squares that each will cover. Demonstrate this. Now put an irregular shaped object on the overhead and again count squares but this time ask for suggestions as to how to cope with squares that are not completely covered. Decide on a rule with the children. Tell them that they are going to find the area of a variety of shapes using a counting squares approach.

Activities (25 min)

Give out geoboards and elastic bands and tell the groups that you want them to make shapes with the elastic bands and then count the squares in their shapes. When the children have got a feel for this process give out the shapes you have assembled and **Copymaster C**. Tell the children that they should choose shapes, draw around them, then count the squares. Encourage different members of the group to try the same shapes to see if they each get the same result. Make sure that everyone tries irregular as well as regular shapes. Tell the children to keep a record of the numbers of squares for each shape they attempt.

Closing the lesson

10 min

Select a variety of the shapes and ask which groups have measured them and what they found. Reinforce the fact that we are measuring the area of the shapes. Finish by telling the class that the measurement of area is important in such things as building, farming, and designing.

Assessment

Child performance	Teacher action
Has few problems with rectangles but has difficulty with other shapes	Work with these children building up their experience in stages starting with rectangles again
Completes a good range of straight sided shapes but not others	Go over the children's achievements then work with them on irregular shapes
Demonstrates understanding with all the different sorts of shape	Move on to the next lesson

Lesson 2

Key questions

How far around the edge is this one?

Are you sure you have counted every side?

Vocabulary

Perimeter, edges, side, total

Introduction

Draw a rectangle on your overhead grid and count the length of the sides using the squares as your measure. Do not, at this stage, be concerned about the fact that one side could be counted and then doubled as this should come out later. Now draw an upper case T and E as shown below. Again count the sides using the squares.

Tell the children that we call the length all the way around a shape the perimeter. Write this on the board.

Activities

25 min

Give out geoboards and elastic bands telling the children to practise working out perimeters using the elastic bands to make different shapes. Tell them to make shapes only with right angles and no sloping lines. Give out **Copymaster C**. Remind them to draw their shapes carefully and to write the perimeter of each next to the shape when they have done their counting and totalling.

Closing the lesson

10 min

Choose some examples and either get the children to show these to the class or you draw them on the board. Use the examples to reinforce the method of determining the perimeter that they now know. Ask if anyone found a quicker way of doing their counting for any of the shapes. Use appropriate comments to encourage the children to think further about their work. Collect the work for checking.

Assessment

Child performance	Teacher action
Makes some errors due to lack of organised counting strategy	Sit with these children and do some more together, talking about ways of keeping a record of counts, then give a further opportunity
Correctly draws and gets the perimeter for a limited number of shapes	If appropriate give some more time
Produces a good range of shapes with their perimeters and has ideas about, for example, doubling strategies in some shapes.	Move on to next lesson

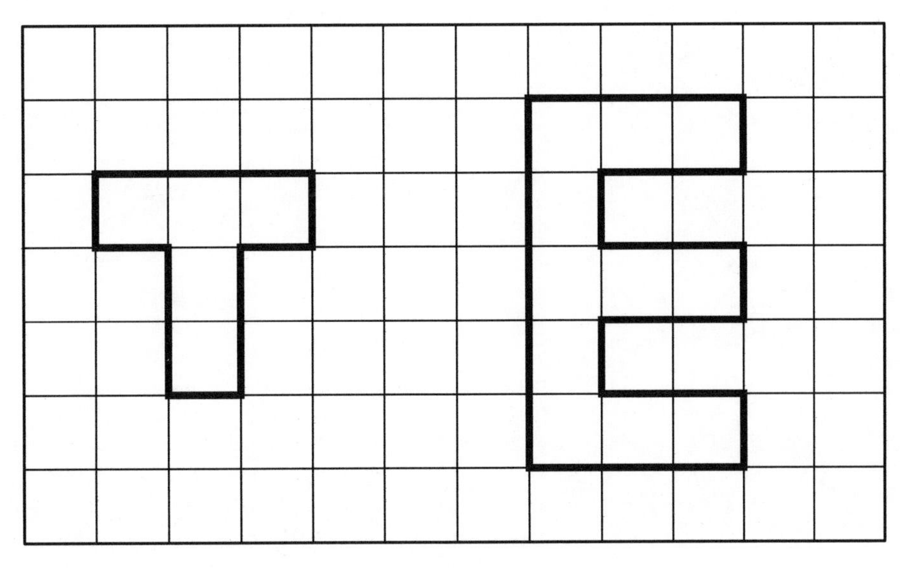

Lesson 3 

Key questions

What is the perimeter and area of this shape?

What do you notice here?

Can you produce any shapes that have these things in common?

Vocabulary

Area, perimeter, total

Introduction 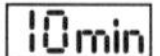

Revise what the children should now know about area and perimeter. Write key points on the board as they arise. Tell the children that in this lesson they are going to use their knowledge to find the area and perimeter of a range of shapes. Tell them that as they do this they should think about any patterns or connections that they see.

Activities 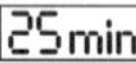

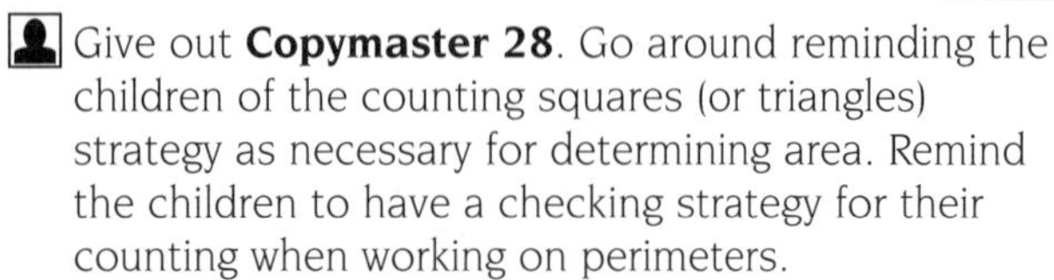

Give out **Copymaster 28**. Go around reminding the children of the counting squares (or triangles) strategy as necessary for determining area. Remind the children to have a checking strategy for their counting when working on perimeters.

Closing the lesson 

Ask a sample of individuals to tell you and the class some of what they have done and to identify any patterns or connections they could see. Use these where possible to excite new ideas on area and perimeter in the rest of the class. Collect the Copymasters for evaluation purposes.

Assessment

Child performance	Teacher action
Copes with some but not all of the shapes	Review what has been achieved then give further exercises
Completes the task but does not see any patterns or connections	Following the class discussion see whether these children can now make some connections
Completes the task and sees patterns and connections	These children have met the learning targets for this theme

HOMEWORK

The children should trace a map of the UK, or be given a copy of one, and, by counting squares, get comparisons of the areas of Scotland, Wales, England and Northern Ireland.

LENGTH, AREA & PERIMETER

THEME **21**

Drawing and constructing shapes

Learning targets

The children should be able to:

1 ➣ Construct triangles using drawing instruments

2 ➣ Construct squares and rectangles using drawing instruments

3 ➣ Construct regular polygons using drawing instruments

Before you start

Subject knowledge

The construction of 2D shapes using pairs of compasses has gone out of fashion in recent years. No doubt this is, in major part, due to the wide availability of plastic templates and the capacity of new technologies to produce 2D images. There are also many books, including this one, which have photocopiable pages of shapes. However, we believe that if children learn how shapes can be constructed this will enhance their grasp of the characteristics of 2D shapes. In this theme we concentrate on three techniques, the production of right angles, the use of intersecting arcs to define points, and the use of circles in constructing regular shapes. These have been chosen as they represent some of the fundamentals in drawing construction. The drawing instruments needed are pairs of compasses, protractors, rulers and sharp pencils. There is a variety of pairs of compasses available on the market. There are three main types: those that lie flat on the paper like a ruler, ones with a straight beam where the pencil is held in a moveable vice, and the traditional ones with a hinge near the holding position. Any of these can be used but it is vital that, once fixed in position, there is no play in the mechanism which allows the pencil point to move laterally. Protractors come in various sizes and designs. We recommend those that are a full 360 degrees.

Previous knowledge required

Familiarity with common 2D shapes – their characteristics and names, angle, experiences of accurate measurement using rulers and protractors, experience in drawing circles and arcs with a pair of compasses

Resources needed for Lesson 1

Pairs of compasses, rulers, sharp pencils, Copymaster 29, a pair of board compasses, if available, for demonstration

Resources needed for Lesson 2

Pairs of compasses, rulers, sharp pencils, Copymaster 30, a pair of board compasses, if available, for demonstration

Resources needed for Lesson 3

Pairs of compasses, protractors, rulers, sharp pencils, Copymaster 31, a pair of board compasses, if available, for demonstration

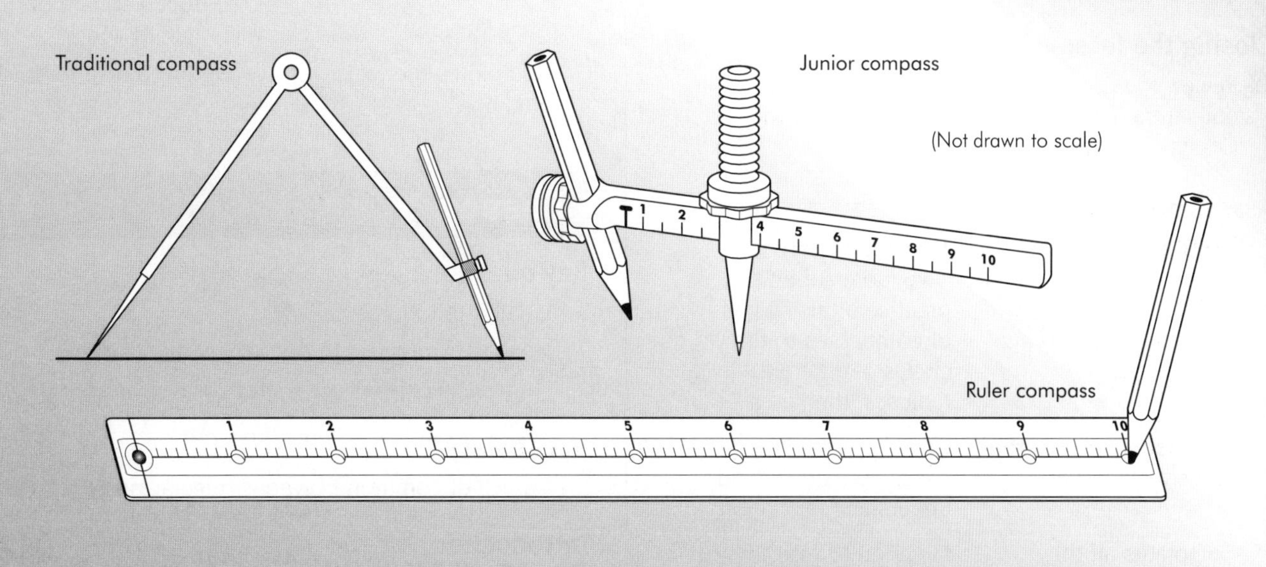

Teaching the lessons

Lesson 1 

Key questions

How do we fix the pencil?

What precautions do we need to take?

What is this angle?

Vocabulary

Pairs of compasses, angle, triangle names, metric length units

Introduction 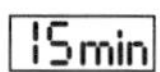

Using either a pair of board compasses or by showing a group at a time ordinary pairs of compasses remind them how to set the pencil and draw circles. Now demonstrate how to use a ruler and pair of compasses to construct an angle of 90 degrees as shown below.

a) 

b) 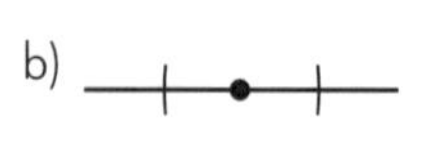

c) 

d) 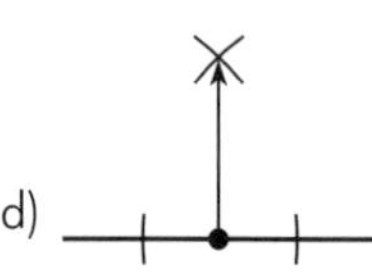

Tell the children that they are going to try this for themselves, then make a right angled triangle. They will have a sheet with instructions and a method for constructing an equilateral triangle. If necessary, remind them what an equilateral triangle is and use the opportunity to quickly revise other triangle names. Warn the children about the sharp point on pairs of compasses and remind them of the need for care.

Activities 

 Give out **Copymaster 29**, pairs of compasses and rulers. Make sure pencils are sharp. The children should follow the instructions. You may need to go around and repeat these for some children.

Closing the lesson 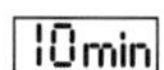

Review the construction of right angled and equilateral triangles on the board. Collect the Copymasters for evaluation purposes.

Assessment

Child performance	Teacher action
Needs a lot of help and has some difficulty with managing the drawing instruments	Give more supported practice on using pairs of compasses to draw circles of different radiuses, then arcs
Completes most of the task satisfactorily	Give more time then check confidence and understanding
Completes all the task readily	Move on to next lesson

Lesson 2

Key questions

How do we make a right angle with a pair of compasses?

How can we use our knowledge to make a square/rectangle?

Vocabulary

Pairs of compasses, right angle, square, rectangle, metric length units

Introduction 10min

Remind the children of the method they have explored for drawing right angles using pairs of compasses. Tell them that they have to use their knowledge to now construct squares and rectangles of a given size.

Activities 

Give out **Copymaster 30**, pairs of compasses and rulers. Make sure that the children have sharp pencils. They have to work through the Copymaster on which there is a reminder of the construction method, and some challenges. Give support as necessary and continue to reinforce the care needed in handling pairs of compasses, and the need for accuracy.

Closing the lesson 10min

Construct a square on the board with advice from the children. Collect the Copymasters for evaluation purposes.

Assessment

Child performance	Teacher action
Can make a right angle but struggles to complete a square or rectangle with reasonable accuracy	Work with these children in a staged way to build a square. Use protractors as an intermediate step if necessary.
Produces most of the figures asked for	Give some more time, then get the children to demonstrate how to construct a square or rectangle to you
Completes the task readily	Move on to next lesson

Lesson 3

Key questions

What is this shape called?

How many degrees in one complete rotation?

How many corners are there?

Vocabulary

Names of common polygons, regular, angle

Introduction 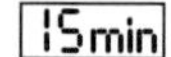

Demonstrate how to construct a regular pentagon

using the approach shown here. Talk about the process and the name and characteristics of the shape as you go along.

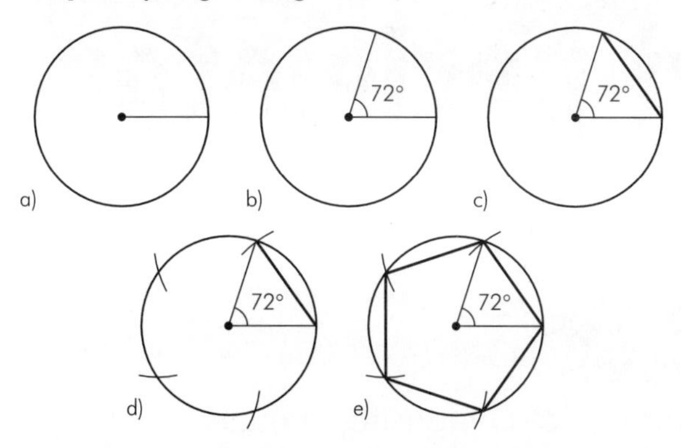

To do this construction one needs to know the angle at the centre for each chosen polygon. For the moment these can be given to the children rather than derived. Write a list of these on the board and talk about what they mean and why the children need them in this lesson. The angles at the centre appear on the Copymaster. Some children may notice that 360 degrees divided by the number of sides, or corners, is the angle at the centre. Remind the children of the need for care and accuracy.

Activities

Give out **Copymaster 31**, pairs of compasses, protractors, rulers and sharp pencils. As you go around check that protractors are being used properly. Encourage the children to go as far as they can with the possible regular polygons.

Closing the lesson

10min

Choose another regular polygon and with the help of the children construct it on the board. Collect the Copymasters to check the progress the children have now made in construction.

Assessment

Child performance	Teacher action
Produces a copy of the example but finds it difficult to progress much further	Consider giving more practice at earlier constructions, and give exercises which support exploration of regular polygons
Produces a limited number of accurately constructed regular polygons	Check on understanding of regular polygons and the notion of internal angle then give further practice on construction
Demonstrates real confidence in accurately producing a range of constructions	These children have met the learning targets for this theme

HOMEWORK

Ask the children to seek out pictures in magazines of designs that use shapes that they think they could now attempt to construct. These could be brought to school to resource a construction challenges display.

LENGTH, AREA & PERIMETER

THEME **22**

Calculating area and perimeter

Learning targets

The children should be able to:

1 ➤ Calculate the area and perimeter of rectangles

2 ➤ Calculate the area and perimeter of triangles

3 ➤ Calculate the area and perimeter of a range of composite shapes

Before you start

Subject knowledge

Children should, by now, know that area means coverage, and perimeter is the total distance around the edge of a shape, having compared areas by the 'counting squares' method, and perimeters by counting unit edges or sides. Some will have made connections between standard units and standard square units, and have developed important informal methods for calculating some perimeters. Here, we build on that experience to help consolidate methods for calculating both area and perimeter of a range of shapes. An understanding of area and perimeter of straight-sided shapes will support the later development of understanding of the equation for the area and perimeter of a circle. In developing equations for rectangles and triangles it is important to link them, and to be clear about the vocabulary that the children might encounter. For example, they might come across a discussion of length times breadth, length times depth, and length times width, all of which actually concern the same area. Rather than restrict the children to one term it is better to use and explain all the synonyms that they might encounter. Other words that will need a clear explanation include the 'base' and 'height' of triangles and 'diagonal' of rectangles and squares.

Previous knowledge required

Basic work with area and perimeter, familiarity with the names and characteristics of common 2D shapes, use of centimetres and millimetres, decimals, partitioning of shapes into rectangles and triangles

Resources needed for Lesson 1

Copymaster 32, rulers, an overhead transparency of a square grid and some rectangles to place on this for demonstration purposes

Resources needed for Lesson 2

Copymaster 33, rulers, protractors, set squares, an overhead transparency of a square grid and some rectangles to place on this for demonstration purposes

Resources needed for Lesson 3

Copymaster 34, rulers, protractors, set squares

Teaching the lessons

Lesson 1 

Key questions

What do we mean by area and perimeter?

What units do we need to use?

Vocabulary

Area, perimeter, rectangle, square, centimetres, square centimetres

Introduction

15min

Show the children the overhead transparency of a square grid and place a rectangle on it to exactly cover a number of the squares. Ask the children how many squares are covered and what we call the coverage. Tell them that if this were a certain number of squares that had one-centimetre sides then we would say that the area was N square centimetres. Write the result for your rectangle on the board using these units. Then show them the abbreviation for this. Repeat the exercise for another rectangle. Now refer to the distance around the sides of your rectangles. All should be familiar with the term 'perimeter' and the counting approach. Ask if there is a quicker way to determine perimeter. From the ideas the children provide, draw a rectangle on the board and produce the equation that area equals length times breadth. Do the same for perimeter which, at this stage can be perimeter equals twice long side plus twice short side. When appropriate you can move the children to perimeter being equal to twice the sum of the long side and the short side. Tell the children they are now going to have a go at solving some problems.

Activities

Give out **Copymaster 32**. Answer queries if necessary.

Closing the lesson

10min

Review the equations from the Copymaster. Collect the Copymasters to see how each child has progressed.

Assessment

Child performance	Teacher action
Hesitant about the equations and leans on counting experience	Work with these children using geoboards and so on and give more exercises
Gets through most of the tasks satisfactorily	Move on to next lesson to confirm understanding
Completes the task with understanding	Move on to next lesson

Lesson 2

Key questions

Can you see a relationship between this triangle and a rectangle?

If this triangle is half this rectangle what is its area?

Vocabulary

Area, perimeter, triangle names, rectangle, base, height, diagonal, perpendicular, apex

Introduction

15min

Start with an overhead grid using card rectangles. Establish the area of one of the rectangles with the children, cut it in half along a diagonal and put the two pieces back as though it was still a rectangle. Ask, if you were to take away one half, what the area of the remaining half would be. Do this with another rectangle. Draw a rectangle on the board and elicit the equation for obtaining its area. Draw in a diagonal and invite suggestions for an equation for half of the rectangle. Work towards an appreciation that it can be half times the length times the breadth. Draw a triangle, with no right angle, on the board. Explain that we measure the base (relating this to length) and draw a perpendicular line from the base to the apex. Do this and work out the area of the triangle using half the height times the base. Tell the children that for the perimeter we measure each side with a ruler. Alert them to use decimals if their answers are not whole numbers.

Activities

30min

Give out **Copymaster 33**, protractors and rulers, and circulate, giving support as necessary.

Closing the lesson

10min

Review and work out examples from the Copymaster. Collect the Copymasters for marking.

Assessment

Child performance	Teacher action
Can solve some but has difficulty and needs much support	Using geoboards, squared paper and card rectangles repeat your introduction. Give more examples to try
Works steadily and makes satisfactory progress	Discuss the children's work then move on to next lesson
Works confidently and accurately with clear understanding	Move on to next lesson

Lesson 3

Key questions

What shapes could we divide this one into?

Can we make this from rectangles, squares and triangles?

What is the area of this shape?

What is its perimeter?

Vocabulary

Triangle names, rectangle, square, diagonal, area, perimeter, total

Introduction

15min

Revise work on calculating the areas and perimeters of rectangles, squares and triangles. Draw a shape from the Copymaster on the board. Ask how we calculate its area. Divide it into rectangles, squares and triangles and ask whether this makes it easier to calculate the area. Work out the area with the children. Tell them they are going to try to work out the areas of some shapes and measure the perimeters.

Activities

Give out **Copymaster 34**. Go around the class reminding and prompting as necessary.

Closing the lesson

10min

Choose one or two shapes and ask individuals how they obtained their findings. Collect the Copymasters for an evaluation of the children's understanding of calculating area and perimeter.

Assessment

Child performance	Teacher action
Copes well with some but finds others too difficult or confusing	Review the successes together then move on to tackle difficulties
Makes good progress	Give more time, then review outcomes
Finds the exercise straightforward	These children have met the learning targets for this theme

HOMEWORK

Where you feel it appropriate, give some extension activities on the calculation of area and perimeter for one or more of the shapes encountered.

THEME **23**

Problem-solving

Learning targets

The children should be able to:

1 ➸ Use their knowledge of length, angle and construction to measure heights
2 ➸ Use their knowledge of length, area and perimeter to explore small objects
3 ➸ Use their knowledge of length, area and perimeter to explore large objects

Before you start

Subject knowledge

The children now have a lot of knowledge and experience about 2D shapes, their characteristics and the calculation of their dimensions. In developing the application of mathematical knowledge it is vital that we offer investigations that actually build on previous experience and excite the interest of the children. Too often application is reduced to the simple repetition of known skills or techniques. Here, we offer three areas of investigation that should allow the creative use of existing knowledge and support the making of real connections between material that may have been taught, and learned, at different times. The role of the teacher in this sort of work is that of listener, prompter, facilitator and resourcer but not problem-solver.

Previous knowledge required

In particular, the children will need to marshal their thoughts about length, area, perimeter, angles, triangles, rectangles, constructional drawing, scale, ratio and the ways in which these are measured or calculated. As with so much applied work there are also data handling ideas such as averages with which the children will need to be familiar.

Resources needed for Lesson 1

Clinometers, tapes, access to a tall object such as a tree, Copymaster C, Copymaster 35

Resources needed for Lesson 2

Small objects including those mentioned on Copymaster 36: dried peas, barley corns, pins, needles, cocktail sticks, small beads, reams of paper, books; rulers, Copymaster C, Copymaster 36

Resources needed for Lesson 3

Access to parts of the school building, the playground and the field, trundle wheels, long tapes, metre sticks, cocktail sticks, Copymaster 37

Teaching the lessons

Lesson 1 ①

Key questions

What height do you think that is?
How did you come to that answer?
What scale should we use?

Vocabulary

Estimate, angle, height, distance, length, scale

Introduction (15 min)

Tell the children that in this lesson they are going to work out the height of an object, which is too difficult for them to measure using tapes or metre sticks. Tell them that to do this they are going to have to use their experience of careful drawing, measurement, and angles and triangles. Draw a tree on the board and ask how we might measure its height. Write the suggestions in note form. When the children run out of ideas draw a right angled triangle on the board with a vertical line running up the centre of the tree, the apex at the top of the tree and a stick figure, as shown below.

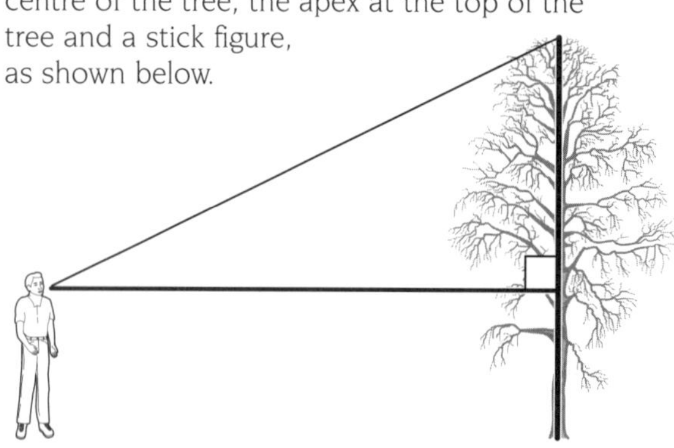

Now ask if this gives any more ideas. Finish by discussing the need to take measurements of the distance we are from the tree, how tall we are, and the angle of the triangle next to our eye and then drawing a scale diagram. Show a clinometer and explain how it works. Tell the children what they are going to measure the height of – if you have a variety of objects then different groups can be given different ones or you might consider taking groups at intervals to the same object.

Activities

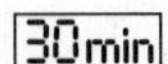

Give out clinometers, measuring tapes, **Copymaster C**, and **Copymaster 35**. The Copymaster has prompts but remind the children of what they must measure in order to draw their scale diagram and work out the height of the object.

Closing the lesson

10min

Let the groups say what they have found. Collect the scale drawings and conclusions.

Assessment

Child performance	Teacher action
Takes measurements but has problems with scale drawing	Check back on the children's work on scales and ratios. Consider giving some exercises to support this area of mathematics
Produces an answer with some help	Review the children's work with them and decide whether to move them on or give more practice
Works through the task readily and produces a sensible answer	Move on to next lesson

Lesson 2

Key questions

How could we possibly find this out?

Vocabulary

This will depend on the strategies and ideas of the children but will include length vocabulary

Introduction

10min

Tell the children that in this lesson they are going to find out some facts about small objects or things. Show a dried pea or corn and ask how long or wide they think it is. Ask how they could find out. Take suggestions, encouraging the idea that if we measured a row of, say, ten we might be able to estimate the average length of one better than trying to measure each one separately. Tell the children they are going to work together to try and find the answers to a variety of questions about small objects.

Activities

30min

Give out **Copymaster 36**, **Copymaster C**, and make available as required the small objects. A range of challenges is offered and you might choose to allocate different ones to different groups or spread the challenges over more than one lesson.

Closing the lesson

10min

Let the children talk about what they have discovered.

Assessment

Child performance	Teacher action
Lacks an organised approach to the tasks	Check on previous experience of practical/ investigative experience. Evaluate and decide on practical investigations to attempt
Makes some progress but has one or two false starts	Discuss achievements to decide whether to give more challenges
Produces solutions with confidence and has a purposeful approach	Move on to the next lesson

Lesson 3

Key questions

How could we possibly find this out?

Vocabulary

This will depend on the strategies and ideas of the children but will include length vocabulary

Introduction

10min

Remind the children of their work with small objects. Explain they will be doing similar work with large objects. Review successful strategies such as looking at the dimensions of a given number of objects and extrapolating from them.

Activities

30min

Give out **Copymaster 37** and make available the measuring instruments as required. Be available to listen to ideas and help with prompts.

Closing the lesson

10min

Listen to what the children have discovered. Collect the notes they have made for evaluation purposes.

Assessment

Child performance	Teacher action
Lacks an organised approach to the tasks	Check on previous experience of practical/ investigative experience. Evaluate and decide on practical investigations to attempt
Makes some progress but has one or two false starts	Discuss achievements to decide whether to give more challenges
Produces solutions with confidence and has a purposeful approach	These children have met the learning targets for this theme

---

HOMEWORK

Consider giving adaptations of the challenges. Encourage the children to seek out published data on dimensions, such as in *The Guinness Book of Records*.

Investigations

- Choose something for which you would like to produce an accurate drawing, take the measurements you think you need, then draw it. Make additional measurements when you need to.
- Produce a book of records about longest, tallest, smallest, and shortest dimensions.
- Produce a dictionary of the words that we use when talking about length and area. Try out your dictionary with friends and family and adapt it if they do not fully understand. Your dictionary may also need drawings.
- Make a collection of catalogues that have furniture and furnishings, and do some measuring of chairs, sofas, tables and so on at home and in school. Work out curtain sizes for windows, cushion sizes for chairs, and walls and wallpaper in order to plan a new look for home or school. When you have finished, work out the wrapping paper you will need for the presents you will give to classmates!
- Do some investigation of length ratios using pictures of faces. Look at, for example, the length of the nose and the distance from the end of the nose to the top lip. Try the width of the eyes and the distance from eye level to the chin and so on. Follow this by doing a similar exercise with area.
- Produce a booklet on the history of measures of length and area. Look for sporting references like furlongs in horse racing, and the fact that a cricket pitch is twenty-two yards (one chain) in length.
- Using plans, scale drawings and blueprints of buildings work out the dimensions of chosen features and their areas as flat shapes. Work out the perimeters too.
- Using seed catalogues and garden books plan the flower bed or vegetable plot you would like to have. How many plants of each kind can you have – how far apart must each plant be planted?
- Work out ways of measuring, accurately, the perimeter and 'width' of circular objects. Work out their area using the counting square approach and then try to make rectangles of the same area.

Assessment

- Estimate lengths then measure and find the differences.
- Measure accurately the lengths of lines in a given drawing.
- Produce accurate measurements of chosen dimensions of given solids and objects.
- Measure the perimeter of the playground, the hall, or the corridor choosing appropriate measuring instruments.
- Give computation of length exercises using addition, subtraction and then multiplication and, finally, combinations of these.
- Use the counting squares method to arrive at good approximations of the areas of 2D shapes.
- Use triangles and rectangles to calculate areas of other shapes.

CAPACITY AND VOLUME

The terms 'capacity' and 'volume' are difficult to define. Some writers suggest that capacity is the space inside a container and the volume how much space the whole container takes up. However, if we think of practical considerations we may have a container that has a capacity of one litre but the actual volume is greater than this because the liquid does not come right to the top. Some suggest that different units should give us an indicator of which term to use so anything measured in cubic centimetres should be called volume and anything measured in litres should be capacity. There may be some merit in this suggestion: that we should think about the context in which we wish to use the appropriate term. So a central heating expert would talk of the volume of a room when considering how big the radiator should be, and a manufacturer of tins of spaghetti would consider the capacity of the box for transporting the tins – the number of tins it will hold.

The systems of measurement for capacity and volume are worth exploring as children get further into the everyday use of standard measures. The metric system is actually very convenient for thinking about volume and its relationship with other measures. The system is designed so that one cubic centimetre of water weighs one gram and is one thousandth of a litre, that is one millilitre. In practice, there are some variations on these if we consider heating or cooling water, but for everyday purposes the system works well. In making the system connect volume and mass it also helps with some important issues. In order to understand volume and capacity we need to make connections to our knowledge of 3D and 2D shapes, length, weight, and our skills in arithmetic. The estimation of volume is a very difficult task. Even for adults it is often the case that we need to test out in practice whether different containers will hold the same amount of liquid. Try this for yourself by seeing how much water an eight-inch (twenty-centimetre) sponge tin will hold. Because of this difficulty we need to give children continuing practice in comparing and ordering containers using sand and water. In doing this we need to be aware that the height of a container often influences our estimates. Indeed it may be this factor of height that can also be important in the orientation of containers. Tilting a bottle can cause some children to suggest that the volume has changed. Thus, as well as comparing and ordering we need also to consider conservation. Making up different shapes using the same number of cubes is part of the experience we should offer children. Finally, we all find difficulty with the idea of displaced volume. In looking at traditional ways of assessing volume which entail dropping a solid object into water and measuring the volume of water displaced, we are using complex connections. These are to do with shape, the linear measure of the volume, and thoughts we have about sinking and floating. We learn how to 'fill' the bath so that it will not overflow when we get into it but few of us have cause to say 'Eureka!' about volume and capacity.

CAPACITY AND VOLUME

THEME **24**

Comparing and ordering

Learning targets

The children should be able to:

1 ➤ Compare the capacity of different containers

2 ➤ Make comparisons and order containers according to capacity

3 ➤ Construct a block graph showing the capacity of different containers

Before you start

Subject knowledge

Young children need lots of practical experience of capacity and volume. They should be given a variety of situations in which they can compare the capacity of different containers using sand and water. In gaining this experience, in the early stages, it is not necessary for them to relate capacity and volume to length or area, and they should not be made to measure using standard measures at first. Rather. the tasks should focus on comparison and ordering, supported by the extension of vocabulary to do with capacity and volume. Such terms as 'holds more', 'holds less', 'full', 'empty', 'half full' and so on should be used appropriately by the children and with the children.

Previous knowledge required

General opportunities in measurement, practical investigations involving comparisons, ordinal number

Resources needed for Lesson 1

A great variety of different sized and shaped containers, sand, water

Resources needed for Lesson 2

A great variety of different sized and shaped containers, including a container that can be used as a non-standard measure, for example, an eggcup or a large spoon, sand, water, Copymaster 38.

Resources needed for Lesson 3

Copymaster D, a measure such as a spoon or eggcup and a variety of containers if you are not doing this lesson close to Lesson 2, otherwise use the results from Lesson 2

Teaching the lessons

Lesson 1 ①

Key questions

Does this hold more than this?

Which of these holds the most or least?

How do you know which holds the most or least?

Vocabulary

Most, least, holds, fills, the language of comparison and ordering

Introduction 10 min

This lesson is an experiential one and you may feel not all the children need do this work all at the same time, depending on their experiences in earlier years. Tell the children that they are going to work in pairs to see what they can find out about a range of different containers and how big they are in terms of what they will hold. Show some of the containers that they will use. Explain that they should investigate them using water or sand or both.

Activities 25 min

The children explore the containers' capacity. Go around asking the key questions and making sure the children use the appropriate vocabulary. Ask them to draw the containers that they believe hold the most and the least and any two containers that contain almost the same.

Closing the lesson 10 min

Get some examples from the children of 'largest' and 'smallest' in respect of capacity. Ask each pair to tell you one thing they discovered. Write these on the board and finish by reading them with the class.

Assessment

Child performance	Teacher action
Lacks a consistent appreciation of the task	Give a lot more opportunities for play with sand and water

Child performance	Teacher action
Carries out the work satisfactorily	Move on to the next lesson but keep an eye on the children's progress in ordering
Carries out the work easily and moves into ordering without any need for encouragement	Move on to the next lesson

Lesson 2

Key questions

Which holds the most / least?

Does this one hold more or less than that one?

Vocabulary

Hold, more, less, most, least, order, compare, comparison, and measure.

Introduction

10min

This lesson builds directly on the target for Lesson 1 but here the children have to go on to make finer judgements in ordering, from smallest to largest capacity. Tell the children that they are going to work together to put containers in order on the basis of what they will hold. Tell the children that they need to use one container to help them work out which of the others holds the most or least, and then to order all the containers. Depending on your resources, indicate which container they should use as their measure. It might be an eggcup or a spoon or another suitable resource, providing it has no scale marked upon it.

Activities

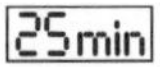

25min

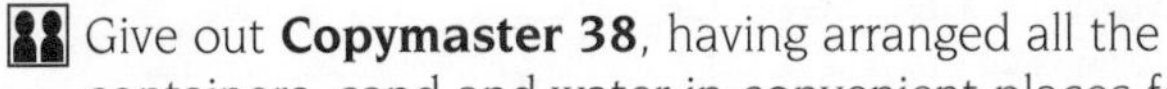

Give out **Copymaster 38**, having arranged all the containers, sand and water in convenient places for each pair or small group. Remind them to use the chosen measuring container and encourage them to work carefully, keeping a note of their results. These notes will allow them to complete the Copymaster.

Closing the lesson

10min

Use a sample of the results to discuss what the children have been doing. Finish by reinforcing that the shape of the container is not always helpful when estimating what it will hold. Ask whether the children were surprised at any of their results. Collect the children's work to use in the next lesson.

Assessment

Child performance	Teacher action
Finds least and most but struggles with ordering	Give more practice with containers, sand and water, then repeat this lesson
Accomplishes an order with some help	Give another opportunity with some different containers
Produces an accurate ordering of the containers	Move on to next lesson

Lesson 3

Key questions

How can we make a picture of what we have done?

How many more or less is this?

Vocabulary

More, less, most, least, block graph

Introduction

10min

Tell the children that, using the results from the previous work on comparing and ordering, they are going to produce a block graph. Remind them of a block graph. In this case, they need to show how many eggcups or spoonfuls fill each of the containers. Draw an example on a graph, but for only a couple of containers.

Activities

25min

Give the children their copies of **Copymaster 38** on which should be a record of the quantity for each container. If the record is incomplete the practical work will need to be repeated. The children have to construct a block graph showing the capacity of each container. Give them copies of **Copymaster D** on which they can construct the block graph.

Closing the lesson

10min

Take an example from the class and reproduce it on the board. Ask the children whether their graphs look like this one and, if not, ask what the differences are. Collect the block graphs to check the children's understanding of comparison and ordering.

Assessment

Child performance	Teacher action
Has difficulties in organising the data to graph	Do more work on simple block graphs
Has difficulties in completing the graph	Give another similar exercise and talk through the process of graphing
Completes the graph satisfactorily	The children have met the learning targets for this theme

HOMEWORK

The children should carry out an informal survey of situations in which the measuring of capacity comes into everyday life at home. Such things as 'don't overfill the bath' and helping with cooking could be the stimulus.

THEME **25**

Measurement

Learning targets

The children should be able to:

1 ➸ Use a scale to measure capacity
2 ➸ Discuss some aspects of metric measures of volume and capacity
3 ➸ Explore packaging and common labelling on packages

Before you start

Subject knowledge

The development of standard measures in volume and capacity has an interesting history in common with all our measures. The key idea with a standard measure is that it supports fair-trading and offers a consistent measure for comparative purposes. Standard measures are approximations in the sense that there will be small but real differences from one measuring device to another. It is important that children come to see that we need to measure as accurately as we can using an appropriate measuring device. When we do so, there is always a small margin of error – which in the classroom, we often describe in terms of 'almost' or 'just about' and 'approximately'. The measurement of liquids is further complicated by the upper surface of a liquid column – the meniscus – being either convex or concave. That the upper surface is not flat should be discussed with the children and the point from which to measure the liquid column is the centre of the curved arc of the surface of the liquid.

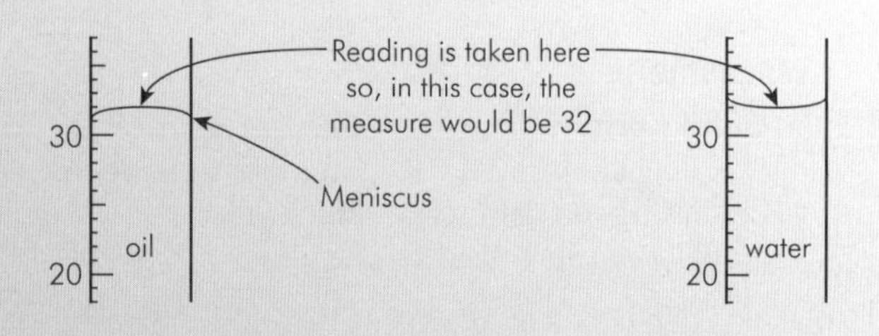

The children need to start using appropriate standard measures – both metric and imperial. They must know that there are 1000 millilitres in a litre and also know what a cubic centimetre is.

Previous knowledge required

Practical experience with capacity using non-standard measures, comparison and ordering of quantities, use of a simple scale such as a ruler, simple fractions and multiples of 10

Resources needed for Lesson 1

A large variety of containers, metric measuring cylinders, water

Resources needed for Lesson 2

Centimetre cubes, metric measuring cylinders, litre and half litre containers, metric measuring jugs (containers now available from manufacturers specifically support volume and capacity work), Copymaster 39, open boxes to take centimetre cubes, for example, empty match boxes (enough for each group to have at least three different boxes)

Resources needed for Lesson 3

A collection of packaging (the children might be able to help by bringing some of this into school) including plastic bottles and different shaped boxes with the labels intact such as cereal boxes, shampoo bottles, drinks containers, cartons, bottles, chocolate wrappers, cheese boxes; Copymaster 40

Teaching the lessons

Lesson 1 ①

Key questions

What is this on the scale?
How much does that container hold?
How easy is it to read the scale?

Vocabulary

Scale, measure, capacity

Introduction

10 min

Tell the children that they are going to measure how much water a number of different containers will hold. Explain that we use the term 'capacity' for how much something will hold. Show them a measuring cylinder and draw part of a scale (see above left) on the board, explaining how to read the level. Put some water in a measuring cylinder and get two children to come out and read the scale. Point out the need to have the surface of the liquid at eye level and have the measuring cylinder standing on a flat surface.

Activities

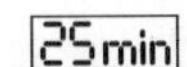

The children should measure the capacity of as many of the available containers as they can. Each person should have a go at reading the scale and all should keep a record of the capacities. Where a container's capacity is greater than the cylinder's, ask for ways of finding out its capacity.

Closing the lesson

10min

Ask the children for their results in measuring the capacity of some containers. For wide variations, measure them yourself as a demonstration. Tell the children that the scales were in measurements called millilitres.

Assessment

Child performance	Teacher action
Makes errors in reading the scale	Use a variety of scales including rulers to check how the children are doing their measuring
Carries out the task satisfactorily though makes some errors	Check the children's arithmetic and work with them measuring large containers
Carries out the task satisfactorily	Give an opportunity to measure and order containers labelling each with their capacity

Lesson 2

Key questions

How does this scale relate to this one?

How many ... in ...?

Vocabulary

Litres, millilitres, cubic centimetres

Introduction

10min

Review the children's work in comparing and measuring capacities of containers. Ask for examples of measures of capacity such as pints of milk, one and a half litre bottles of fizzy drinks and litres of petrol. Tell them that this lesson concentrates on metric measures and that there are 1000 millilitres in 1 litre. Write this on the board in full and with the abbreviations 'ml' and 'l'.

Activities

25min

Give out **Copymaster 39**. The children have to work through this but when they get to the final part on cubic centimetres, stop them and talk to the class about the fact that we can measure volume in cubic centimetres. On the board write this and the 'cc' abbreviation (later you can introduce cm^3). Working in small groups, the children then have to estimate the capacity of three chosen boxes with the help of centimetre cubes.

Closing the lesson

10min

Review samples of work on millilitres from the Copymaster and check some results of the work with centimetre cubes. Collect the Copymasters.

Assessment

Child performance	Teacher action
Makes some errors	Check the arithmetical capabilities of these children and work on fractions and decimals
Finishes most of the work satisfactorily	Give more time to complete, check orally
Completes all tasks confidently and accurately	Move on to the next lesson

Lesson 3

Key questions

What is the amount here?

Which has the greater capacity?

Vocabulary

Capacity, volume, 'weight'

Introduction

10min

Select containers and talk about the information on the labels. Tell the children that they are going to investigate how manufacturers label the capacity or volume of their products. They must identify the quantities and write them in a table.

Activities

25min

Give each child **Copymaster 40** and a collection of packaging to each group. Ask them to think about each package's shape and whether they are surprised at the labelled capacity or volume. Ask the children to note any questions about labels to ask at the end of the lesson.

Closing the lesson

10min

Ask the children for their queries, for example, they may ask what 'weight by volume' is. Use any figures available to explain. Finish by asking the children to tidy up their work for display. Put the packaging and the children's work on display.

Assessment

Child performance	Teacher action
Finds the task organisationally demanding	Give more practice working with tables as an organisational device
Completes most of the table but generates very few questions	Let the children help with a display and discuss items with them
Completes all the table and raises queries or ideas	The children have met the learning targets for this theme

HOMEWORK

Ask the children to quiz their family, friends and relatives on where they use volume and capacity, for example in cooking, washing or gardening.

CAPACITY AND VOLUME

THEME **26**

Calculating capacity and volume

Learning targets

The children should be able to:

1 ➤ Calculate the volume of rectangular blocks
2 ➤ Make containers of given capacity
3 ➤ Calculate the volume of some three-dimensional shapes

Before you start

Subject knowledge

As children progress in their understanding of capacity and volume, it is possible and necessary to start to connect volume with what they know about area and length. Whilst, at this stage, we are not looking at the application of given formulae, we are setting the foundations for that sort of work later. It is important to use apparatus at this stage that has a clear connection to standard measures of volume. Apparatus such as Cuisenaire®, Dienes® and Centicubes® are essential. You certainly need as many one-centimetre cubes as you can gather. In coming to an understanding of how to calculate the volume of a cuboid, the children first need to make different three-dimensional objects using a given number of one-centimetre cubes. Then, they need to fit cubes into containers. Only after this can they make the connections of length, height and breadth.

Previous knowledge required

Comparing and ordering, work with nets of cubes and cuboids

Resources needed for Lesson 1

Rectangular based open containers such as empty matchboxes, centimetre cubes (as many as possible)

Resources needed for Lesson 2

A large number of centimetre cubes, Copymaster C, scissors, glue or sticky tape or both

Resources needed for Lesson 3

Copymaster 41

Teaching the lessons

Lesson 1

Key questions

Which shapes can you make that have the same length and breadth?

Is the volume of this one the same as that one?

How many fit in here?

Which do you think will hold the most?

Vocabulary

Centimetre cube, volume, capacity, container, length, breadth, width

Introduction 10 min

Ask the children to tell you what they know about capacity and volume. Explain that they will be making three-dimensional shapes using centimetre cubes and finding out how many cubes different containers hold. Show them the cubes and explain why they are called centimetre cubes. If you have Dienes® apparatus, show how many centimetre cubes there are in a long, a flat and a large cube.

Activities 25 min

Each pair needs at least 20 one-centimetre cubes for the first part of the activity. Working collaboratively, the children should make a variety of shapes from the cubes using the same number of cubes for each. Ask the class which shapes have the same length and breadth and whether any have the same height. Discuss whether each shape made has the same volume. Give out the open containers to pairs or small groups and ask the children to estimate how many centimetre cubes will fit into each container. They must then check their estimates practically.

Closing the lesson 10 min

Select children to give their estimate and then their result for a container. Discuss that the volume or capacity of their containers is measured in cubic centimetres. Show that this can be written: 'cu.cm.' 'cc' or 'cm^3'. Emphasise that they have made approximations as there may have been noticeable gaps into which it was not possible to fit centimetre cubes.

Assessment

Child performance	Teacher action
Makes the shapes and fills containers but has difficulty relating this to ideas about volume	Give more supported practice. If necessary, give more work on comparison and ordering
Carries through the activities satisfactorily	Move on to next lesson
Carries through the activities satisfactorily and indicates an appreciation of the relationship of height, length and breadth	Move on to next lesson

Lesson 2

Key questions

Why not make a container and try it out?

How can we work out the net that we need?

Did your container hold what you thought?

Vocabulary

Centimetre cube, net, volume, capacity, rectangle

Introduction

10min

Remind the children of their work on containers and cubic centimetres. Tell them that they will be making containers that hold a certain number of cubes. Remind them how to make an open-topped rectangular based container. They can make a net before the lesson using large squared paper and sticky tape to hold the sides. If they are experienced with nets, let them make flaps and use glue. On the board, write the challenges: to make a container that will hold exactly 16 cubes and one that will hold exactly 30 cubes.

Activities

Give out **Copymaster C**, sticky tape or glue, scissors and at least 30 cubes to each pair or small group. Tell the children to discuss what shape and size their net might be. If they are not sure, encourage them to make a container and try it out. If they unfold their trial container, they might then be able to work out a way of predicting the required dimensions to meet the challenges.

Closing the lesson

10min

Use a selection of the containers made by the children to talk about dimensions and how they worked out which nets to use. Remind them that they made containers with a particular capacity. The volume of the cubes put together was almost exactly the same as the capacity of their containers.

Assessment

Child performance	Teacher action
Makes containers, but not the important connections	Give further practice on using centimetre cubes with different containers then try the activity again
Trial and error and then prediction leads to at least one solution	Review the children's findings and then offer more challenges
Meets the challenges with a variety of appropriate responses	Move on to the next lesson

Lesson 3

Key questions

What is the volume of this?

What is the connection?

Vocabulary

Cubic centimetres, length, breadth, width, height

Introduction

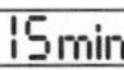

Discuss with the children the connections they have made between the numbers of centimetre cubes and the capacity of a container. Use Multilink® or similar apparatus to demonstrate that we can calculate the number of cubes in a cuboid by multiplying the height, length and breadth or width. Do this also for rectangular prisms, like those shown below.

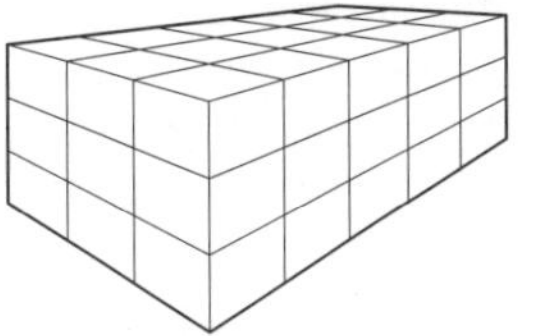

This rectangular prism is $3 \times 5 \times 3 = 45$

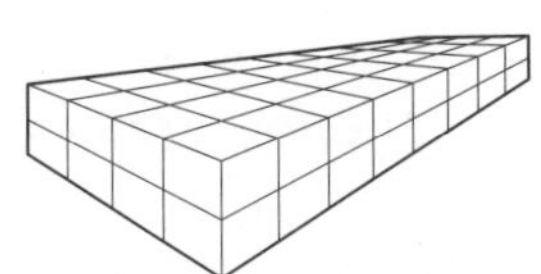

This one is $2 \times 8 \times 4 = 64$

Activities

Give out **Copymaster 41**. The children have to work out how many cubes are in each of the shapes. As you go around the class, encourage them to think about why the volume of the shape is recorded in centimetres cubed or cubic centimetres.

Closing the lesson

10min

Review some of the examples using the children's ideas to support the learning. Collect the Copymasters for checking.

Assessment

Child performance	Teacher action
Works through the first part of the Copymaster but relies on counting	Give more practice on the earlier activities in this theme
Works through most challenges satisfactorily	Give time to complete the Copymaster and review the work
Completes the Copymaster readily	The learning targets for this theme have been met

HOMEWORK

Let the children collect information from packaging labels about measurements used. Looking at quantities used in recipes could form the basis of some technology work.

CAPACITY AND VOLUME

THEME **27**

Displacement, area, mass and volume

Learning targets

The children should be able to:

1 ➤ Use displacement of water to measure the volume of some objects

2 ➤ Develop information about the mass and volume of water

3 ➤ Investigate connections between volume and surface area and their effects

Before you start

Subject knowledge

At this stage, the children should be very familiar with the idea of measuring volume using centimetre cubes. On this basis, they can now move on to look at how to use the displacement of water as an indicator of volume. This emphasises the idea of volume being about the amount of space an object takes up. Once the principle is established, then it is possible to develop some factual knowledge about the particular characteristics of water. At this stage and level, we want the children to realise that 1 cubic centimetre is the same as 1 millilitre and, therefore, 1000 cubic centimetres are equivalent to 1 litre, which is 1000 millilitres. It is possible, also, to investigate the surface area of objects in relation to their volume. All these experiences will eventually lead the children to being capable of investigating density, using the fact that 1 cubic centimetre of water has a mass of 1 gram.

Previous knowledge required

Knowledge of cubic centimetres, use of the appropriate measuring equipment, line graphs

Resources needed for Lesson 1

A variety of irregular and regular shaped objects which will sink, measuring jugs, beakers or cylinders with metric scales, water

Resources needed for Lesson 2

Measuring jugs, beakers or cylinders with metric scales, accurate balances for weighing objects, water and two 1 litre cooking oil bottles, one full of oil and the other empty

Resources needed for Lesson 3

Centimetre cubes, Copymaster G

Teaching the lessons

Lesson 1 ①

Key questions

How do you read the scale?

Which object has the largest or smallest volume?

Vocabulary

Volume, capacity, displace, displacement

Introduction — 10 min

Tell the children that they are going to find out the volume of a number of different objects. Remind them of work they have done previously using centimetre cubes. Revise how to read a scale accurately when measuring the volume of a liquid. Write a table on the board with three columns headed 'Volume of water', 'Reading with object in the water', 'Volume of the object'. Use these headings to explain what the children have to do.

Activities — 25 min

Using the measuring devices and the range of objects that you have provided, the children should put water into the container and read off the amount. Then they should carefully place each object into the water and read the scale once more. Taking one result from the other will give the volume of the object. They can then order the objects in terms of their volume. They should complete the table using the headings that you have shown them on the board.

Closing the lesson — 10 min

Using a sample of the objects, recap some of the work. Finish by talking about the fact that volume is the amount of space that something takes up. If there is time, tell the story of Archimedes getting into his bath and seeing the rise in water due to his volume, and how this led to his profound work on density.

Assessment

Child performance	Teacher action
Makes errors in reading the scale	Give more practice and then try the exercise again
Completes the work satisfactorily	Move on to the next lesson

Child performance	Teacher action
Completes the work satisfactorily and raises ideas about the 'weight' of the objects	Move on to the next lesson

Lesson 2 ②

Key questions

How much does that weigh?

What is the volume of the water and what is its weight?

Vocabulary

Volume, capacity, cubic centimetre, millilitre, litre

Introduction — 10min

Tell the children that, in this lesson, they are going to be collecting together a number of ideas in order to establish some facts about water. These facts are to do with volume and mass. Tell them that they will measure out different quantities of water and 'weigh' them. They should start out by finding out the mass of the empty container so that they can then work out the mass of each different amount of water they use. Tell the children to keep notes of their results for a discussion at the end of the lesson. Remind them of the need for accuracy.

Activities — 20min

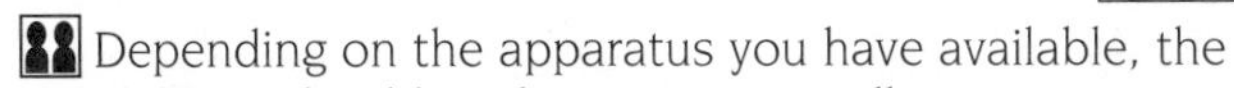

Depending on the apparatus you have available, the children should work in pairs or small groups, carrying out the instructions you have given them. Go around the class reminding them of the need for accuracy and careful measurement and that they should find the mass of several different amounts of water.

Closing the lesson — 15min

Write results from each group's efforts on the board. If the children have not yet made the connection, help them to see that, for example, 250 millilitres or 250 cubic centimetres weighs 250 grams. There will be a range around this due to the errors in measurement or the accuracy of the instruments. Finish by demonstrating that 1 litre of cooking oil and 1 litre of water do not have the same mass. Pour a little of the oil onto the water afterwards and ask the children to think about why the oil might float. This is a good starting point for work on density if you want to pursue this lesson further before looking at surface area and volume.

Assessment

Child performance	Teacher action
Gets wide variation in results	Give more practice at measuring but also check the arithmetic
Works through satisfactorily	Move on to the next lesson
Works through satisfactorily and produces ideas about different liquids having different masses for the same volume	Move on to the next lesson but consider doing some work with these children on density

Lesson 3 

Key questions

What happens?

What shape are your graphs?

Do they ever cross?

What effects might these things have in everyday life?

Vocabulary

Surface area, volume, line graph, scale, axes

Introduction — 10min

This is quite demanding so be sure that the children are ready to tackle this investigation. Show the children a single one-centimetre cube. Ask them what the length of a side or edge is. Then ask them what its volume is and its surface area. Put the results of this on the board. Now work out these same measurements for the next largest cube with the children. Assemble the eight one-centimetre cubes necessary to make this and ask what it is in terms of the length of the edge, the volume and the surface area once more. Tell the children to repeat the exercise for themselves and then to try and go on to work with at least five cubes of increasing size. Put headings for a table on the board and ask them to make their own and fill it in.

Cube	Length of edge	Volume	Surface area
1			
2			

Activities — 35min

The children work through the tasks described to them in your introduction. When the majority have got results for the first five cubes, stop the class and tell them that we can plot graphs of the surface area and volume using our results as shown below.

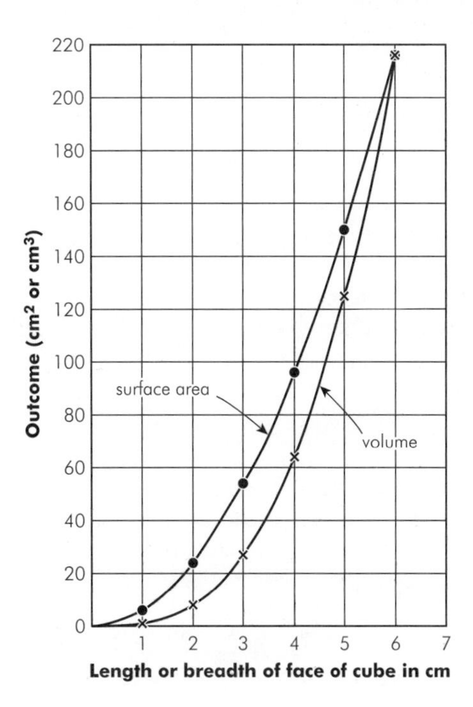

Give out **Copymaster G** and show the children how to mark each of the scales. Then let them plot the surface area and the volume. Use the key questions as they progress.

Closing the lesson

10min

Draw the graphs on the board or an overhead transparency. Talk about the shapes and what seems to be happening. If anyone has got to the sixth cube, they may have some very interesting information to share with the class. Finish by pointing out that small creatures like babies and mice have a larger surface area than volume so they can lose heat very quickly.

Assessment

Child performance	Teacher action
Carries out the first part but finds the graphing too difficult	Do some revision work on line graphs and then try again
Carries out most of the task but doesn't finish	Give some more time
Completes all the task	These children have met the learning targets for this theme

HOMEWORK

The children can further investigate families of volume measures and find out more facts about the characteristics of water. This may allow you to go on to some work on density. Finally children could investigate surface area and volume for shapes other than cubes.

Investigations

- Make some cakes using a recipe that includes measures of volume. Now make up a fruit juice cocktail drink giving the quantities of each juice that needs to be put in for the perfect taste.
- Using apparatus like Multilink® build different shapes from the same number of pieces. Do you think they all have the same volume? At a later stage this could be tested by displacement of water.
- Make your own calibrated measuring device. Choose a suitable container and think about how to calibrate it so that it will help you measure accurately.
- Make a collection of packaging on which there are statements about volume. Keep a note of the cost of the items. Can you work out value for money using these prices and the stated volumes?
- Turn on a tap so that it drips. How many drips would it take to make a litre of water? How could you find this out without waiting too long? Can you work out the volume of each drip? Could you use these ideas to work out the volume of water in a raindrop?
- Look at a set of Russian dolls. Can you make a series of containers that will fit one inside the other? How?
- Using the work you have done in 3D shapes make some containers that will hold a given volume of sand.
- If the school has goldfish or tropical fish, or some of the children do, look at manufacturers' literature about fish medicine. They often give quantities of medicine, in drops that have to be put into differing amounts of water. How can we find the volume of our fish tank?
- Make a conversion book for cooks. Include measures of volume in metric, imperial, cookery measures such as 'tablespoon', and American units including cups.
- Car manufacturers use volume to talk about the size of engines, and the amount of fuel the tank can carry. They also produce figures for the distances you can travel on given volumes of fuel. Investigate these figures.

Assessment

- Compare and order a wide variety of tall, short, wide, narrow, curved, cuboid and conical containers.
- Use a variety of measuring instruments to measure given amounts of water or sand.
- Put given statements of the volume of things in order from smallest to largest.
- Convert a recipe from one system of volume measures to another.
- Draw a conversion graph to convert litres to pints.

MASS AND WEIGHT

There is a familiar story that Isaac Newton sat under an apple tree and an apple fell on his head giving him the inspiration for his work on gravity. We commemorate the significance of this work through the use of the Newton as a measure of force. For instance, if you hold a small apple in your hand you experience the force of about one Newton. However, we do not commonly use the Newton though it would help us in distinguishing between mass and weight. There has been much discussion over the years as to whether, and how, we should try to teach Primary children about mass. In our view we should continue to talk about 'weight' with children and leave the development of ideas about mass until later. The exception to this is the convention that most of us find acceptable when talking about 'masses' in a box of 'weights'. It is there that we can at least introduce the term to children.

In working with 'weights' and in the process of weighing the children will encounter a variety of weighing machines. These range from the balance which consists of a beam balanced on a fulcrum, to spring balances and bathroom scales. If we took our beam balance to the moon it would still work in the same way with its identical 'weights'. But our bathroom scales would not work as these depend upon the force of gravity for their accuracy. It is important that children have the opportunity to use a variety of weighing instruments and that, as they progress, they learn something of how these instruments work. Through this they will eventually be able to resolve for themselves the 'mass' and 'weight' problem.

In learning about 'weight' and weighing there are two issues that can cause confusion and uncertainty and which may lead children to developing profound misconceptions. These are to do with 'weight' and shape, and 'weight' and size. Many youngsters believe that changing the shape of something will increase or decrease its weight. Try this with some children to see what happens. Take some Plasticine® or similar material and make a sphere. Let the children handle it and then roll it into a sausage shape. Ask whether they believe it now weighs the same. If any of them say it has changed you have a clear indication that more practical work using malleable objects is necessary. The other problem is that we often associate height with weight, so a taller object is often believed to be heavier. Again there is much practical investigation to be made available in order to ameliorate such false understanding.

MASS AND WEIGHT

THEME **28**

Comparing and ordering

Learning targets

The children should be able to:

1 ➤➤ Compare how much each of a set of objects weigh

2 ➤➤ Order a set of objects

3 ➤➤ Use kilograms and half kilograms

Before you start

Subject knowledge

In the early stages of their developing a concept of 'weight', close attention should be paid to the development of appropriate vocabulary. Comparative terms such as 'heavier', 'heaviest', 'lighter' and 'lightest' and technical language such as 'scales', 'balance', and 'weight' are examples of words the children should know and use. As with all our explorations of the world, touch and feel are important in appreciating the concept of mass. The children should be encouraged to discuss the feel of different objects in terms of their weight. Ordering by feel and then testing one's decisions by use of a balance or scale is an essential experience. The development of standard measures has, as is so often the case with measurement, an interesting history. At the heart of the development of standard measures is, of course, the need for fair trading. Also, the importance of weighing can be seen in the production of alloys, chemical mixtures and cooking. Finally, there are key skills that we need to introduce, such as the reading of scales.

Previous knowledge required

General work on comparing and ordering, simple fractions

Resources needed for Lesson 1

A variety of objects sufficient for work in small groups, balances

Resources needed for Lesson 2

A variety of objects sufficient for work in small groups, balances

Resources needed for Lesson 3

Balances, kilogram and half kilogram balance weights, a variety of objects that can be grouped and weighed, for example, bags of stones, boxes of nuts and bolts, Plasticine®, wooden bricks and, for demonstration purposes, one kilogram, half kilogram and quarter kilogram packages of, for example, flour, sugar, tea

Teaching the lessons

Lesson 1 ①

Key questions

Which is heavier?

How do you know?

Can you find objects that balance each other?

Vocabulary

Balance, comparative vocabulary like heavier, lighter, lightest

Introduction — 10 min

Using a few of the objects ask the children to look at them and decide whether they can judge which is the heaviest, which the lightest. Then let individual children handle them and describe the feel of 'heaviness'. Show a balance and remind them how to use this. The key idea is getting the arm level. Tell them that they will be working together to find out all they can about a variety of objects by using a balance.

Activities — 25 min

The children investigate the objects by comparing them and keeping a record of for example which they think is the heaviest, and which the lightest. Ask them to find objects that weigh almost the same and state how they know.

Closing the lesson — 10 min

Let individuals tell the class about some other things they have discovered. Reinforce the need, in such experiences, to be as accurate as possible and to be well organised so that comparisons made are not forgotten.

Assessment

Child performance	Teacher action
Works through the task but is poorly organised	Give more practice at tasks that need to be thought about in respect of organising themselves
Works satisfactorily	Move on to next lesson
Works well, making perceptive observations	Move on to next lesson

Lesson 2 (2)

Key questions

Which is heavier/lighter?

Where does this one come in your order?

Vocabulary

Balance, the language of comparison and order

Introduction

10min

With the help of the children, revise the work done on comparisons in Lesson 1. Tell the children that they are going to do a similar exercise in this lesson with the addition of comparing the weight of objects and also putting them in order from heaviest to lightest. Remind them of the way to judge the balance at eye level.

Activities

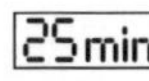

The children should have at least six different objects for each group. Judicious movement of objects around during the lesson may mean that additional ordering can take place. As the children work through the task, keep reminding them of the need to be organised and to keep a record of what they find out.

Closing the lesson

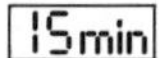

Let some of the groups present their order to the others. Ask the children whether any of the items were difficult to put in order. Ask all the children how they kept a record of what they did.

Assessment

Child performance	Teacher action
Lots of repetition because of lack of organisation	Do the exercise again with these children, reviewing the sorts of information they need to organise and how this might be done
Orders the objects satisfactorily	Move on to next lesson
Orders the objects readily and extends the order by adding more objects	Move on to next lesson

Lesson 3 

Key questions

What is the relationship between these weights?

How many did you need?

Could you get it exactly balanced?

Vocabulary

Kilogram, balance

Introduction

10min

Show the children kilogram and half kilogram weights. Write the names on the board in full and in abbreviated form. Tell the children that, in this lesson, they are going to find out how many items from a variety of objects make a kilogram and how many a half-kilogram. Remind them of the way to accurately use a balance, demonstrating as you do this that two of the half kilogram weights balance the one-kilogram weight.

Activities

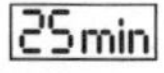

Depending on the number of balances available to you, the children should work in pairs or small groups to establish, for example how many wooden bricks there are in one kilogram and how many in half a kilogram. Reinforce the need for them to keep a record of their findings. If the balance cannot be exactly levelled, tell the children that they should decide which number of items gives them the nearest to a perfect balance.

Closing the lesson

Write a table of the objects on the board and write in each group's results. Discuss any differences that appear. Point out that the kilogram is an important weight today and show some common products that come in one and a half kilogram, one kilogram, half kilogram or quarter kilogram packages.

Assessment

Child performance	Teacher action
Can do the task but doesn't make the connections between numbers of items and a relationship between the number for a kilogram and a half-kilogram	Check on understanding of simple fractions and then repeat this exercise
Carries through most of the task satisfactorily	Give time to complete and check their understanding of all the ideas in this theme
Carries through the task readily and talks about other fractions of a kilogram	These children have met the learning targets for this theme

HOMEWORK

Ask the children to find out at home the kinds of common packages and what they weigh in kilograms, for example for potatoes, sugar, flour, butter and chocolate.

MASS AND WEIGHT

THEME 29

Conservation and estimation

Learning targets

The children should be able to:

1 ➤➤ Conserve 'weight' when the shape of an object is changed

2 ➤➤ Use grams as well as kilograms

3 ➤➤ Estimate weights and then check their estimates

Before you start

Subject knowledge

Conservation of weight, in common with other measures and with number, is vitally important in the development of children's understanding. To explore conservation in weight, we can work with both elastic and non-elastic constructional materials. Malleable materials such as Plasticine® offer us opportunities to check a child's understanding of change and constancy. The use of constructional materials such as Multilink® give us opportunities to get children to see that, while overall design can change, there is still the constancy of 'weight'. If the opportunity is available, the making of pots with a given 'weight' of clay and then a measure of the finished product after firing can help bring into sharp focus what has changed and what has not. In support of conservation, we need to be able to measure 'weight' with increasing accuracy and finer measures. To this end, the children need to extend their appreciation of families of measures. Here, we start to make use of the gram, though one gram is rather too light to give the children a feel for weight, so multiples such as 25, 100 and 250 grams need to be emphasised. Finally, in order to gauge just how well the children are getting on with their understanding of 'weight', we need to give plenty of opportunities for them to estimate 'weights' against standard measures. At first, you might find that children guess but, given consistent practice, they can and should become adept at making reasonable and reasoned estimates of common 'weights'.

Previous knowledge required

Comparison and ordering of weights, the kilogram and simple fractions of the kilogram, use of a balance or other appropriate instrument

Resources needed for Lesson 1

Plasticine®, Multilink® or similar constructional apparatus, Copymaster 42, balances, a variety of weights which can be counted, as for example, three blue ones, two red ones, and so on

Resources needed for Lesson 2

A variety of objects to be weighed, a variety of balances, balance weights, other measuring instruments

Resources needed for Lesson 3

A variety of objects to be weighed, a variety of weighing instruments, Copymaster 43

Teaching the lessons

Lesson 1 ❶

Key questions

What did that weigh?

Is it the same now?

Vocabulary

Weight, weighing, compare, comparison

Introduction 10 min

Remind the children of their work on weighing objects with accuracy. Tell them they will be experimenting with 'squashable' and rigid materials to see whether changing their shapes makes any difference to their weight. Plasticine® moulded into different shapes and ten pieces of Multilink® made into new shapes will be weighed to see whether the same number of weights balance with the Plasticine® and Multilink® each time.

Activities 25 min

Depending on the numbers of available weighing instruments, the children should work in pairs or small groups. They have to complete **Copymaster 42** including explaining what they have found out. Encourage the children to count the numbers of weights they use and not, at this stage, to be concerned about the total number of grams.

Closing the lesson

10min

Use the children's work to show that when shapes change the weight remains the same. Collect the Copymasters to evaluate the children's understanding.

Assessment

Child performance	Teacher action
Believes the shape change should make a difference to the weight	Do more work on conservation in this and other areas of measuring
Carries out the task and is happy with the results	Move on to next lesson
Understands conservation of weight and uses grams rather than numbers of weights	Move on to next lesson

Lesson 2

Key questions

How many grams in half a kilogram/quarter kilogram?

What does this weigh?

Vocabulary

Kilogram, gram

Introduction

15min

Tell the children that to accurately weigh a wide variety of objects they need to know more about standard metric measures. Remind them of their work using kilograms and fractions of a kilogram. Tell them that there are 1000 grams in 1 kilogram. Write some fractions of kilograms on the board (half, quarter, three quarters, one fifth and so on) and ask the children what these are in grams. Let children handle the balance weights. Show examples of the types of weighing instruments and how they are used.

Activities

20min

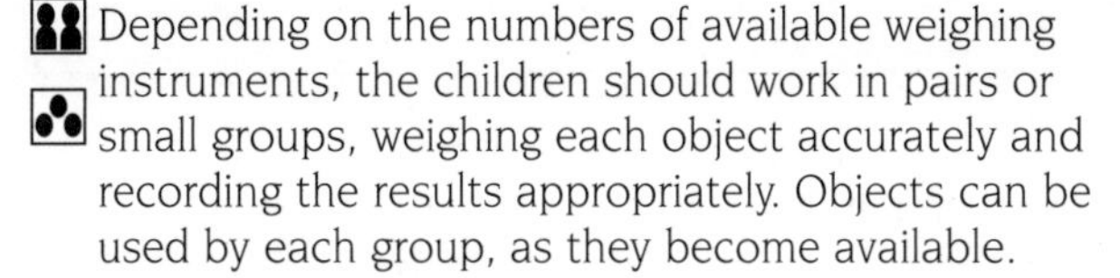

Depending on the numbers of available weighing instruments, the children should work in pairs or small groups, weighing each object accurately and recording the results appropriately. Objects can be used by each group, as they become available.

Closing the lesson

10min

On the board write some of the objects and groups' results. Where there are differences in results, measure the objects yourself as a demonstration. Recap on the number of grams in a kilogram and some fractions of a kilogram.

Assessment

Child performance	Teacher action
Has difficulty in using the instruments	Do more work on measuring weight skills
Weighs a number of objects with reasonable accuracy	Give further opportunities, then move on to the next lesson
Demonstrates a facility with this task	Move on to the next lesson

Lesson 3

Key questions

What do you think this weighs?

Were you close?

Were you surprised?

Vocabulary

Estimate, estimation, kilogram, gram, appropriate fractions and general weighing vocabulary

Introduction

10min

Tell the children that, in this lesson, they are going to estimate the weight of each object before weighing it. Demonstrate and talk about not guessing but really trying to estimate. Tell the children to use the range of metric weights they know and to think of familiar weights, for example some chocolate bars weigh about 50 grams. Tell them to work out the difference between their estimation and the weight they find when they measure it.

Activities

25min

Give out **Copymaster 43**. Go around the class asking individuals to estimate an object, then watch them weigh it. The children need to fill in as many attempts as they can in the time available. They also need to work out the difference between their estimate and the actual weight as they go along.

Closing the lesson

10min

Write some examples in a table, on the board. Discuss how the table should have been completed. Ask the children which objects they found easiest to estimate and which the most difficult. Collect the Copymaster for checking the understanding of the task and the appropriate use of the standard measures.

Assessment

Child performance	Teacher action
Carries out the task but is inconsistent in approach and the use of standard measures	Give these children more general practical activity using balances and weighing exercises
Makes satisfactory attempts with few errors using standard measures in calculation of difference	Check the work with the children and then let them try it again
Completes the task satisfactorily	The learning targets for this theme have been met

HOMEWORK

The children could do a survey of friends and family asking on which occasions the weight of something needs to be known. This survey could be used to further extend discussion about the meaning of 'weight'.

MASS AND WEIGHT

THEME **30**

Families of measures

Learning targets

The children should be able to:

1 ➤➤ Use appropriately common weights
2 ➤➤ Convert measures in different weight families
3 ➤➤ Make and test their own balances using standard measures

Before you start

Subject knowledge

In many areas of life in the UK, imperial units of weight continue in use. Even though many shops have moved to labelling in metric measures, it is still the case that we still use, for example, stones and pounds for a person's weight. Indeed, as long as people continue to ask for a pound of apples or tomatoes rather than half a kilo, we need to be familiar with common imperial units. In introducing and using these, however, we must be careful not to give children the impression that different units mean that objects have a different weight. While there are different systems and units, each performs the same function and it is possible and necessary to be able to convert one to the other. Weights that we need to teach currently are kilograms/grams and stones/ pounds/ounces. The conversion information (top right) gives the units and their relationships. The systems are extended here to larger weights, as these can often stimulate children's thinking and you might choose to use them for this purpose.

We can use 2.2 pounds (lbs) as being equivalent to 1 kilogram (kg) at this stage.

Metric

1000 grams (g)	=	1 kilogram (kg)
1000 kilograms (kg)	=	1 metric tonne

Imperial

16 ounces (oz)	=	1 pound (lb)
14 pounds (lb)	=	1 stone
8 stones (112lb)	=	1 hundredweight (cwt)
20 hundredweights (cwt)	=	1 imperial ton

Previous knowledge required

Practical experience of weighing and the use of balances, the construction of straight line graphs

Resources needed for Lesson 1

Balances, objects to be weighed, sets of metric and imperial weights

Resources needed for Lesson 2

A balance and metric and imperial weights for demonstration purposes, Copymaster 44

Resources needed for Lesson 3

Coat hangers, yoghurt pots or similar, string, sticky tape, card, scissors, a variety of small objects, standard weights

Teaching the lessons

Lesson 1 ①

Key questions

What does this weigh in grams/kilograms?

What does this weigh in ounces/pounds?

Vocabulary

Weight vocabulary for both metric and imperial units

Introduction — 15min

Talk to the children about the different units and systems of weight in use in the world. Explain that in the UK, we have decided to use the metric system and units, but we still use imperial units like stones and pounds. Copy the conversion table above on to the board and discuss the relationship between measures. Tell the children you want them to weigh a collection of objects, finding the weight in metric and then imperial units.

Activities — 20min

Using the balances and given weights, the objects you have provided should be weighed and each weight recorded. Where the children cannot obtain an exact balance, they should get as close as they can and indicate in their results that this is an approximate answer. They must not mix weights from the two systems when they are weighing.

Closing the lesson — 15min

Review some of the children's results. Give more examples of imperial weights in use or ask the children to do so. Use examples, such as hearing people asking for a pound of sugar or reading stories where youngsters bought a quarter of sweets (four ounces) to make a list of rough equivalents that the children can use in everyday experiences like cooking and shopping.

Assessment

Child performance	Teacher action
Performs the task but indicates through their statements that there is confusion about the different systems	Give more practice with the units separately and then try this activity again
Performs the task satisfactorily	Move on to the next lesson
Performs the task satisfactorily and suggests equivalents in their results	Move on to the next lesson

Lesson 2

Key questions

If this is equivalent to that, can we make a graph?

What is the equivalent of...?

Vocabulary

Weight vocabulary in metric and Imperial systems, straight line graph, equivalent

Introduction

Demonstrate equivalents for 1 kilogram, 500 gram, 250 gram and 100 gram weights and then for 1 lb, 8 oz, 4 oz and 1 oz weights (see below).

Equivalents using a balance and weights

1kg	=	2lb 3oz
500g	=	1lb 1oz or 1lb 2oz
250g	=	8 or 9oz
100g	=	3 or 4oz
1lb	=	450–455g
8oz	=	225–230g
4oz	=	110–115g
1oz	=	25–30g

For our purposes we can use
1kg = 2.2lb
as a base for developing equivalents

Write your results on the board to use later. Explain that we can obtain equivalents by using a straight-line graph. The two points needed to make the graph are zero (g and oz), and the fact that 2.2 lb is equivalent to 1 kg.

Activities

Give out **Copymaster 44** for the children to draw a straight line graph then use it to answer the questions.

Closing the lesson

Using their graphs, the children should check the practical results that you got at the start of the lesson. Collect the Copymasters to check for accuracy in the graphs and the answers.

Assessment

Child performance	Teacher action
Makes errors/false starts in producing the graph	Do some more work on straight-line graphs
Constructs the graph and completes most of the questions	Give children time to complete the work and review it together
Completes the task satisfactorily	Move on to the next lesson

Lesson 3

Key questions

Did you get it level?

How did you check?

What is good about your balance?

Vocabulary

The common weight vocabulary

Introduction

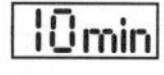

This lesson will support your evaluation of the children's understanding of weighing and the use of standard units of weight. Explain that the children are to work together to design and make their own balance using the given materials and that accuracy and robust construction is important.

Activities

The children design and make their balances then test them out. Move around the class, encouraging the process, then testing the balances.

Closing the lesson

10min

Select some children to demonstrate their balances to the class. Arrange all efforts on display so that everyone has an opportunity to evaluate the work.

Assessment

Child performance	Teacher action
Finds collaboration difficult	Think about situations in which you can help these children to see the benefits of working together
Works well but needs more time to complete the work	Give more time and then test out the balances
Helps produce a working and usable balance	These children have met the learning targets for this theme

HOMEWORK

The children should carry out a survey as to where they, their friends and family use or encounter imperial measures. These need not be restricted to weight but could be used as an opportunity to support all your measure work.

MASS AND WEIGHT

THEME **31**

Estimating and testing

Learning targets

The children should be able to:

1 ➤ Estimate the weight of very light objects

2 ➤ Estimate the weight of very heavy objects

3 ➤ Make a spring and test it for elasticity

Before you start

Subject knowledge

This theme brings a range of skills and ideas together. These include the application of arithmetical skills to problem solving, including an ability to make sensible and sustainable estimates. Also, there is a need for the children to be well organised, reflective and thorough in their record keeping. There is, of course, a need to know systems for weights and the relationship between the units within any system. In order to keep the impetus with the investigative work within this theme, it is necessary to be able to access appropriate information, as it is needed. Some of this information might come from books but much needs to be gained through first-hand experience. For example, working out the average weight of a brick, a roof tile, a plank of wood, or the number of sheets in a pack of paper or an exercise book has to be done first hand. There are opportunities here for extending the work into projects, for example, finding the weight of a single sheet of paper could be linked to a project on standard paper sizes (A3, A4 and so on) and an investigation about the weights of papers claimed by the manufacturers. This 'weight' refers to the heaviness of papers designed for particular uses. For example, a typical sheet of paper is labelled as 80 gsm (grams per square metre). The children could investigate why there are papers of other weights.

Previous knowledge required

Wide range of weighing experience, units and systems – particularly metric. Calculating skills including averages and graphing – particularly line graphs

Resources needed for Lesson 1

These or similar light objects: quantities of A4 paper, exercise books, access to library books, dried peas or beans, a large quantity of paper clips, Multilink® or centimetre cubes, pins, calculators, weighing instruments, Copymaster 45

Resources needed for Lesson 2

Examples of building objects to show including a brick, a carpet tile, a vinyl floor tile, a roof tile, if possible, a plank of wood (all need to be weighed by you). Additional supervision, escorting groups of children to different parts of the school, may also be needed

Resources needed for Lesson 3

Wire that can be wound on a pencil readily but won't snap, weights with a hook or a hook on which a pan or yoghurt pot can be suspended, clamps and stands, sheets of card or other stiff paper, rulers, a spring balance for demonstration purposes, Copymaster G

Teaching the lessons

Lesson 1

Key questions

How can we estimate the weight of this?

What does that weigh?

Does a … weigh more or less than…?

Vocabulary

Quantity, average, decimal, estimate

Introduction 10min

Show the children one or two of the items you have collected together. If, for example, you have dried peas hold one up and ask the children to suggest how we might find its weight. If they suggest weighing it, demonstrate that it is too light for most weighing instruments. Through question and answer, develop the idea that if a known number, say 100 dried peas, are weighed, then we can get an average weight for one pea. This can be done with other light objects, such as a sheet of paper or a paper clip. Tell the children they are going to find out the weights of many light things.

Activities

30 min

Using the available weighing instruments and the range of available items, the children should complete **Copymaster 45**, working out the average weight of one of each of the items. Because the results will be very small with many decimal places, calculators should be used to support the averaging process. Collect some results as you go around the class and do calculations yourself along the lines of how many pins are needed to balance a chocolate bar.

Closing the lesson

10 min

Using some of the results, contrast the weights that the children have completed. Where there are differences review work on the board, checking the position of the decimal point. Using the results you collected earlier, give some comparisons of, for example, the number of dried peas needed to balance the weight of a packet of crisps. Consider starting a display on 'light' and 'heavy' that can be further developed in the next lesson on heavy objects.

Assessment

Child performance	Teacher action
Has problems with averaging	Consider revising mean averages and look at the children's facility with the use of decimals
Completes a small number of items satisfactorily	Give time to extend the children's experience, looking at sticking points and working on problem areas
Completes many items satisfactorily	Move on to the next lesson

Lesson 2

Key questions

How can we estimate the total weight of...? How can we estimate the number of...?

Vocabulary

Total, estimate, estimation

Introduction

10 min

Remind the children of their work for the previous lesson in the estimation of light objects. Tell them that, in this lesson, they are going to estimate the weight of heavy objects, such as the tiles on the floor in the school corridor. Show them your heavy objects and write what each of them weighs on the board. Ask the children how they might go about estimating the weight of a house or the school wall or the weight of carpet in the school reception area or the Head's office. Depending on your resources, allocate a different problem to each group.

Activities

30 min

The groups have to discuss and work out a plan for finding the weight of the item you have allocated to them. Check their plans and help modify them where necessary. The children should then attempt their planned activity, coming back to work out the total weight of the roof, the corridors, the wood on the hall floor or whatever it may be.

Closing the lesson

15 min

Write a table on the board of the investigations you gave and let each group give feedback. Discuss their findings. Ask whether the children are surprised at some of the weights. If possible, contrast them with, for example, the weight of a herd of elephants or the weight of a car. Consider adding the outcomes of this work to your display, perhaps giving additional time for the children to make drawings and set out their working out neatly.

Assessment

Child performance	Teacher action
Does not complete the task as their plans were not well thought out	Work with the children on their plan and then let them try again
Does not complete the task even though they have a reasonable plan	Give some more time to complete the work
Completes the task	Move on to the next lesson but consider them helping organise the display

Lesson 3

Key questions

How will you measure the stretch?

What is the weight now?

Have you marked the position of the spring now?

Will the spring go back to its original shape?

Vocabulary

Weight vocabulary, stretch, and elastic.

Introduction

10 min

Tell the children that, in this lesson, they are going to make and test a spring. Show them a spring balance and discuss its key characteristics. Now demonstrate how to make a spring by winding a piece of wire around a pencil. Point out the need to leave straight wire at each end which can be bent and twisted to make a loop to hang the spring by and to allow something to be hung on its loose end. The challenge is to make a spring, work out how to measure its stretch when weights are added and then to plot a graph of the weight against the length.

Activities

35 min

Working in small groups, the children have to plan how they will make the spring balance using the apparatus you have provided. They should then implement their plan and try some weights to see if they can check the length of the spring accurately.

When they have reached this point, stop the class and talk about doing the graph. Explain that you want them to add weights progressively and measure the length of the spring each time. They should keep records of the lengths and the weights. They need to be as accurate as possible. Talk about the scales needed for the graph and give out **Copymaster G**. The children then work in small groups to complete the activity.

Closing the lesson

10min

The children should get a straight-line graph until the spring is stretched beyond the point that it can spring back. Use the children's results to demonstrate this.

Assessment

Child performance	Teacher action
Takes a rather haphazard approach and cannot co-ordinate results	Work with these children on planning and organising and then let them try again
Gets the balance to work and takes some readings but does not complete the graph	Support the completion of the graph and then discuss it with the children
Completes the activity satisfactorily	These children have met the learning targets for this theme

HOMEWORK

Let the children find out about the range of weighing instruments they have at home and the maximum amounts each will weigh. They can also ask relatives whether there are weighing instruments in their places of work and what they are used for. This information could be collated and could contribute to the class display.

Investigations

- Make a beam balance where you can move the beam from side to side. Make it balance with the same weights on the end. Now put a heavier weight on one end. Can you make it balance with the smaller weight by sliding the beam along? How far did you have to slide it? Try with other weights. What do you think is happening?
- Make up a funfair where all of the rides and challenges depend upon weight. Make a poster advertising the attractions at your funfair.
- You want to buy some weights (or masses) for your new weighing machine. Each mass will cost you £1. You want to be able to measure in grams with the smallest measurement being one gram and the largest being 50 grams. What is the least amount of money you need to pay to do this?
- Make 10-gram and 50-gram Plasticine® weights using a beam balance and a 20-gram mass.
- Make a spring-balance and calibrate it. To make a spring wind wire around a pencil. Work out how to fasten the spring at the top, and how to hang weights on the bottom. Where will your scale go and what is the range of weights your spring balance will be able to measure? Be careful not to overload the spring.
- Find ways of estimating the weight of a tree; and the weight of leaves on a tree.
- Lorries have maximum loads they can carry. How are lorries weighed. On the sides of some rolling stock on the railway there are weights. What purpose have these? Container lorries have containers on which there is information. What does it tell you?

Assessment

- Make up parcels of different sizes with different weights inside. Make sure that the largest or smallest parcels do not contain the heaviest or lightest weights. Get the children to order them by feeling their weight then check by measuring their actual weights.
- Given a collection of objects put them in order by feeling their weights. Now try and estimate either by using standard units or by comparing with, say, a bag of sugar. Weigh the objects.
- Using shopping bills and information about weights on packaging, work out costs and value for money of a range of products
- Weigh a range of objects accurately including using decimal places. Work out the total weights of combinations of these objects.

TIME

Time is a difficult idea. We cannot touch time but only experience its passing through changing seasons, anniversaries, day and night and so on. It is also probably the most important of all the measures we learn about. Time is not just about telling the time, and not merely a device. There are many aspects of time that we need to address with children. Some of these can be illustrated by some commonly used phrases: 'time for tea', 'the time is just flying by', and 'time's up'. In a historical context we use devices such as time-lines. We look at some events in respect of their duration: the time something lasts or the time it takes. We also, of course, need to learn to tell the time and use this as a prompt for action.

Time is first experienced by all of us in terms of cycles. These include day and night, the seasons, moon phases, and sequences of activities like getting up, going to school, coming home and going to bed. As is often the case with teaching and learning it is a good idea to use these routine experiences of time passing as starting points with the children. Even though we cannot hold time we can relate things we observe and experience to the idea of time passing. It is only after a good grounding in order and sequence of events that we should impose the clock as a measure of the time when things happen. In telling the time there are several connections that need to be made. These include the rotation of the hands or fingers on an analogue clock. We need to use simple fractions too. We must also come to appreciate that there are sixty minutes in an hour, and sixty seconds in a minute. Finally, in using twelve-hour clocks children learn about ante-meridian (a.m.) and post-meridian (p.m.). The meridian is an imaginary line that runs from the North Pole to the South Pole passing through Greenwich, from which arises the term 'Greenwich Mean Time'. With digital clocks we need to consider the twenty-four hour clock, and make genuine connections between the displayed numbers and the time.

The children's knowledge and understanding of time will be much enhanced if they are offered a wide variety of experiences beyond learning to tell the time. Time is a key element in such things as navigation, global communications, and space travel. Time has a fascinating history. Certainly records of the attempts people have made to make clocks and watches, to predict regular natural events, and to keep calendars of the passing days, months and years are all worth bringing to children.

TIME

THEME **32**

Calendars and seasons

Learning targets

The children should be able to:

1 ➤ Discuss cycles of time using years, leap years and months

2 ➤ Explore a calendar for patterns

3 ➤ Investigate day length

Before you start

Subject knowledge

The Gregorian calendar we now use was introduced into England and Ireland on 1 January 1752. It replaced the Julian calendar, which was introduced by Julius Caesar. Other countries had been using the Gregorian calendar since 1582. Scotland had been using the first day of January for the New Year since 1600. England and Ireland were 11 days behind other places. To rectify this, 2 September 1752 was followed by 14 September in England and in Scotland 3–13 September was dropped. Many people felt they had been robbed of time. As with most arrays of numbers, there are patterns to be found in calendars. If we take any four numbers in a square on any month, we see that the numbers sum to the same total diagonally and the same applies for nine numbers in a square, as shown below.

			1	2	3	4
5	6	7	8	9	10	11
12	13	14	15	16	17	18
19	20	21	22	23	24	25
26	27	28	29	30		

In the square →

2	3
9	10

2+10 = 12
3+9 = 12
also 2+3 is 14 less than 9 + 10
and 2+9 is 2 less than 3 + 10

In the square

5	6	7
12	13	14
19	20	21

5+13+21= 39 as do 19+13+7, 6+13+20 and 12+13+14

also 39÷3=13, the centre number in the square

The further we are from the equator, the greater the variation in day length over a year. Indeed, in the north of Scandinavia, there are some days in the summer that have little darkness and, in the middle of the winter, little daylight. This variation in daylight hours led to the introduction of clock changes designed to capitalise on the available daylight. It is important that children appreciate that changing the clocks is something that happens in parts of the world, but not everywhere. For example, in equatorial Africa, every day and night is about 12 hours long and there is no point in altering the clocks. Every year there is a debate in this country about whether we should continue to change our clocks. Much of this debate is to do with safety and particularly the safety of children coming to and from school, so the children should be involved in a discussion about British Summer Time.

Previous knowledge required

Basic awareness of calendars, seasonal change and year length

Resources needed for Lesson 1

As wide a variety as possible of information sources such as books, CD-ROMs, articles from newspapers and magazines which relate to events that have a time cycle to them, for example, the Olympics, sports seasons, hibernation, migration, anniversaries, holidays and festivals

Resources needed for Lesson 2

As many examples as possible of any months on calendars of any years, Copymaster 46

Resources needed for Lesson 3

As many newspapers as you can assemble over as great a time period as you can manage which show lighting up times, Copymaster 47, Copymaster 48

Teaching the lessons

Lesson 1 ➊

Key questions

How often does this happen?

When will this occur next?

When did it happen last?

What date is…?

Vocabulary

Names of months, leap year, season, event

Introduction

10min

Quiz the class on their knowledge of days in the year and a leap year, the months (chant the common rhymes) and the seasons. Ask for examples of things that happen regularly every year, then every few years (leap years, Olympics, elections for example). Tell them they will work in groups to produce a class booklet on interesting facts based on years, leap years, months and seasons.

Activities

30min

Using the reference materials that you have made available, each group of children must search for such things as anniversaries, holidays, celebrations, events, phenomena which occur on a regular (or reasonably regular) basis. They should make notes about what they find in order to report back to the class at the end of the lesson.

Closing the lesson

15min

Let each group report one different interesting fact they have discovered. Write their information on the board. Collect the lists and follow up the exercise by creating a 'Time Facts' booklet.

Assessment

Child performance	Teacher action
Uncertain of some quite basic facts about years and months	Do some work on time telling, months, seasons and year lengths
Helps to produce a good range of facts	Move on to the next lesson
Understands the task and has a good grasp of the facts	Move on to the next lesson

Lesson 2

2

Key questions

How many days in...?

Can you see a pattern?

Vocabulary

Names of the months, general number vocabulary

Introduction

10min

Recap, with the children, the months and how many days in each month. Tell them some of the history of calendars. Explain that they will be looking at some calendar months and searching for number patterns.

Activities

25min

Give out **Copymaster 46** and calendars or parts of calendars. As the children work on the Copymaster, go around the class, probing their exploration of the patterns and eliciting ideas. Share good ideas with the class and invite others to try them out.

Closing the lesson

15min

Review the key questions on the Copymaster, using invited individual children to tell the class what they have discovered. Put the 'Time Facts' booklet from Lesson 1 on display and add the investigation of the patterns in a calendar to it.

Assessment

Child performance	Teacher action
Struggles with pattern identification	Do more work on number patterns particularly the common number ones
Finds the major patterns	Move on to the next lesson
Finds the major patterns and less obvious ones	Move on to the next lesson

Lesson 3

3

Key questions

When do you think the longest /shortest days are?

How many hours of darkness in...?

What do you know about changing the clocks?

Vocabulary

Sunrise, sunset, seasons, line graph, British Summer Time

Introduction

10min

Tell the children that they are going to do some work on the days and nights in an imaginary place called Tempus Town. To do the work, they will need to construct line graphs. Remind them how to do this. Explain that they will have two Copymasters and they need to do the one with the graph first.

Activities

30min

Give out **Copymaster 47** and **Copymaster 48**. As queries arise on the graph, use them to help and guide the whole class. Tell them to join the points with as smooth as line as they can manage.

Closing the lesson

10min

Review the questions on Copymaster 48 as a means of reinforcing the work. If there is time, discuss some of the implications of British Summer Time.

Assessment

Child performance	Teacher action
Manages the graph with some help	Talk through the graph and give the questions again
Manages the graph and starts the questions	Give more time, then talk through the answers
Completes the task	These children have met the learning targets for this theme

---

HOMEWORK

The children can do some history work looking at the development of calendars and the changing of clock times, including wartime use of Double British Summer Time.

TIME

THEME 33 Check the time

Learning targets

The children should be able to:

1 ➸ Produce a schedule for the cooking of a meal
2 ➸ Investigate some aspects of timetables
3 ➸ Graph temperature against time

Before you start

Subject knowledge

There are several key ideas in the development of concepts of time in this theme. While the children will have done work in earlier years on flow diagrams and the sequencing of actions, there is still a need to support their understanding of planning through the ordering of events. Here we are interested in backward chaining of events so that a given deadline can be met. This is a skill that we all need to develop to cope with many demands of 'ordinary living'. Time describes not only what time of day it might be but also can be employed in comparative exercises where time taken for events can be analysed. In this theme, we are concerned with two ideas. The first is so that we can make comparisons. We have to learn to calculate in hours and minutes and because of our use of 60 as the base number, there is a need to move 'place' at different intervals from when we were doing base 10 calculations. Also, in using line graphs, it should be recognised that in the great majority of situations, time is the measure to use on the x-axis. If we think about any graphs that depict change, such as those including distance, speed, temperature, air pressure, growth and decline, we realise all of them involve a measure of time.

Previous knowledge required

Basic work on time and timing, simple arithmetic using hours and minutes, simple line graphs

Resources needed for Lesson 1

Copymaster 49

Resources needed for Lesson 2

Copies of the class timetable with times of day, Copymaster 50

Resources needed for Lesson 3

Copymaster G, room thermometer or apparatus for looking at the cooling of water linked to a science lesson or sensors, depending on your choice of approach

Teaching the lessons

Lesson 1 ①

Key questions

Which should be first/last?

What time do you need to start?

Vocabulary

Times, timing, order

Introduction — 10 min

Tell the children that a grown up needs to plan the preparation of a meal for some friends. They have to work out the order in which to cook the dishes so that everything will be ready to eat at the right time.

Activities — 25 min

Give out **Copymaster 49**. Remind the children to read all the information before they start their ordering. Tell them you don't like cold soup or lumpy gravy!

Closing the lesson — 10 min

With the children's help write up a sensible order on the board. Where there is a difference of view, discuss it so that everyone is happy and understands the decision.

Assessment

Child performance	Teacher action
Produces an order but struggles to get everything into the sequence	Review the task again, with the children
Produces a workable list	Move on to the next lesson
Produces a workable list and indicates that they have thought about additional pressures, such as laying the table and other preparation	Move on to the next lesson

Lesson 2

Key questions

How much time do we spend doing…?

Why do you think we do this much…?

Vocabulary

Timetable, total, amounts

Introduction

10min

Tell the class that you want to work out how much time is being spent on all the subjects they do. Explain that you want them to look at the class timetable and use it to answer a set of questions that you will give them. Ask them to think about where any time might be wasted and what you might be able to do about that.

Activities

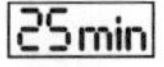

Give out copies of the timetable unless the children already have them. Give out **Copymaster 50** that has a set of questions about the balance of the work that they do. As the children progress, check for arithmetical problems regarding the addition of hours and minutes. If necessary, remind the class that, for example, one hour and 63 minutes should be written as two hours, 3 minutes. Copy the table on the Copymaster onto the board while the children are working.

Closing the lesson

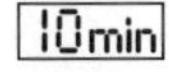

Fill in the table, using the figures from the children. Ask them what they think about the amounts of time spent on the different activities. See if they have any good ideas about any waste of time and how they might use it more effectively.

Assessment

Child performance	Teacher action
Makes error in the totalling of time and/or in working out amounts of time	Give some calculation work on adding and then subtracting hours and minutes
Completes the main part of the task	Discuss the work with them, eliciting any ideas that they have
Completes all of the task	Move on to the next lesson

Lesson 3

Key questions

What scale should we use on a graph?

What does the line show us?

How long does it take to change this much?

Vocabulary

Temperature, line graph, cooling, curve

Introduction

10min

This lesson could use data from a related science experiment or could be based on room temperature collected over a day or a week at set times. If these are not used, then either get the children in pairs or small groups with hot but not boiling water and thermometers and tell them to take the temperature of the water every two minutes and keep a record of time and temperature. If resources are tight, then do this as a demonstration. If sensors are available, these could be used to produce the graphs. Discuss with the children the fact that we need regular temperature readings and that we are going to use these to make a temperature/time graph.

Activities

25min

Give out **Copymaster G** together with the apparatus or, before you demonstrate the cooling of water over time, if you have recorded room temperatures, then make those data available. The children have to produce a temperature/time line graph. As they discuss this, encourage them to think about the best way to make the x-axis (time) and the y-axis (temperature).

Closing the lesson

10min

Write an example of a graph on the board and use this to discuss what the children could identify as key features of the graph. Finish by telling them that most line graphs work only if time is used for the x-axis.

Assessment

Child performance	Teacher action
Has difficulties with data collection and understanding the available data	Give more experience of data collection and then move to analysis
Has difficulties with the graph	Check the children's general work on line graphs through exercises with given data, then try this work again
Completes all parts satisfactorily	These children have met the learning targets for this theme

HOMEWORK

There is a range of possible activities. More planning and sequencing might be appropriate for some children. Give exercises such as producing a plan for organising a class trip or camp. Timetables for other classes could be analysed and compared with their own. Holiday brochures can be used to explore temperature/time graphs over a year.

TIME

THEME 34

24-hour system

Learning targets

The children should be able to:

1 ➤➤ Relate 12 and 24-hour statements

2 ➤➤ Convert between 12 and 24-hour systems

3 ➤➤ Solve problems involving 24-hour timetables

Before you start

Subject knowledge

The measurement of time passing has become more and more precise over the years. Now we commonly have battery-operated watches and clocks which we can choose to indicate the time in either analogue or digital form. Digital clocks and watches customarily give us the choice of displaying the time in 12- or 24-hour clock fashion. Many of the children will have digital watches. The ability to use both sorts of representation, together with the 12- and 24-hour clock system, is important. Indeed, the fact that children may read off digital time at quite an early age faces us with even more challenges – they may be able to read the number, but that is no guarantee of their understanding of time. It is necessary to expose the children to a sustained set of experiences using 12- and 24-hour time to consolidate their appreciation of telling the time. Vocabulary is important in this understanding. In order to operate with a 12-hour clock, we have to understand 'a.m.' and 'p.m.' and special words like 'midday' and 'midnight'. In using the 24-hour system, we have to understand and employ the appropriate vocabularies. For example, '20 past 3 in the afternoon' needs to be articulated as '15.20 hours' in the 24-hour system. This, of course, can raise interesting issues about decimals, whilst 15.20 will be described as 'fifteen point two' in the decimal system, this is not the convention when we come to 24-hour time. So, there is much to do regarding vocabulary in the context of understanding time.

Previous knowledge required

Number lines, telling the time, some experience of work on time passing and time taken, use of tables for obtaining information

Resources needed for Lesson 1

Copymaster 51, an overhead transparency or a drawing on the board of a clock face marked in 12- and 24-hour systems.

Resources needed for Lesson 2

Copymaster 52

Resources needed for Lesson 3

Copymaster 53, atlases

Teaching the lessons

Lesson 1

Key questions

What time is this?

What is the equivalent in 12-/24-hour time?

Vocabulary

12-hour clock, 24-hour clock, equivalent, convert, a.m., p.m., hundred hours

Introduction 15min

Show the children the overhead transparency of the clock face or use a previously drawn copy on the board. Put different times on the diagram, starting with hours only. Ask the children to tell you the time for each example you give them in 12-hour language. Then, ask them to tell you what those times are in the appropriate 24-hour language. For example, 9 o'clock and 09.00 hours or 9 o'clock and 21.00 hours. Then introduce minutes. Tell the children that they will be telling the time in both the 12- and 24-hour systems.

Activities 25min

Give out **Copymaster 51**. The children should work through the problems on their own.

Closing the lesson 10min

Recap the relationship between 12 and 24-hour time. Then ask some of the children to give you answers to a sample of the questions from the Copymaster. Use these to reinforce the ways in which the two systems work, giving particular attention to the appropriate vocabulary. Collect the Copymasters for evaluation purposes.

Assessment

Child performance	Teacher action
Works instrumentally and is not relating the systems with understanding	Check the children's time-telling expertise and give appropriate follow up activities
Completes the Copymaster but has a few errors	Discuss their responses and then decide whether more practice is needed
Completes the task with no errors	Move on to the next lesson

Lesson 2

Key questions

What is this time in the 12-/24-hour system?

Vocabulary

12-hour system, 24-hour system, o'clock, hundred hours, equivalent, convert

Introduction

Get the children to focus on the 12- and 24-hour systems by recalling what they have done so far. Tell them that, this lesson, they will be able to demonstrate their understanding of both systems and how each relates to the other. Remind them of the relationship between those systems.

Activities

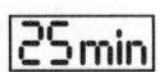

Give out **Copymaster 52**. Support the children as necessary and be prepared to help with ideas on the final part of the Copymaster.

Closing the lesson

Use the final part of the Copymaster to revise times and timings in both 12- and 24-hour systems. Collect the Copymasters to check the children's understanding of the 24-hour system.

Assessment

Child performance	Teacher action
Carries out some of the task but makes a number of errors	Work with these children using clock faces and time lines in both 12- and 24-hour systems, then try this exercise again
Carries out most of the task without major errors	Give the children some time to complete the activity
Carries out all of the task	Move on to the next lesson

Lesson 3

Key questions

What time does...?

How long will it take?

How soon do you have to start?

Vocabulary

Timetable, journey, general time vocabulary

Introduction

10min

Give a range of times in the 12-hour and 24-hour systems and ask the children to tell you the time in the appropriate system. Tell them that they are going to use their knowledge to explore some journey times. Remind them to check carefully when adding or subtracting time.

Activities

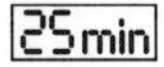

Give out **Copymaster 53**. Working collaboratively, the children have to answer the questions on the Copymaster and then develop further questions of their own to try out on their classmates. The children can use their atlases to check the location of places and the regions the trains travel through.

Closing the lesson

10min

Do a sample of the questions on the board and then collect the Copymasters to select a range of children-produced questions that can then be used in a follow-up exercise.

Assessment

Child performance	Teacher action
Finds timetable difficult to interpret	Work with these children using a local bus time-table in order to find out more about where they are uncertain
Completes the questions but doesn't generate any of their own	Discuss the work done and, if appropriate, give more time to generate their ideas
Completes the questions and generates some of their own	These children have met the learning targets for this theme

HOMEWORK

The children could collect holiday brochures and timetables and plan a journey they would like to make, giving the times for this journey and the places they travel through and to.

TIME

THEME 35

Time machines

Learning targets

The children should be able to:

1 ➤➤ Relate time to the movement of the sun

2 ➤➤ Relate time to other regular motions

3 ➤➤ Investigate motion and the measurement of time

Before you start

Subject knowledge

Quintessentially, our measurement of time uses regular motion. Whether that motion is like the apparent passage of the sun across the sky, or whether it is based on phenomena such as gravity or the burning of a candle, the key notion is that predictably regular occurrences can act as a standard for the passage of time. Sundials depend on a regular movement of the earth, candle clocks on the consistent burning of a candle and water clocks on gravity. Clockwork driven clocks depend on the unwinding of a regulated spring, regulated by a pendulum, which in its turn depends on gravity. In this theme, this idea of regular motion in relation to measuring time passing is explored through the use of sundials and the pendulum. There are a number of important features of the sundial. Sundials have to be made for the latitude at which they will be placed. In the Copymaster for making the sundial, we have the style or gnomon, with an angle of 54° which is the latitude of about the centre of the UK. If you want to make your own more accurately, then you need to make the base angle the angle of latitude at your location. In determining the angles for the times on the baseplate, some compromises have been made to support the idea of regular motion and to accommodate rounding effects. A sundial needs to be positioned with twelve o'clock pointing north. Account needs to be taken of the changing of the clocks, of course.

The pendulum was the mainstay of accurate timekeeping for many centuries. Indeed, it is still in use today even though we now have electronic timing. There are three variables in any pendulum – the weight of the bob, the length of the pendulum and the degree of the swing. Of these, only the length makes any difference, but it is important to support the children in finding this out for themselves. As with the other themes in this unit, this work could be linked to science or a project on time.

Previous knowledge required

General construction skills, telling the time, possibly Roman numerals and simple timing of events

Resources needed for Lesson 1

Copymaster 54, thick card, scissors, glue, sticky tape, a magnetic compass or compasses, access to an area in the sun where the children can leave their sundials and periodically check them

Resources needed for Lesson 2

Commercially produced timers that rock and time in seconds, a range of different timers, a pendulum, balances and weights, stop watches or stop clocks

Resources needed for Lesson 3

String, hangers for weights, weights, somewhere to fix the pendulum for testing, possibly clamps and stands, second timers or stopwatches or stopclocks, Copymaster 55

Making a sundial

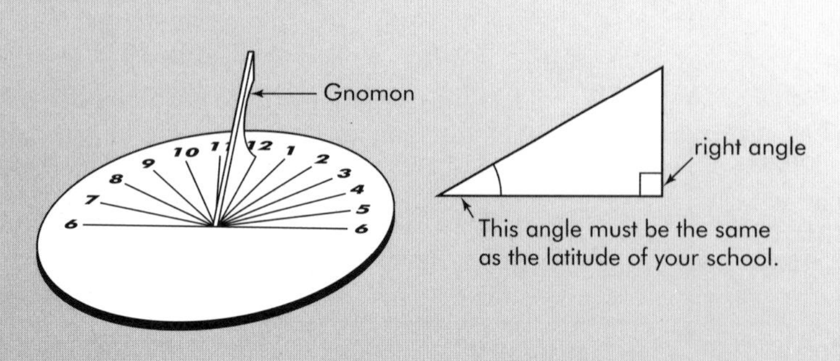

Demonstration of a pendulum

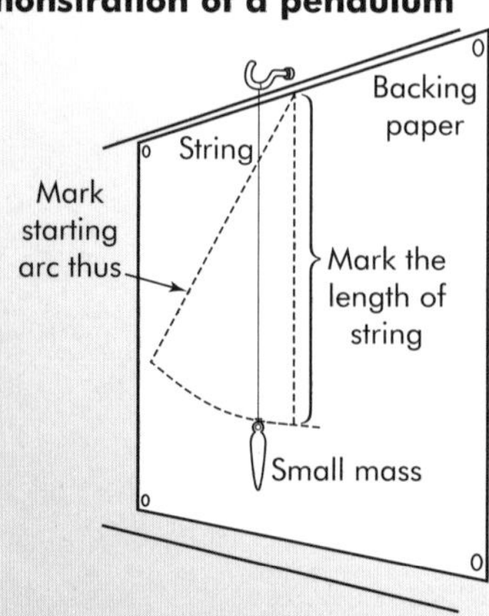

Teaching the lessons

Lesson 1

Key questions

Which direction is north?

What time is it now?

How accurate is your sundial?

Why does it seem to be one hour out?

Vocabulary

North, south, style, gnomon

Introduction

10min

Ask the children what happens to their shadow at different times of the day. If they do not know, tell them that the sun rises in the east and sets in the west and we can use this with a shadow to help tell the time. Explain that they are going to make sundials and that sundials have been used for many hundreds of years. Ask the children if they have seen them in gardens or have seen vertical ones on houses.

Activities

30min

Give out **Copymaster 54** together with the other resources. The children need to stick their cut-outs from the Copymaster onto thick card. When they have done this, show them how to position and fix the upright style onto the base. Then explain that we can track the shadow around to read off the time, but it only works if the twelve o'clock line is pointing north. You can explain this using the east/west idea from the introduction to the lesson. Take the children to a location in the sun and let the pairs place their sundials, using the magnetic compass to check north. Tell the class the time and ask the pairs to make a pencil mark where the shadow is. Ask if it is near the time they expect. Leave the sundials in place and give the children an opportunity to return regularly to check them.

Closing the lesson

10min

Review the work, drawing a sketch of the sundial and the sun on the board to explain what is happening. At appropriate times, ask the children to check the shadow on their sundial.

Assessment

Child performance	Teacher action
Carries out the practical work but struggles with ideas	Do some revision work on changing seasons and the days, then try this exercise again
Carries through the task and understands some of the ideas	Move on to the next lesson but take opportunities to give more work on the relationship of the earth to the sun
Carries through the task and understands all of the main ideas	Move on to the next lesson

Lesson 2

Key questions

What makes these timers work?

What makes them able to measure different numbers of seconds?

Does it matter how far you tilt it?

How tall is it?

What do they weigh?

Vocabulary

Measure, seconds, timer

Introduction

10min

Demonstrate how to use one of the timers or remind the children of their use if they have used them before. Tell them they are going to investigate how these timers work. Advise that there are balances and that they can use rulers.

Activities

25min

The children should investigate the design of the timers. Encourage them to check and record dimensions including their weight, height, width and breadth. They could also try starting the timers at different angles. If children ask for stopwatches or clocks provide them.

Closing the lesson

10min

Through questioning, your aim is to identify three characteristics that might affect how the timers work for different times. These are weight, height and angle of swing. Finish by showing a pendulum, linking it to the work they have done, so that the children can see that the timers are really pendulums.

Assessment

Child performance	Teacher action
Investigates some attributes but lacks organisation	Work with the children in setting out a plan and then let them try again
Investigates some attributes	Check what they have done and encourage them to think about all possible effects
Investigates all attributes and raises ideas about what are significant characteristics	Move on to the next lesson

Lesson 3

Key questions

What happens when...?

Can you make your pendulum measure these exact seconds?

Vocabulary

Pendulum, bob, words for different dimensions

Introduction

10 min

Remind the children of the work they have done using timers. Show them a pendulum, write its name on the board and ask where pendulums might be found. Tell them that they are going to investigate a pendulum to find out what makes a difference to the time of its swing, be it weight, length or the starting angle of the swing. Point out that one swing is difficult to time, and lead them to suggest counting, say, ten swings, and then dividing by ten to get the time of one swing. Discuss, what a swing is and whether it is from, say, the left to the right, or left to right and back again?

Activities

30 min

Give out **Copymaster 55**. Using the apparatus you have provided, the children should make and then investigate a pendulum. Keep reminding them of the need to keep careful records and to measure everything precisely. Encourage them to repeat trials.

Closing the lesson

10 min

Ask the children what they have discovered. If they are not clear at this point that it is only the length that makes a difference to the time of a swing, then give them further opportunities to find this out.

Assessment

Child performance	Teacher action
Does not test all the attributes	Give more time, possibly working closely with them
Carries through the investigations but lacks confidence in their findings	Talk through their findings and let them test again if they wish
Clear about the length being the important factor	These children have met the learning targets for this theme

HOMEWORK

This theme supports a historical project where the children could find out about ancient time-keeping devices or about the history of the pendulum. Alternatively, they could attempt to design and make a timer of their own.

TIME

THEME 36

Distance, speed and time

Learning targets

The children should be able to:

1 ➤➤ Appreciate that travelling takes time and that speed affects that time
2 ➤➤ Show graphically relationships between distance, speed and time
3 ➤➤ Relate their knowledge to large distances and high speeds

Before you start

Subject knowledge

We use the connection between distance, speed and time a good deal in everyday life. Sometimes we fix the distance and then work out the time and speed. For example, in a 400-metre race, we are interested in the time of runner and then use that comparison, treating speed implicitly. Sometimes we fix the time. For example, getting to school by a certain time means we make judgements about when to start, based on our experience of the distance we need to travel and about how fast we can travel. The formula that links these things is speed equals distance divided by time, and, of course, we can use this formula to complete any one if we know the other two. In calculating speed, we are, at this stage, actually using the notion of mean average speed. It is unlikely in real life that a constant speed is maintained but the children do not need, yet, to be working with changes in velocities except in relation to graph work where journeys include time where speed is zero. These two points are illustrated below.

Previous knowledge required

Timing, measures of distance and speed, line graphs, calculating skills including ideally some work with powers of ten, estimation experience, use of simple scale maps

Resources needed for Lesson 1

Copymaster 56, rulers, atlases

Resources needed for Lesson 2

Copymaster 57, a measured distance of about 200 metres in the playground or on the field, stopwatch or stopclock

Resources needed for Lesson 3

Copymaster 58, calculators

Distance – time graph of someone walking 120 metres in 70 seconds. This ignores any acceleration or deceleration.

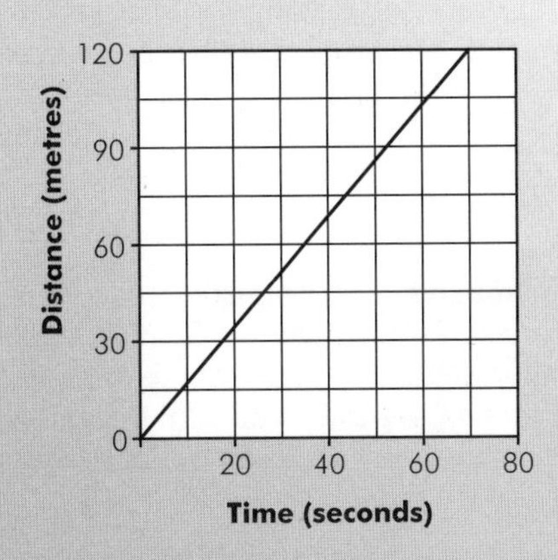

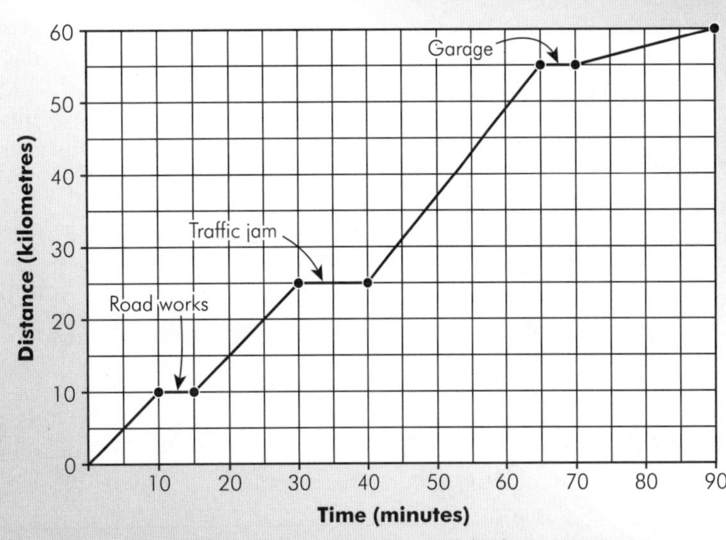

Graph of a car journey including periods when car is stationary

Teaching the lessons

Lesson 1 ①

Key questions

Where are we on the map?

How do we use a scale on a map?

How far...?

How long...?

Vocabulary

Scale, distance, time

Introduction 10min

It has been commonplace for human beings to try and communicate over long distances. Various signalling technologies have been developed but a common method, still used today on occasions, is the use of fire. In 1588 the Spanish Armada was sighted off Plymouth and fires were lit to warn of possible invasion. In this lesson, the children have to work out how long it would take for the message to reach them. To do this, you need to give some key information. Tell the children that the maximum distance that a fire could be seen from was 25 km. This means that they have to take a bonfire route with no gaps. Bonfires would also have been built near communities, so open areas have to be avoided. So, for example, a straight line from Plymouth to Glasgow would not work, as the distance across parts of the sea is greater than 25 km. Tell them it takes five minutes to light the bonfire and another ten minutes for it to be visible. For convenience, tell them the first fire was lit in Plymouth at six p.m. If you live in or are close to Plymouth, then ask them how long it took Elizabeth I to find out in London or how long it would have taken for a friend or relative elsewhere in the country to get the message. If you live on an island more than 25 km from the mainland, then assume a boat brings the news for the last part of the journey and the time for its sailing must be added to the bonfire time.

Activities 25min

Using the information from the Introduction, atlases and **Copymaster 56**, the pairs of children have to work out the time it might have taken to get the news. If questions are raised about the time taken for the firelighters to get to the bonfire, then make some estimates with the children.

Closing the lesson 10min

Explore the solutions the children have come to. If there are wide variations, get the children to discuss how they got their solutions. Finish by contrasting the time taken then to the possibilities nowadays. This lesson could be linked to a history project or could be extended by looking at other forms of signalling such as semaphore.

Assessment

Child performance	Teacher action
Makes errors in developing a solution	Give more time and then talk through the work with them
Reaches a reasonable solution	Take time to discuss the investigation and see if more ideas can be generated
Does the work readily and produces many ideas	Move on to the next lesson

Lesson 2 ②

Key questions

How far have they walked?

How long did it take?

How can we make a graph of this?

Who was fastest/slowest?

How long did it take to cover a half/quarter/third of the distance?

Vocabulary

Line graph, distance, time and some speed related words

Introduction 15min

Before the lesson, decide on a measured distance to be walked and ask some children to help you obtain an accurate measurement. It needs to be a distance that can be walked in a reasonable time. At the start of the lesson, identify three children who are going to walk the measured distance. They have to walk at a steady, natural pace. Depending on how many stopwatches or stopclocks you have, arrange for the time of each of the three to be measured. Emphasise it is not a race but rather you want to collect data for the class to use in the lesson. When you have those data, put them on the board and discuss how a straight-line graph might be produced with time on the horizontal x-axis and distance on the vertical y-axis. Agree how to scale the axes. Tell the children that they need to plot the results of all three children on the same graph and then answer some questions.

Activities 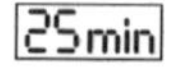

Give out **Copymaster 57**. The children need only two points for each straight line – the origin and the co-ordinates for the time taken over the measured distance for each of the three children. Encourage them to discuss their responses to the questions on the Copymaster.

Closing the lesson 10min

Make your own copy of the line graphs on the board and, with the children's help, work through the questions on the Copymaster.

Assessment

Child performance	Teacher action
Has problems with constructing the graphs	Look at the children's experience in respect of graphical work and consider giving them more opportunities
Answers most of the questions but uncertain about some of them	Discuss their interpretation with them
Completes the task	Move on to the next lesson

Lesson 3

Key questions

How far is...?

How long does it take to travel from...?

Vocabulary

Light year, names of planets and some stars/systems

Introduction

10min

Tell the children that they are going to work out some distances and times using the speed of light. Write on the board that lights travels at about 300,000 km per second. To attempt to put this into context, tell them that the earth has a circumference of about 40,000 km so if you could beam some light around the earth, it would take about one eighth of a second to go all the way round. If the children have worked with powers of ten, then remind them that you can write 300,000 as 3 times 100,000 or 3 times 10 to the power 5. This means you can do your calculation using 3 and then multiply by a 100,000 or ten to the power 5 at the end.

Activities

30min

Give out **Copymaster 58** and calculators. The children can work together if you wish. Children commonly enjoy working with big numbers like these so you should get some good positive feedback as they work through the challenges on the Copymaster.

Closing the lesson

10min

Get the children to share some of their solutions. Tell them that sound travels much more slowly than light and this is why you hear thunder after you see the lightening. Sound travels at about 344 m per second in air and about 1,500 m per second in water. If you wish, the children can go on to look at the time taken in relation to sound. Finish by telling them that there are other waves that travel near the speed of light and this is why radio and TV can be used to send messages around the world, using satellites, almost instantaneously.

Assessment

Child performance	Teacher action
Makes some progress but has problems handling the calculations	Do some general work on big numbers and check computational confidence, then try this exercise again at a later date
Gets through a good proportion of the Copymaster	Talk through what they have achieved and decide whether more time or practice or both is needed
Clearly capable of handling the challenges	These children have achieved the learning targets for this theme

HOMEWORK

Let the children work on more graphical representations of journeys in respect of distance and time. Alternatively, invite them to make an information collection on distances in light years in the universe.

Investigations

- Make a clock. Look at the ways in which you can make sand clocks, water clocks and candle clocks and then design and make one of your own.
- Make a pendulum with a container filled with sand or salt as the bob. A small hole in this container will allow the sand or salt to run out and regular patterns can be made on sugar paper. If there is wet paint or glue on the sugar paper then when it dries the patterns can be preserved.
- Find out about the history of calendars. How do you make a perpetual calendar?
- Time is very important for navigation. Find out why. Why are there ship's bells for telling the time and how often and when are they rung?
- Find out about time zones and the International Date Line. The millennium really occurs at 2001 AD – why is that?
- Produce the 'Big Book of Time' including time records, facts about time units, and time phrases. Add any other ideas you have.
- If you have access to any electronic sensors use them to measure change over time. This could involve sound, light, and temperature.
- There are many instruments that have been used over the centuries that involve time. Find out about some of these including those that have rotating drums on which pens trace a line.
- Do some work planning journeys and working out distances, speeds and times.
- Make a collection of books and stories that have time as an important ingredient. Examples include 'Around the World in Eighty Days', and 'The Time Machine', and films such as 'The Time Bandits'.
- How does the speaking clock work?
- Why do we change the clocks twice each year in the UK? Make a list of all of the clocks and timers that need to be changed at home, on your journey to school, and at school. (See if the children identify timers or clocks in such places as the central heating system and the family car.)
- Make a collection of old postcards and envelopes. Look at the postmarks. When were they posted, at what time and where?

Assessment

- Using clock faces and later digital displays get the children to tell the time and then go on to work out the time intervals between two times.
- Using today's date work out the date in six weeks time, two weeks ago and three and a half months from now.
- Practice mental addition and subtraction of seconds and minutes.
- Using such things as alarm clocks and video-recorders find out how to set the time and then have a go at doing so.
- Collect data and draw charts and graphs with time as the x-axis.

1 Pegboard patterns

Using five each of two different coloured pegs, make a symmetrical pattern on your pegboard. Copy the pattern onto these squares using coloured pencils.

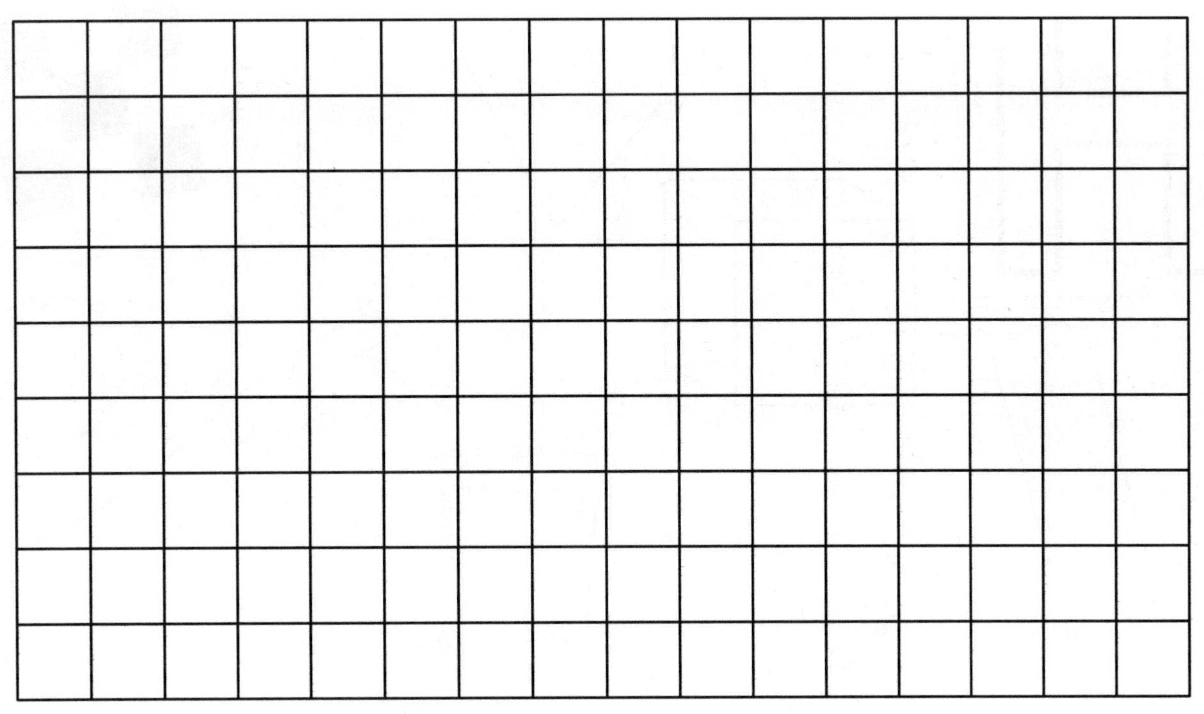

Now try no more than five each of three different colours and record your pattern here.

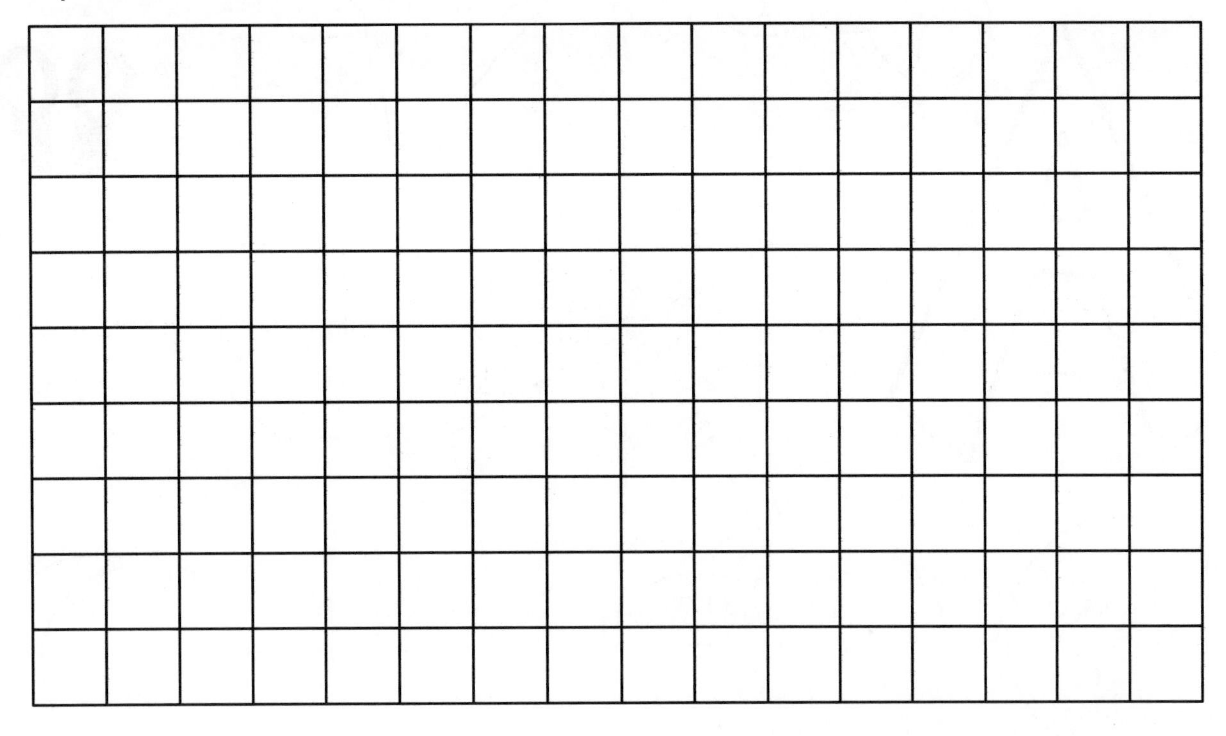

2

Line symmetry

Put a cross next to the drawings that have no line of symmetry.
Draw the line or lines for the others. Use your mirror to check.

3 Triangles

Name these triangles. Some of them may have two names.

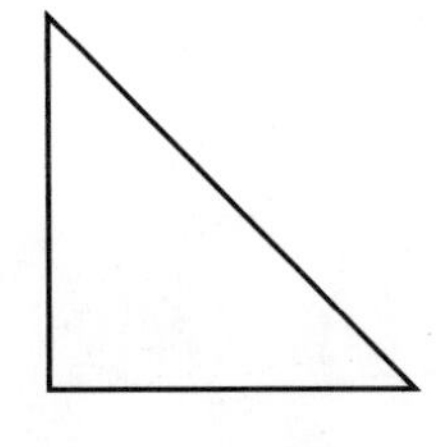

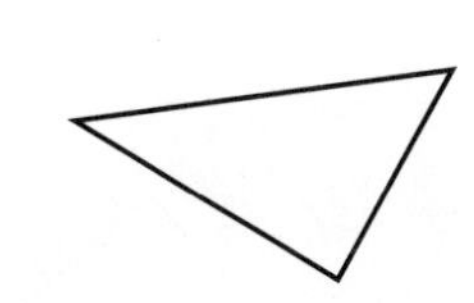

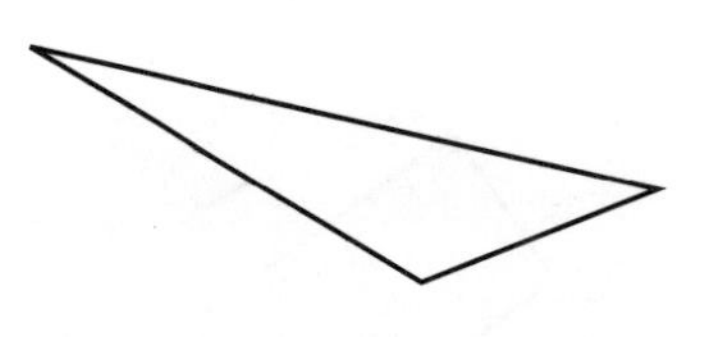

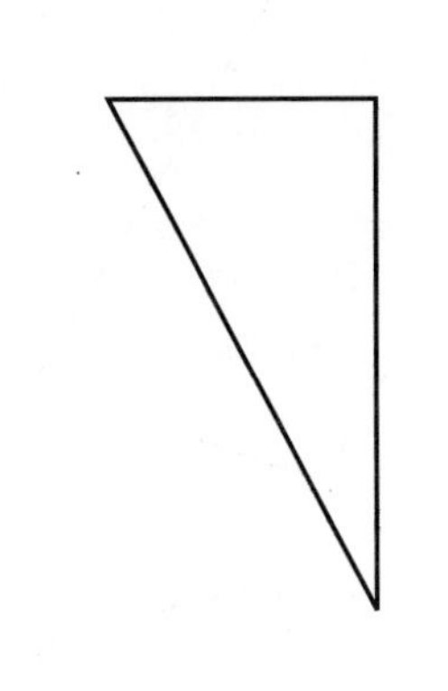

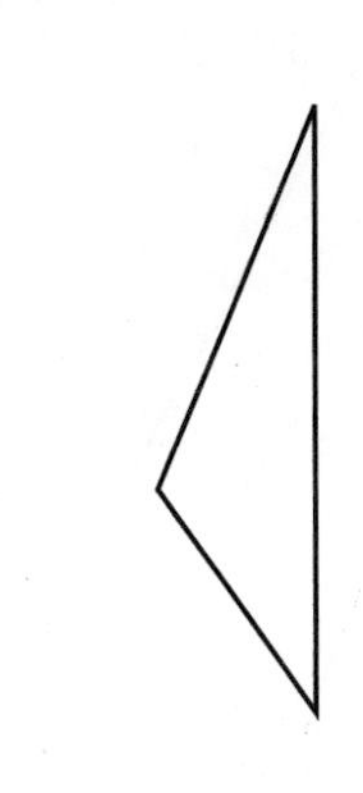

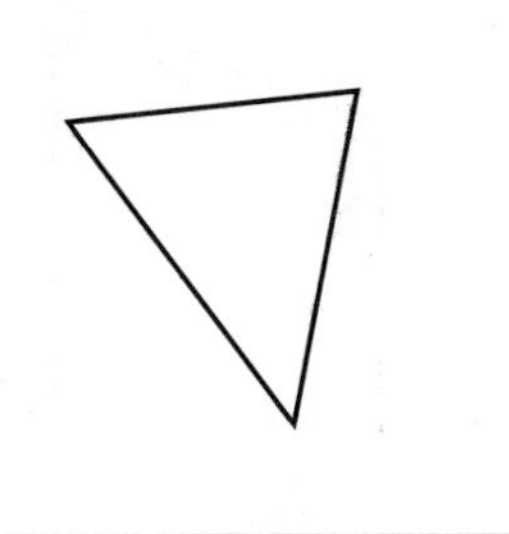

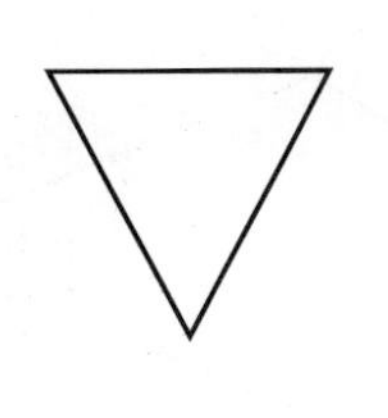

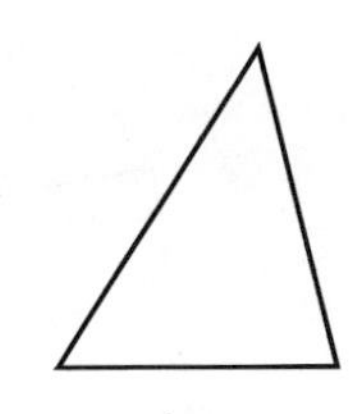

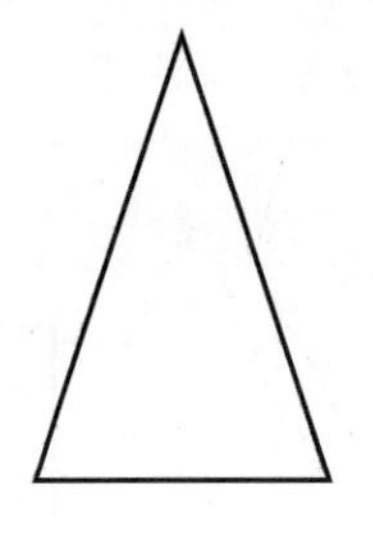

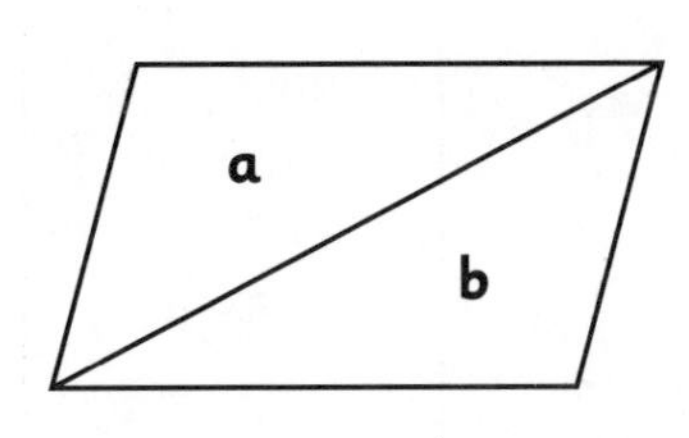

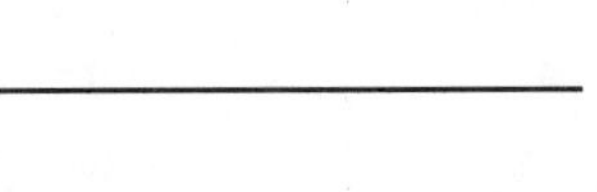

a

b

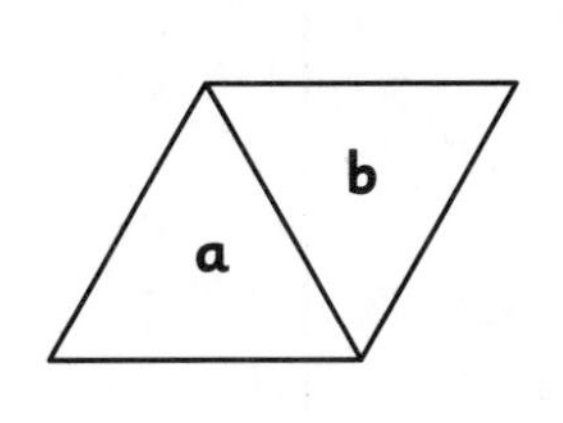

a

b

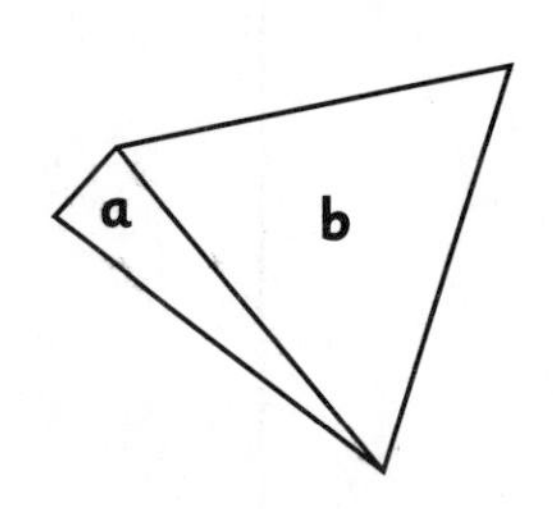

a

b

Quadrilaterals

Colour all the quadrilaterals of the same kind in the same colour. You could make all the squares red and the rectangles blue and so on. Then write down what you know about each group of shapes.

Mark in the colour of each group and make notes below.

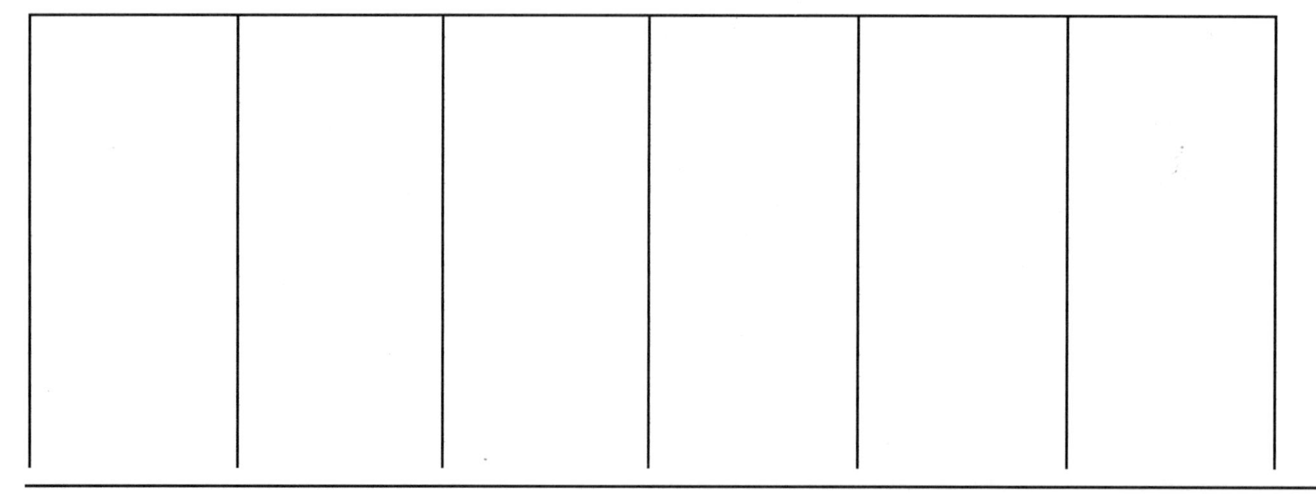

Naming 2-D shapes

Name these shapes.

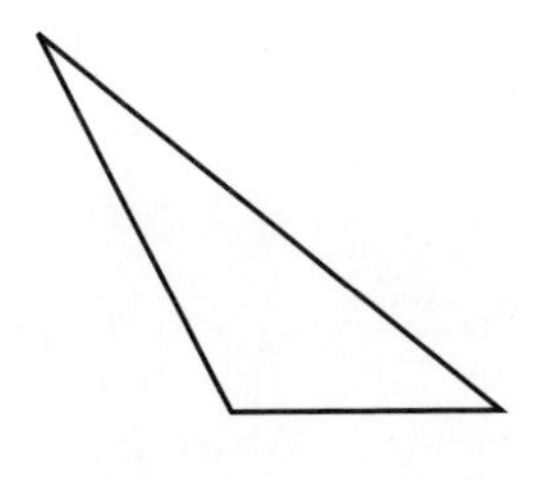

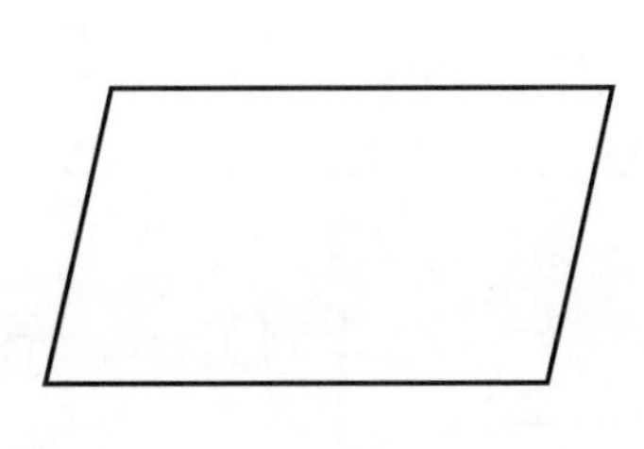

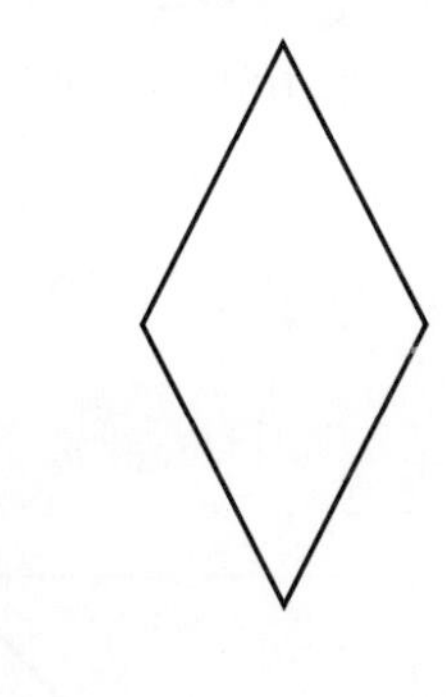

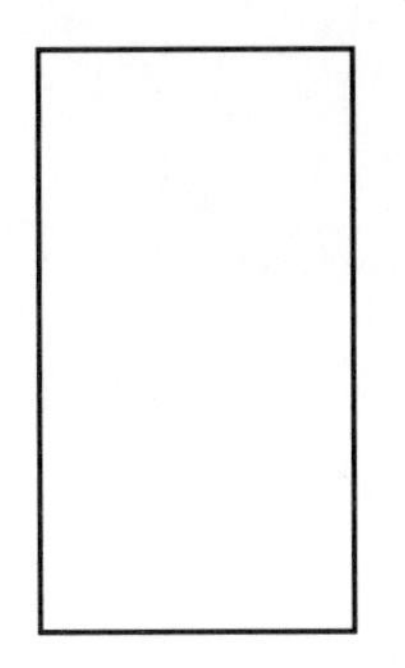

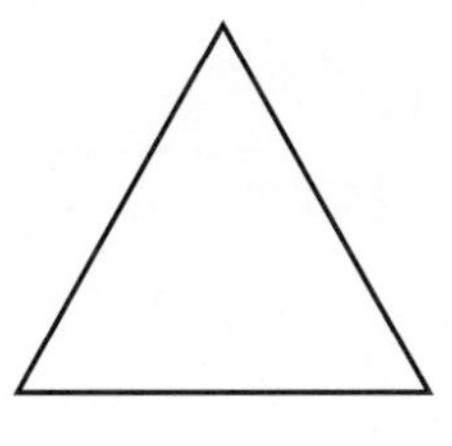

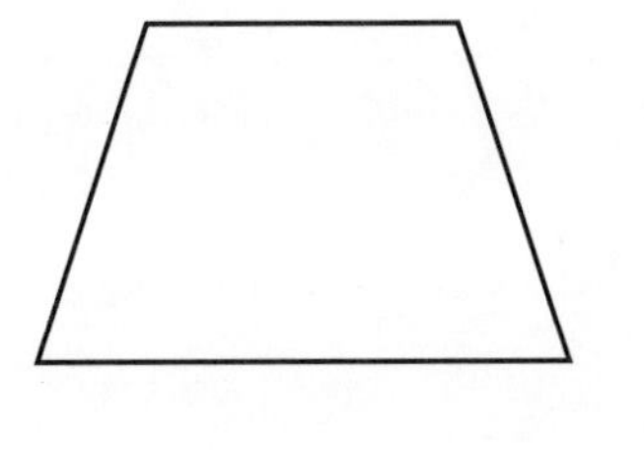

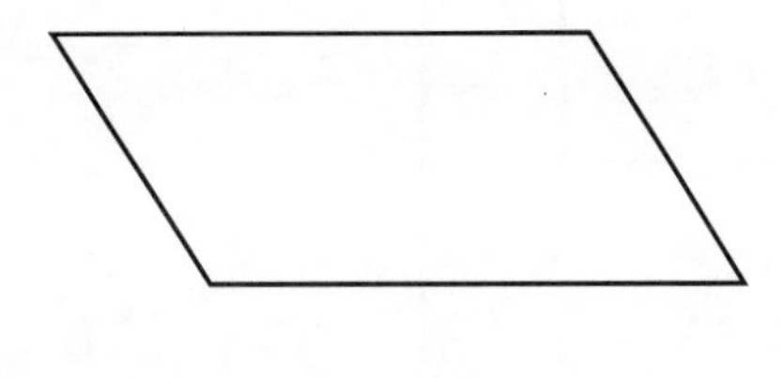

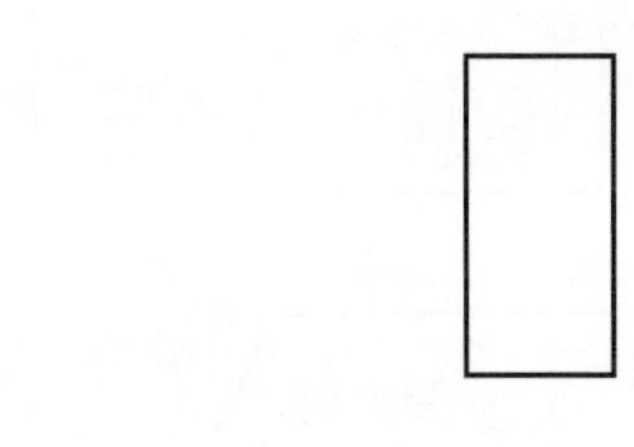

Find and name as many shapes as you can here.

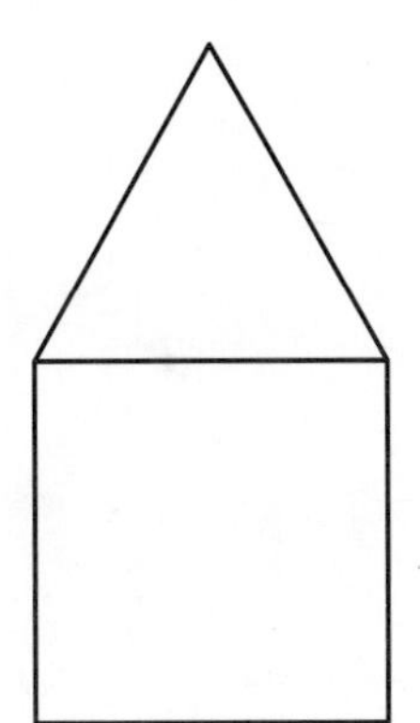

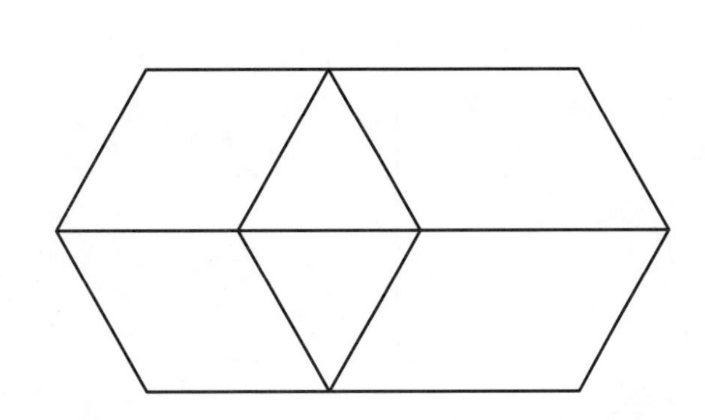

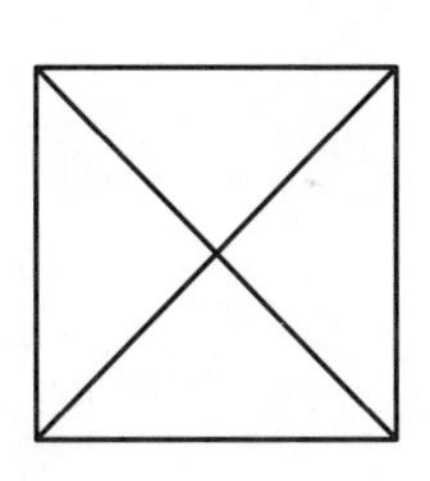

Dividing 2-D shapes

Using your ruler, draw lines across each shape to divide it into triangles or squares, or a mixture of triangles and squares. How many triangles and squares can you cut each shape into? Draw more of the shapes in the right hand column if you need to, to show your ideas.

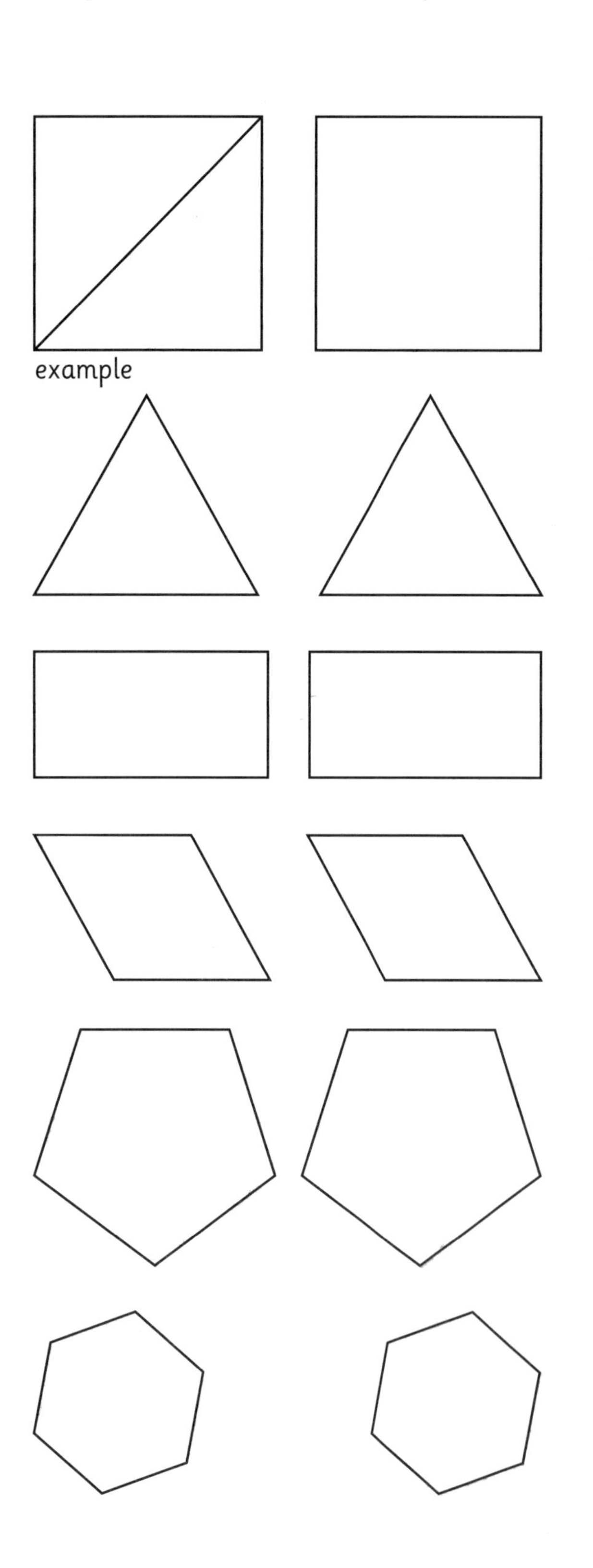

Draw more here.

7 Similarity

Draw lines to join the shapes that are similar.

Look carefully at these shapes. Write number 1 inside all the shapes in set 1, number 2 inside the shapes in set 2 and number 3 inside those in set 3. Write what you notice.

Set 1	**Set 2**	**Set 3**
Number of sides	Number of sides	Number of sides
Number of corners	Number of corners	Number of corners

Naming 3-D shapes

Write the names for these shapes.

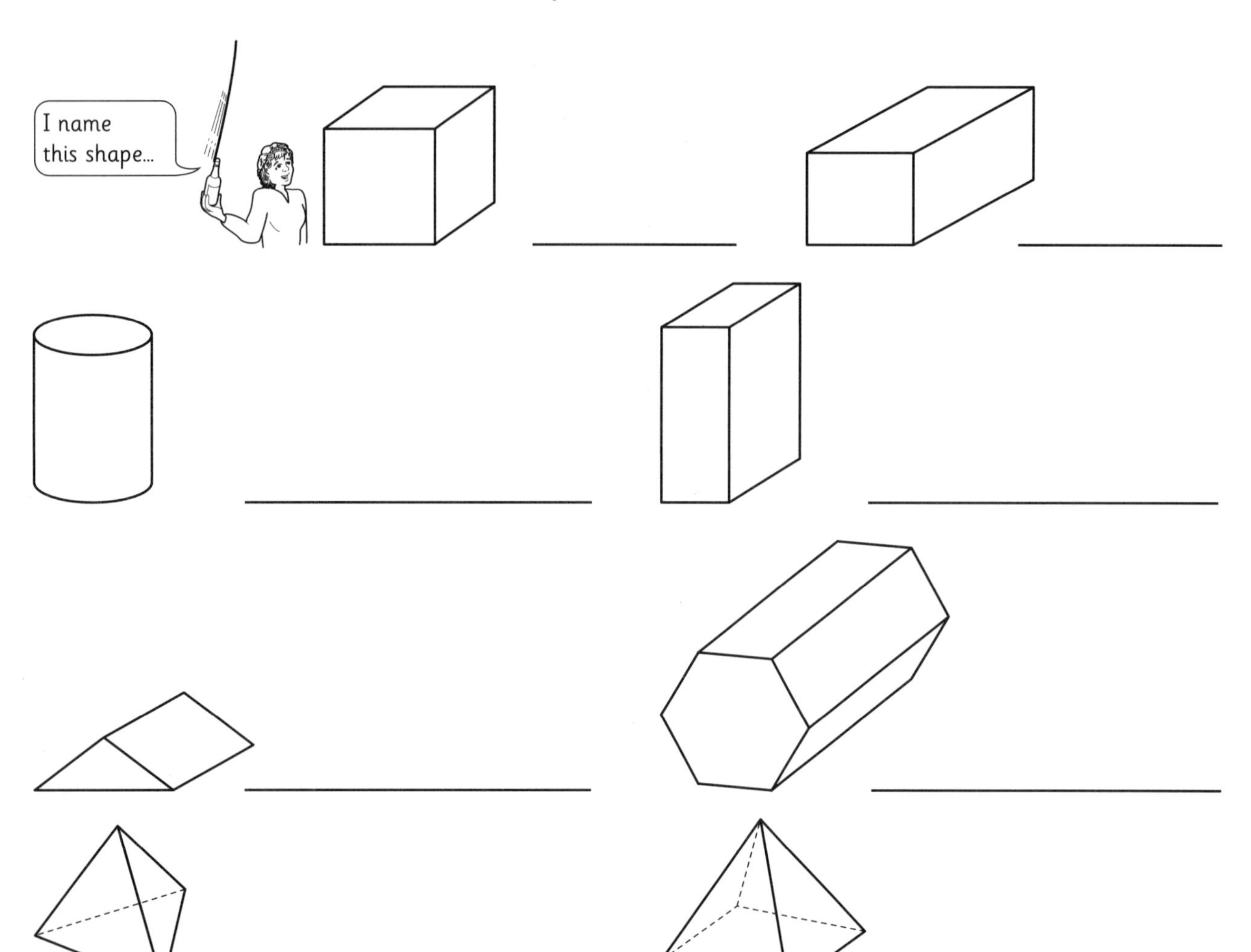

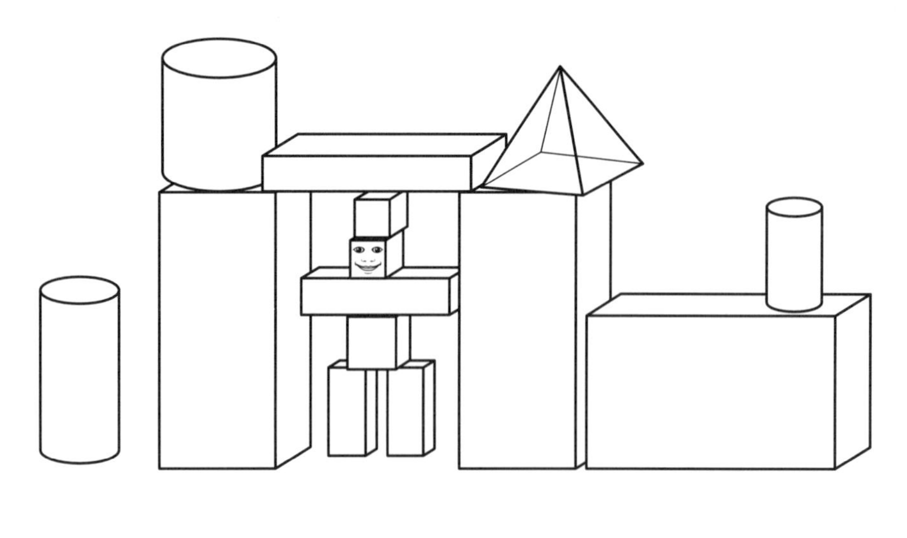

Colour the cuboids blue, the cubes red, the prisms yellow and the cylinders black. Do not colour the pyramid.

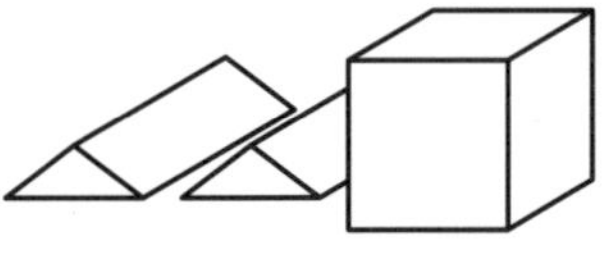

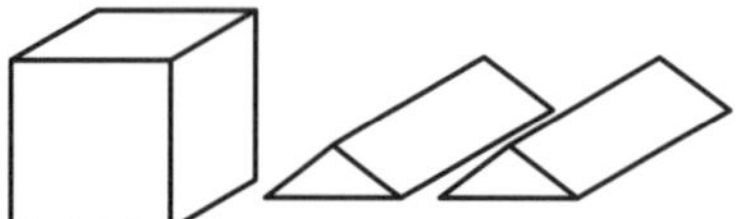

Naming nets

Name these nets.

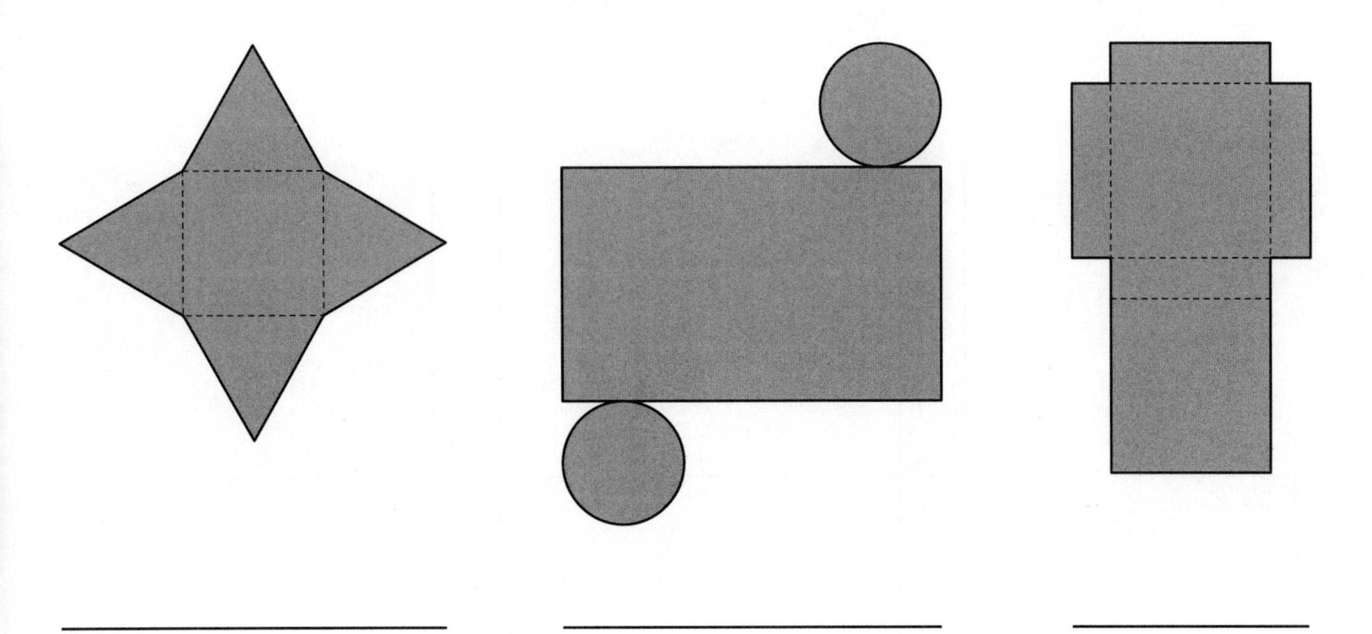

These nets are not complete. Draw in what is missing.

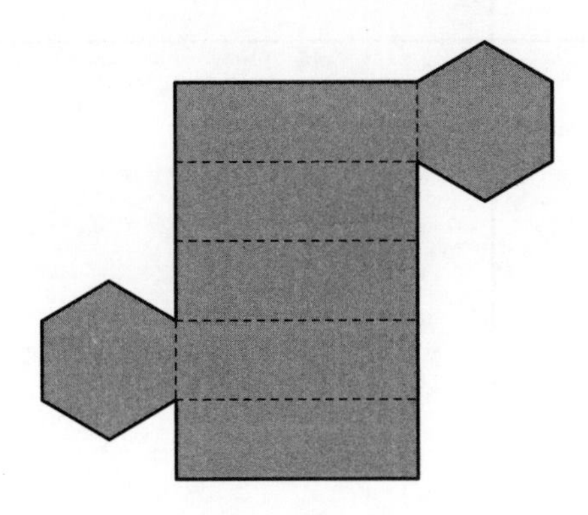

hexagonal prism

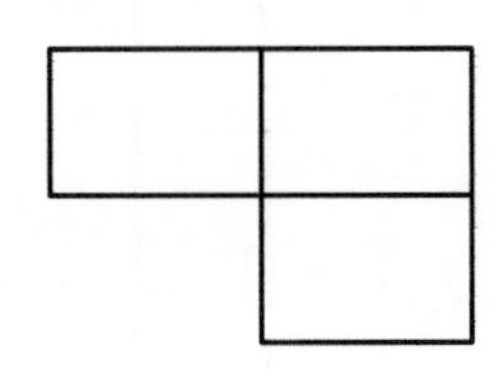

cuboid

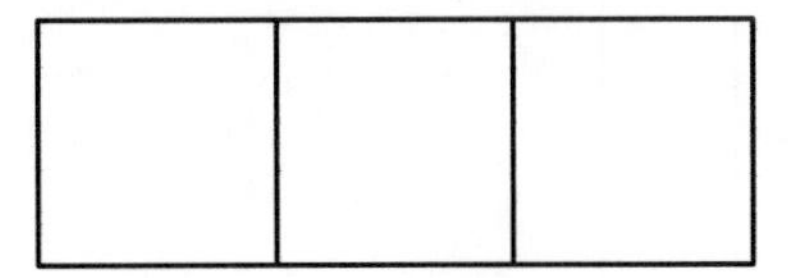

cube

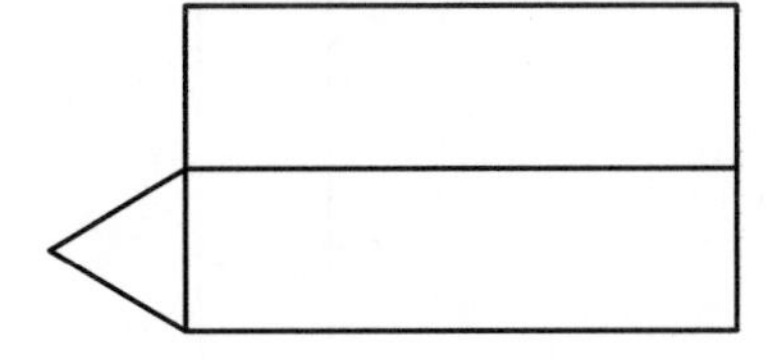

triangular prism

Cube box

Use this net to make a cube.

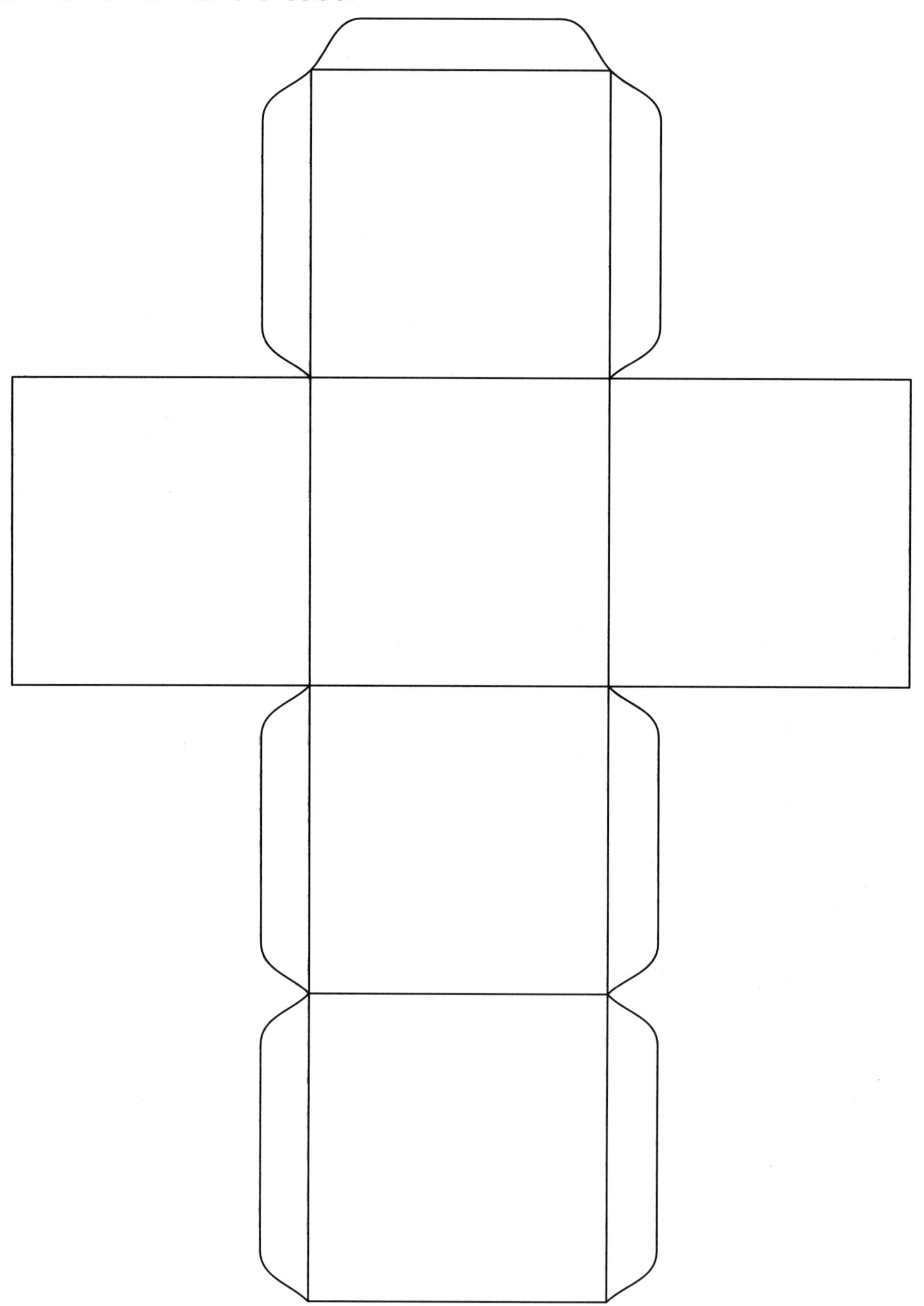

Pyramid

Use this net to make a square based pyramid.

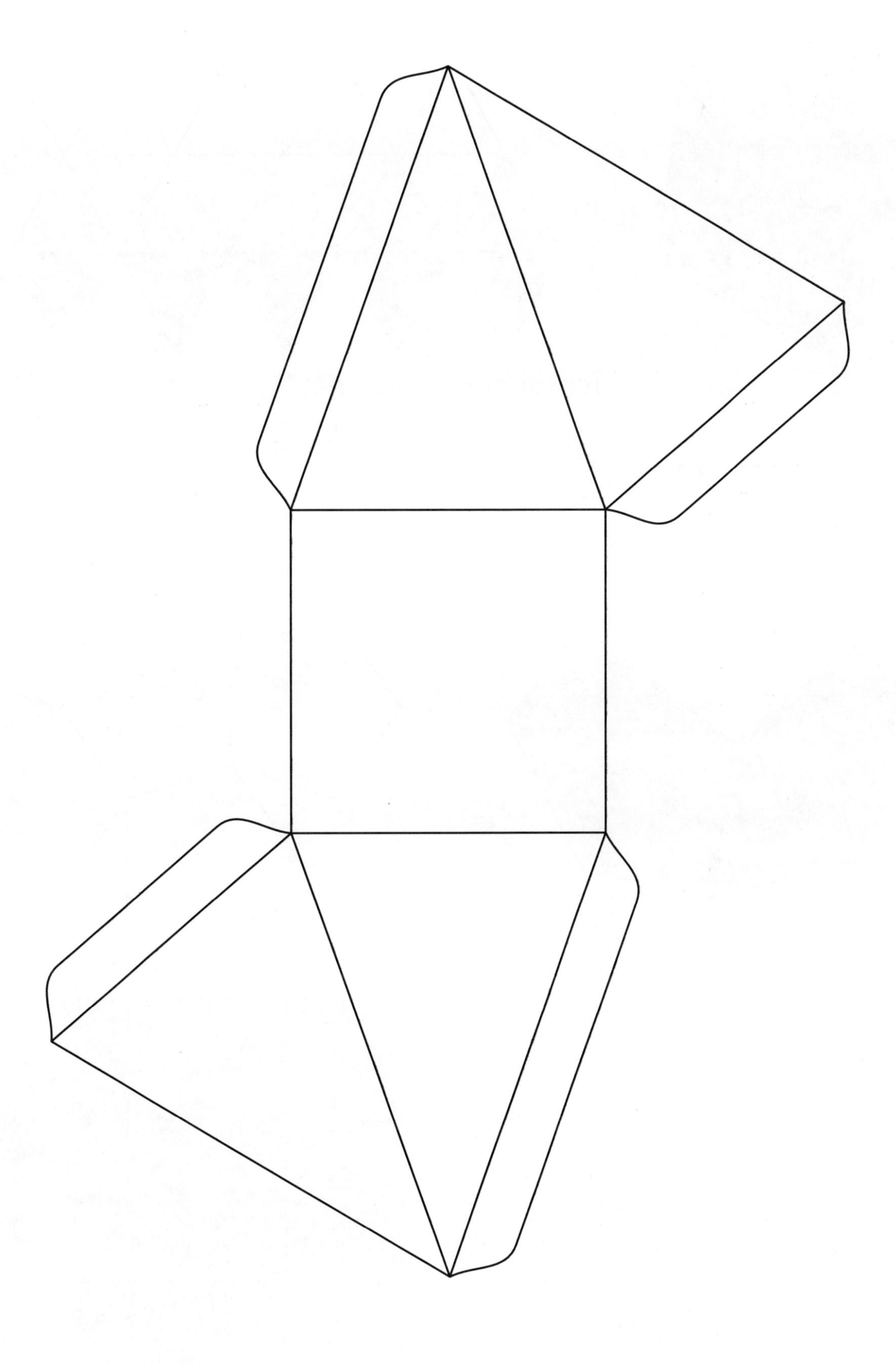

12 Icosahedron and dodecahedron

Using the nets, make an icosahedron and a dodecahedron.

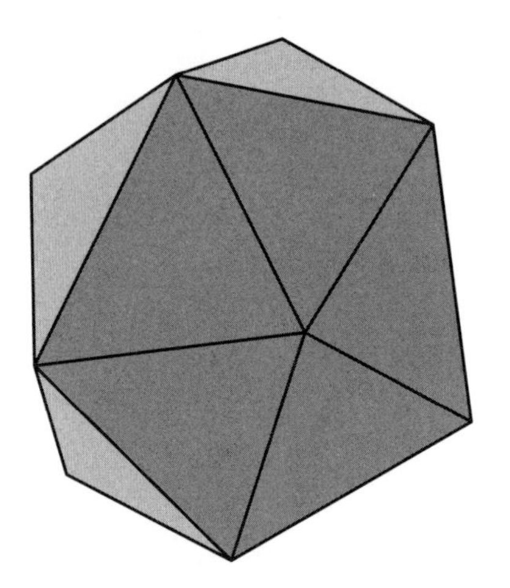

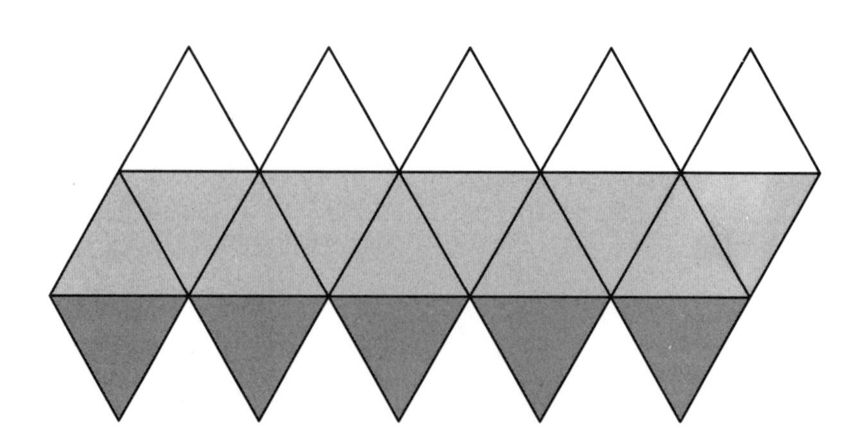

Icosahedron and net

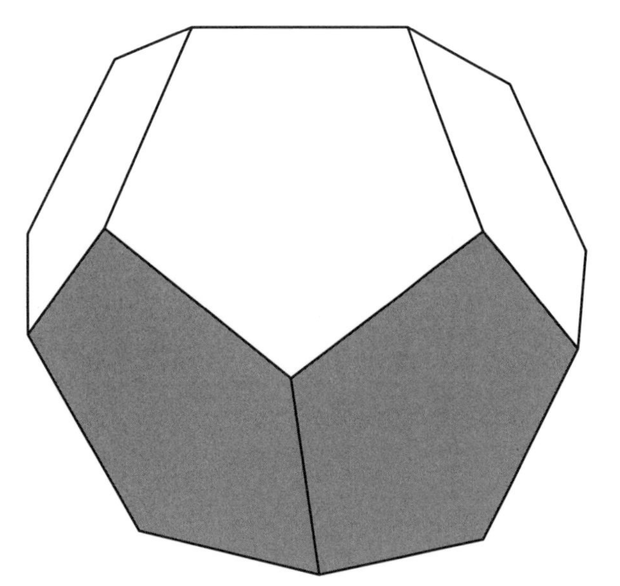

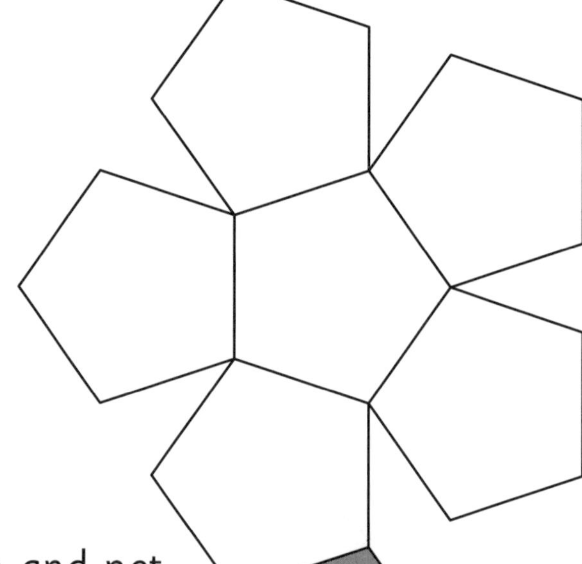

Dodecahedron and net

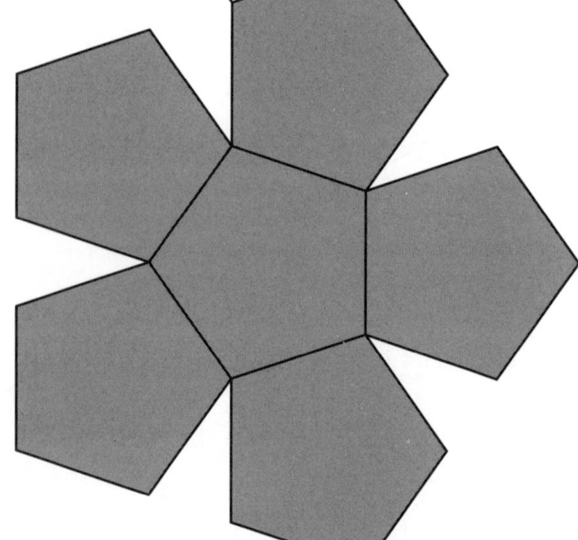

13 Cut faces of 3-D shapes

Imagine these solid shapes are sliced up. What shapes would the cut faces be? Join the dotted lines to the correct names of the cut faces.

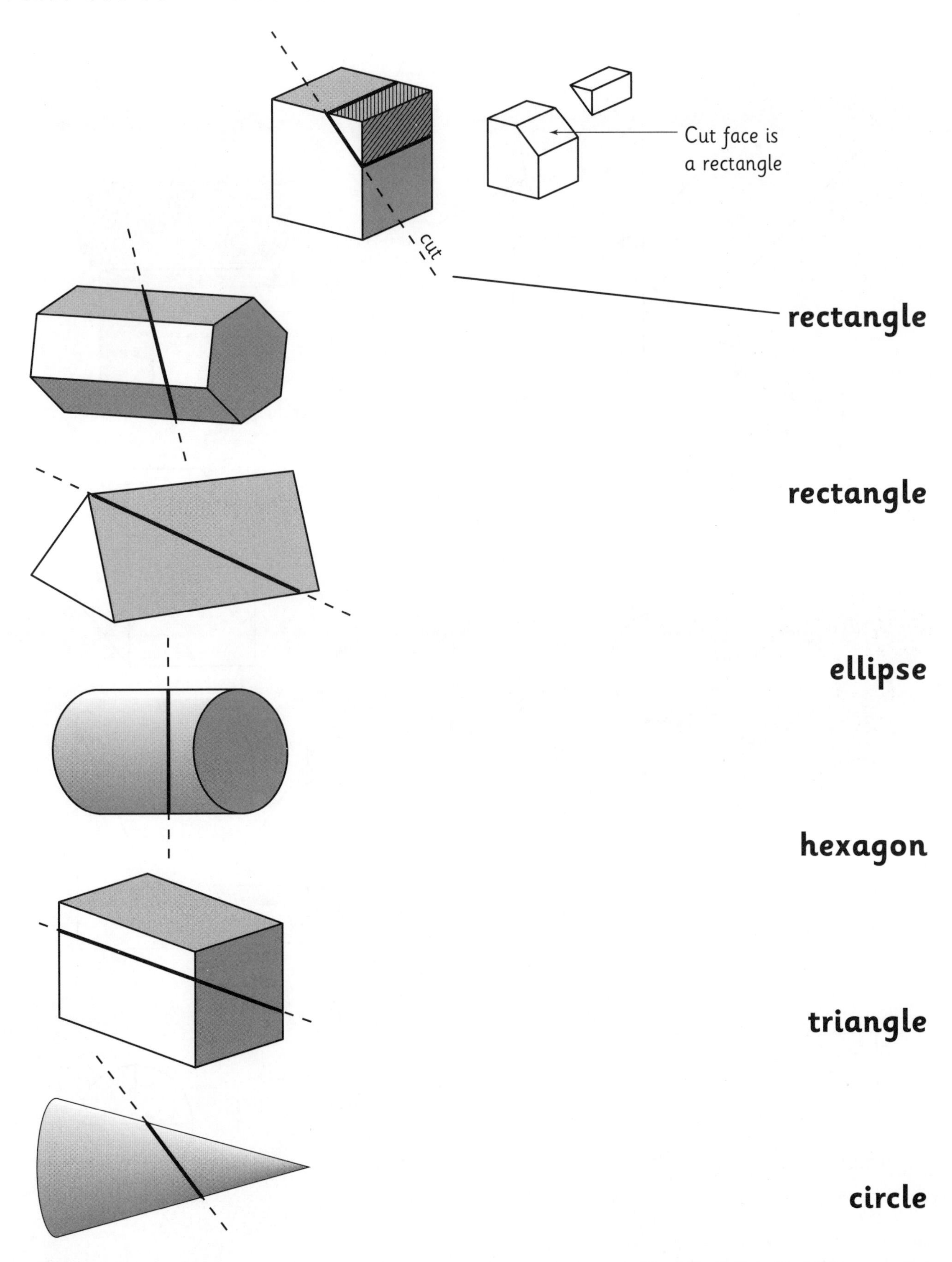

Right angles

Draw ⦜ where you see a right angle.

Grid locations

Mr and Mrs Stick, and Sally and Simon want to reach their pets.

They can only move in these directions: ←↑→↓ .

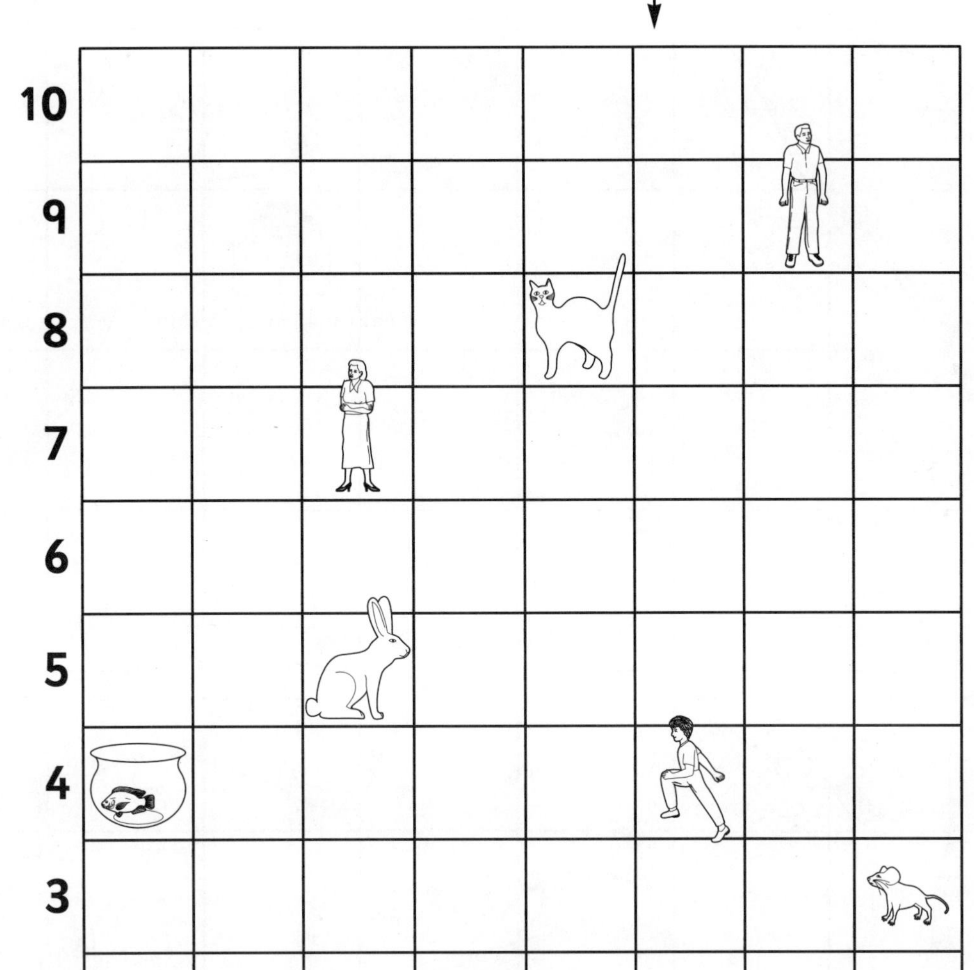

1 Write down the grid square each pet is in.
2 Write down the grid square each member of the Stick family is in.
3 How many squares must Sally travel through to get to her rabbit?
4 How many squares must Simon travel through to get to his cat?
5 Mr Stick keeps a fish and Mrs Stick a mouse. Through how many squares must each travel to get to their pet?
6 Write down all the grid squares Sally must travel through to get to her rabbit.

16 Map puzzle

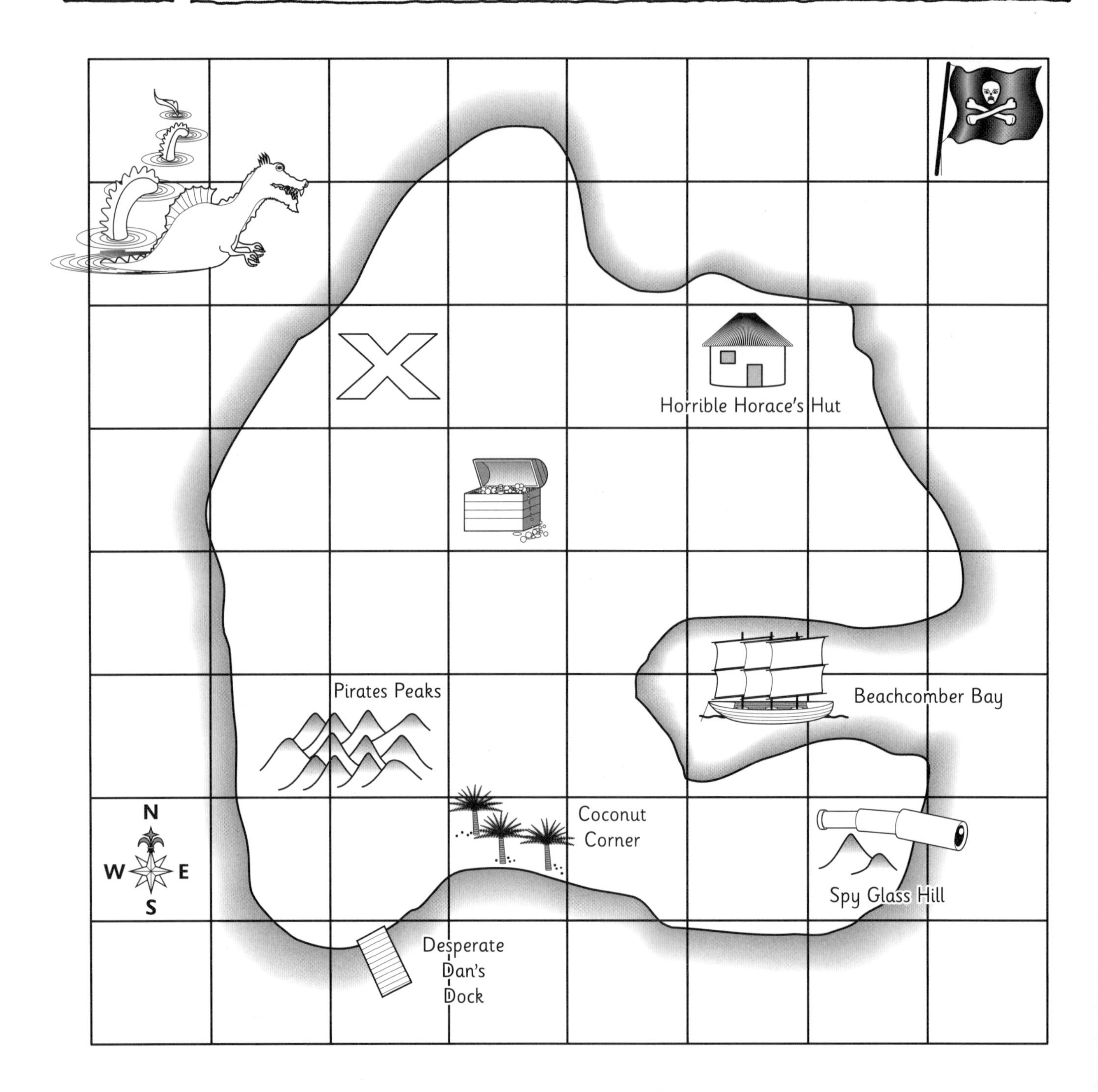

1. In which direction is the treasure chest from Coconut Corner?
2. In which direction is X from Pirates Peaks?
3. In which direction is the ship from Horrible Horace's Hut?
4. What is north of Desperate Dan's Dock?
5. In which direction is Coconut Corner from Spy Glass Hill?
6. Mark a trail from Spy Glass Hill to the treasure.
7. Give directions for your trail using compass points.

17 Fractions of a turn

Draw the correct compass point in each circle. Write what fraction of the whole circle has been made in each.

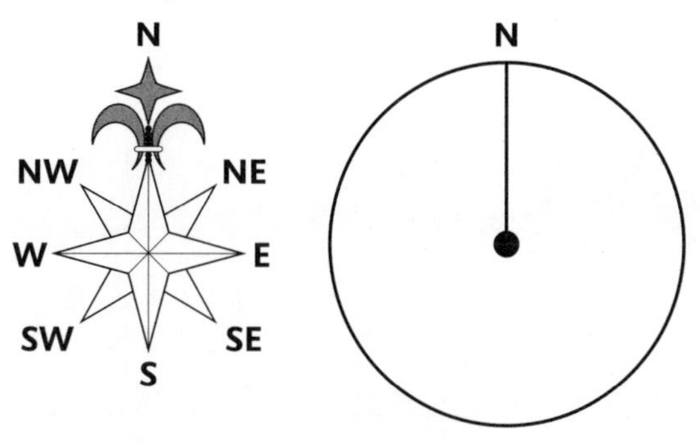

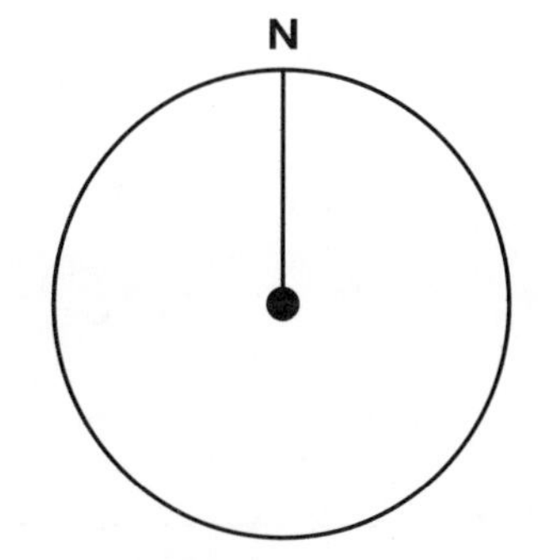

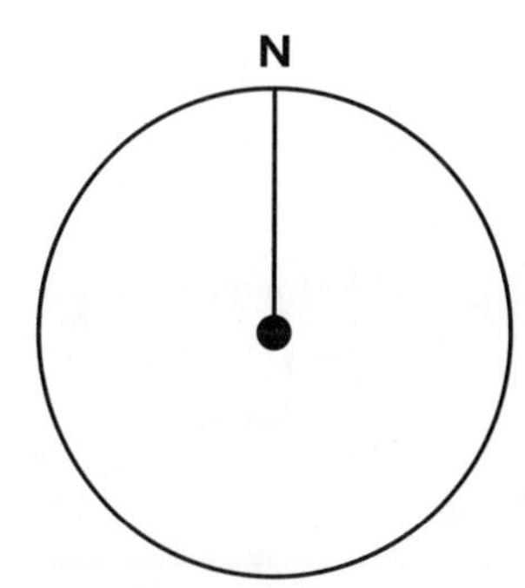

Put in east.
What fraction of
a turn is that?

Put in south.
What fraction of
a turn is that?

Put in north-east.
What fraction of
a turn is that?

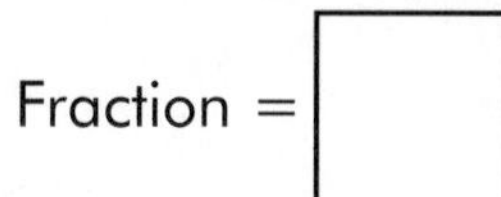

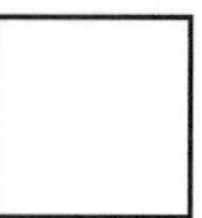

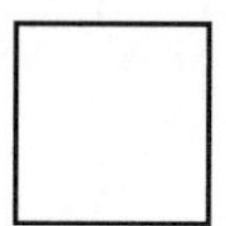

Draw the hands for the time on each clock face. Write what fraction of a turn there is between the hands.

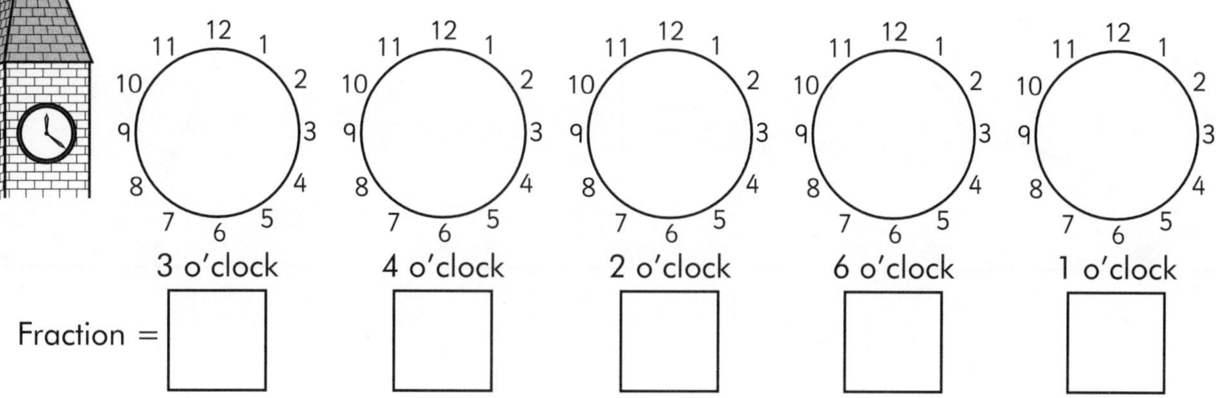

Draw four clock faces. Draw the hands on each but do not make the time "o'clock" (twenty past two is an example).
Work out the fraction of a turn between the hands for each one.

What direction is $\frac{5}{8}$ of a clockwise turn from N?
What direction is a $\frac{3}{4}$ turn? Try some other fractions and directions.

18 Naming angles

Write the name of each angle.

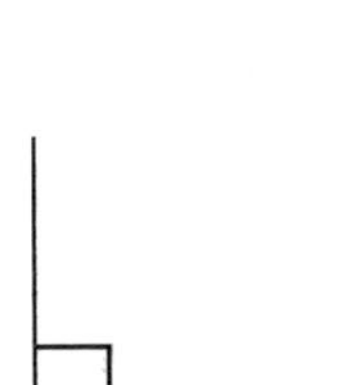

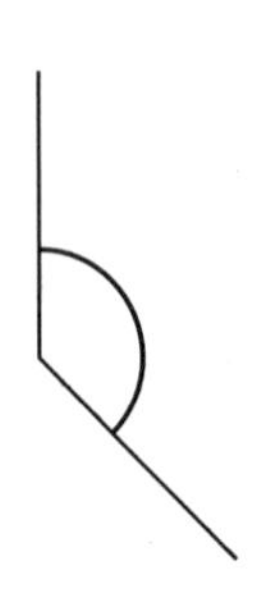

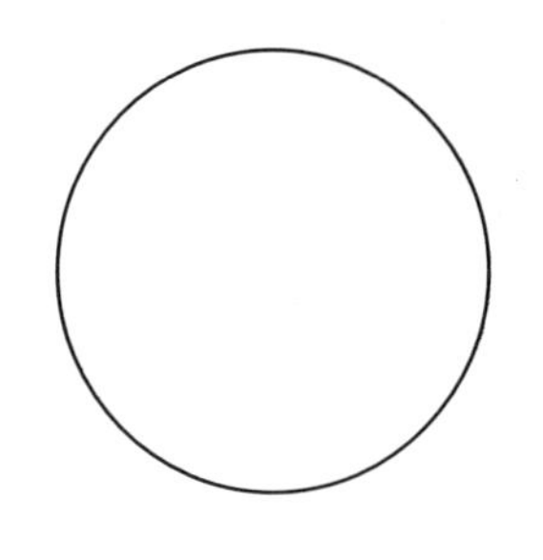

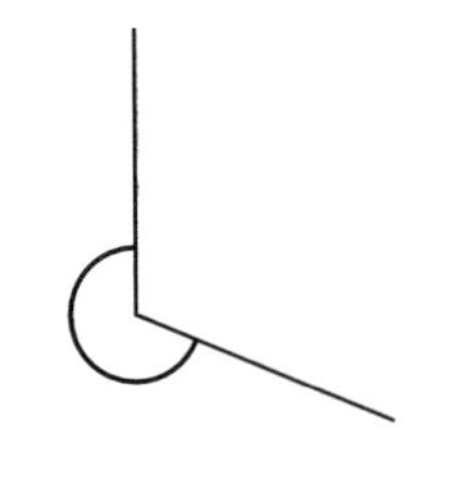

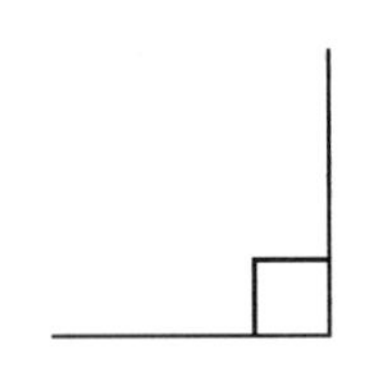

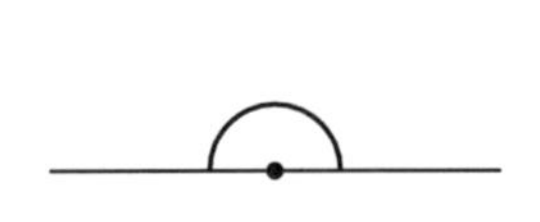

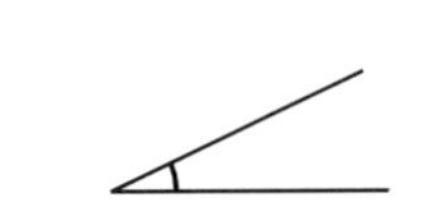

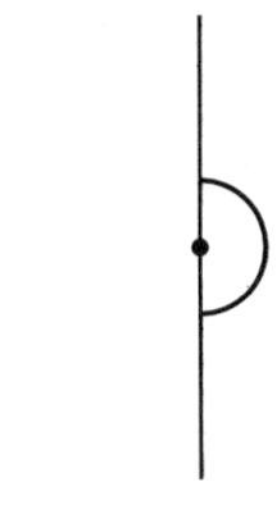

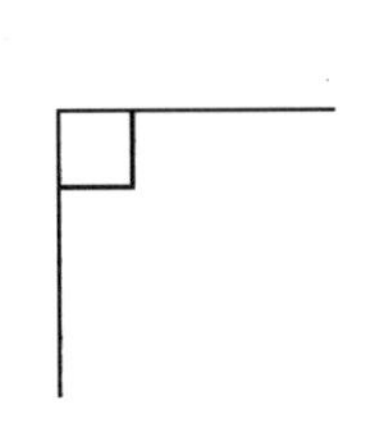

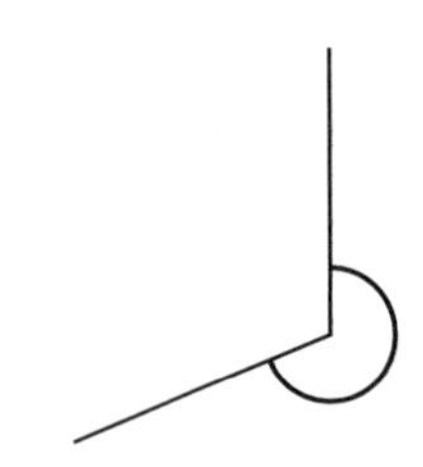

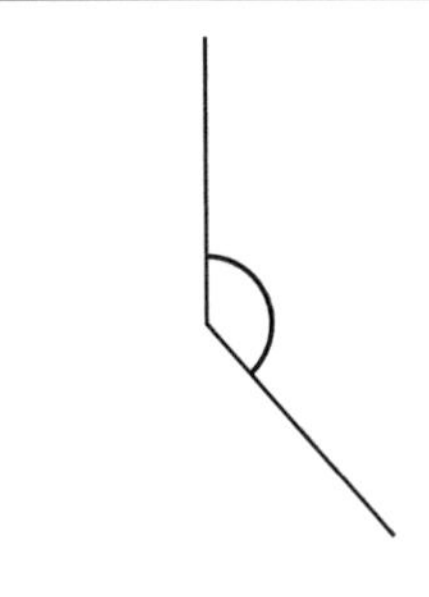

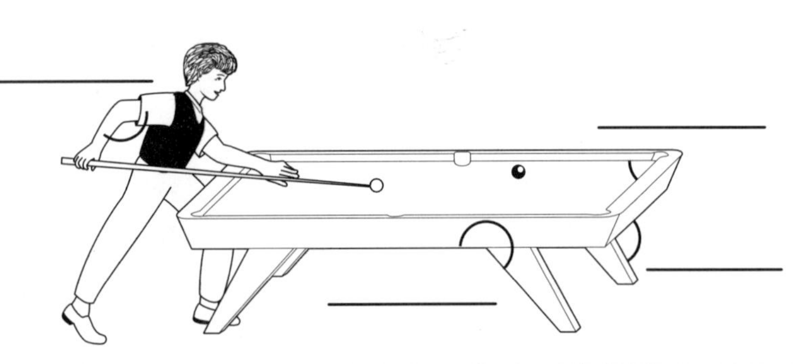

19 Measuring angles

Use a protractor to measure how many degrees there are in each angle.

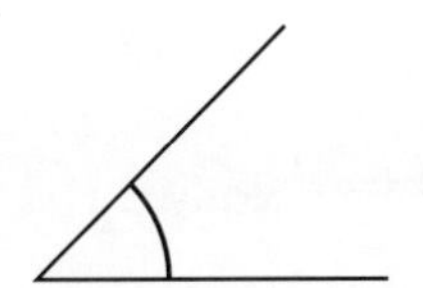

________ degrees

________ degrees

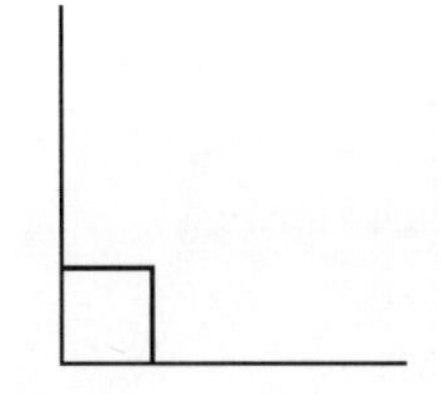

________ degrees

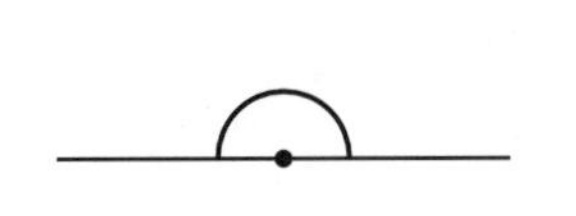

________ degrees

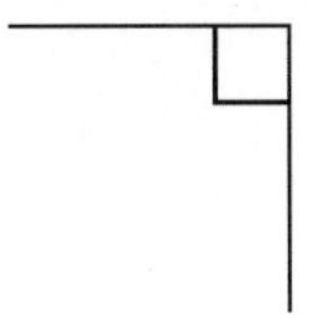

________ degrees

________ degrees

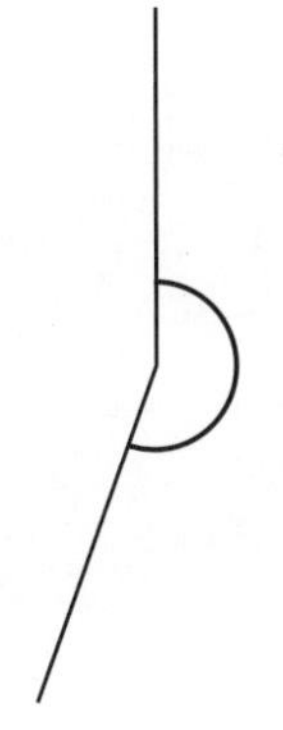

________ degrees

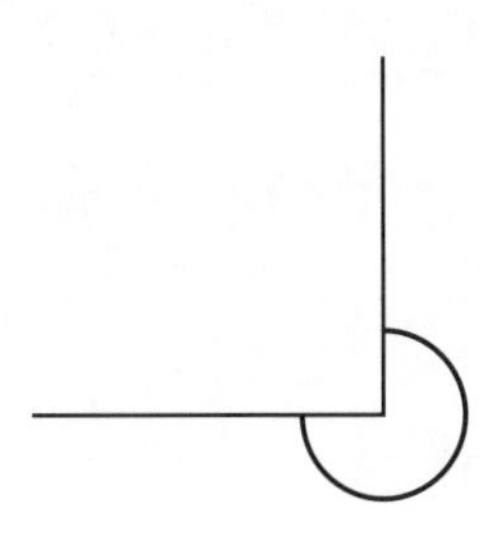

________ degrees

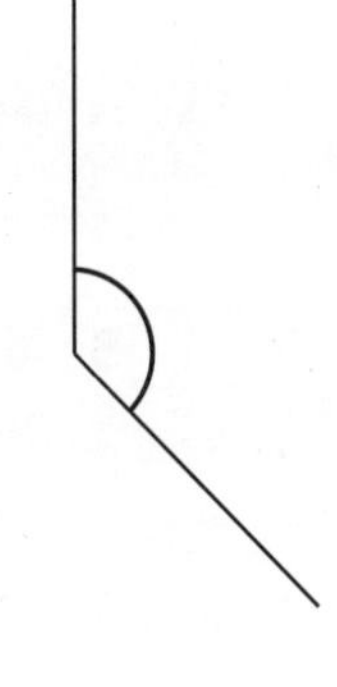

________ degrees

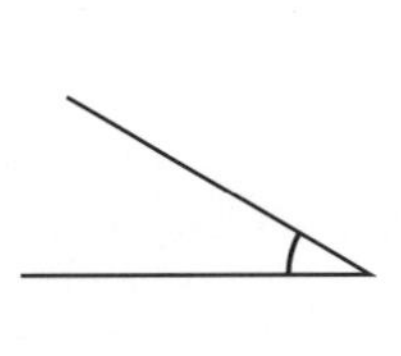

________ degrees

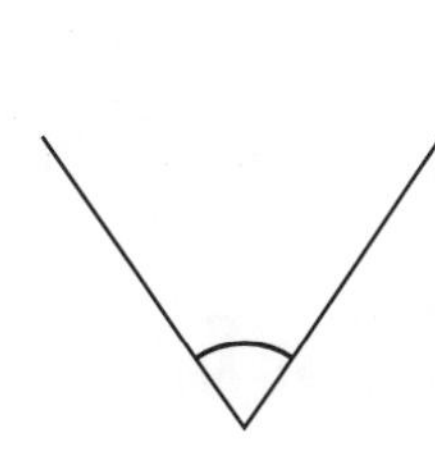

________ degrees

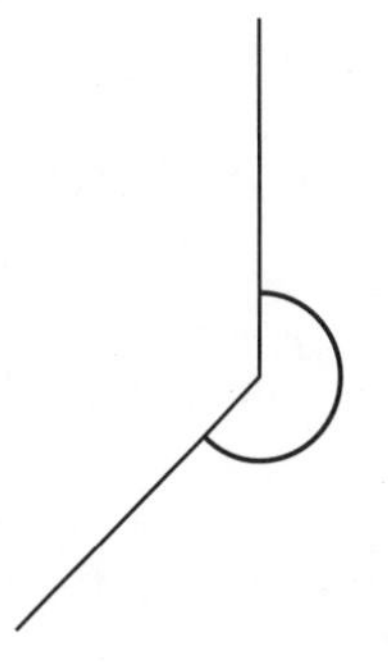

________ degrees

Co-ordinates: mapping

Study this map of the District of Willowbank.

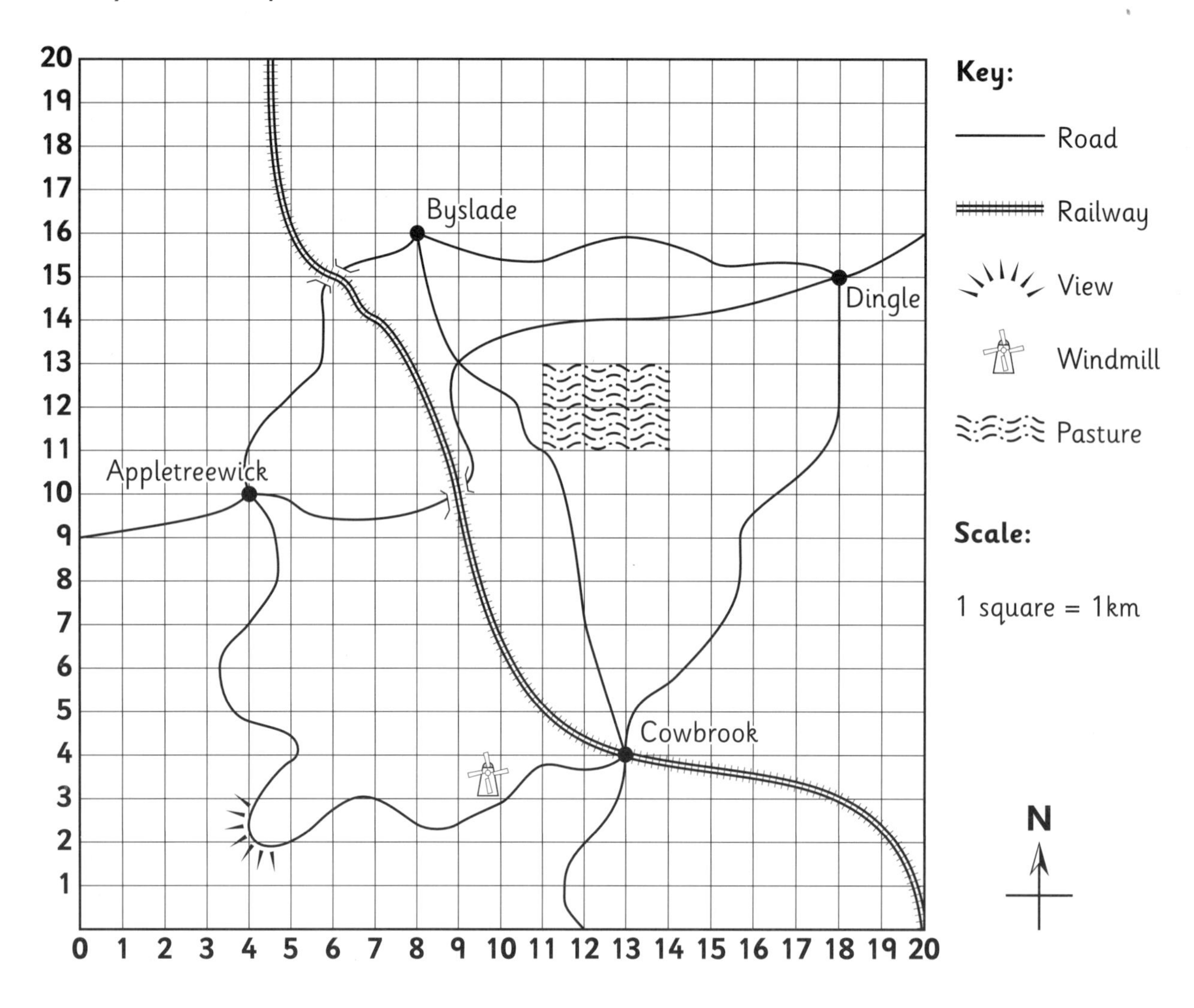

1 What are the co-ordinates of each of the four towns?

2 The road from Appletreewick to Dingle crosses another road. What are the co-ordinates of this junction.

3 At which point does the big pasture meet the road.

4 Where is the old windmill?

5 Where do people go to see the view?

6 There is a level crossing at Cowbrook but the railway has two bridges over roads. Where are these bridges?

21 Co-ordinates: drawing shapes

Draw and name the shapes.

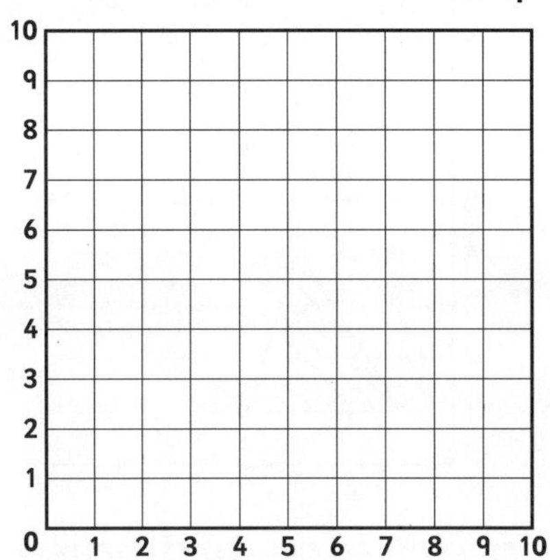

Co-ordinates (2,2) (7,2) (2,6) (7,6)

Shape ____________________

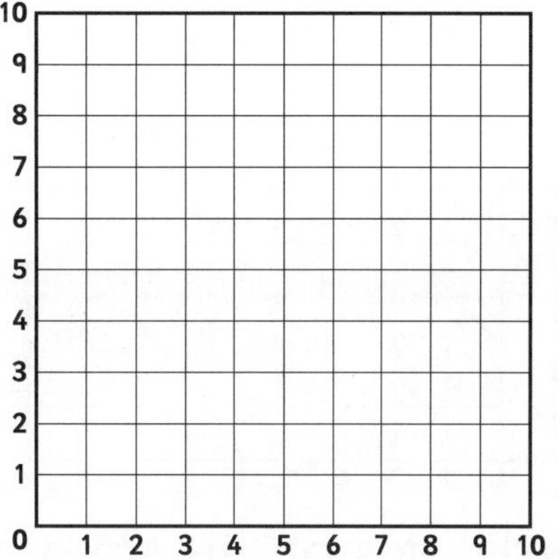

Co-ordinates (3,2) (4,6) (9,1)

Shape ____________________

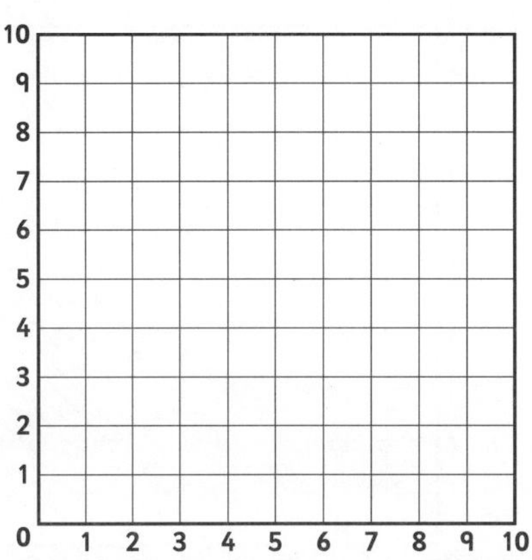

Co-ordinates (2,3) (4,2) (6,3) (2,6) (4,7) (6,6)

Shape ____________________

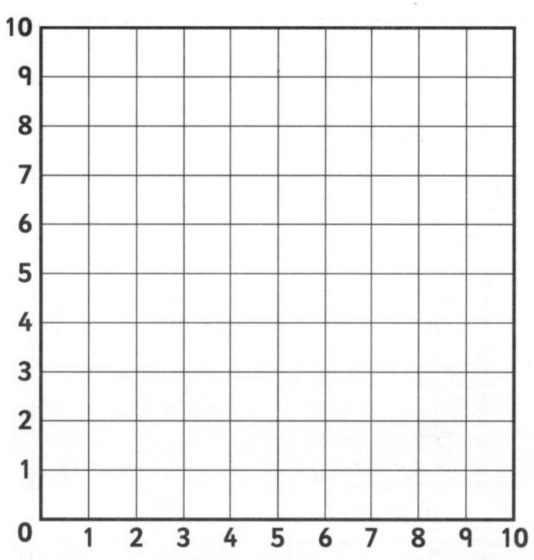

Co-ordinates (2,3) (3,6) (8,3) (7,6)

Shape ____________________

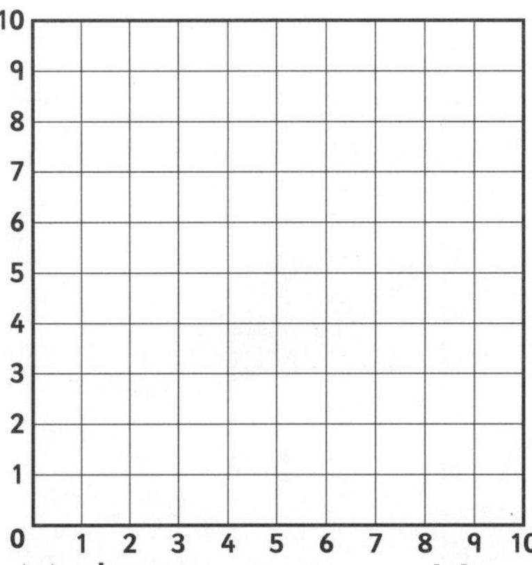

Make a square. Use (2,2) and (2,8) to start. Write its co-ordinates here.

____

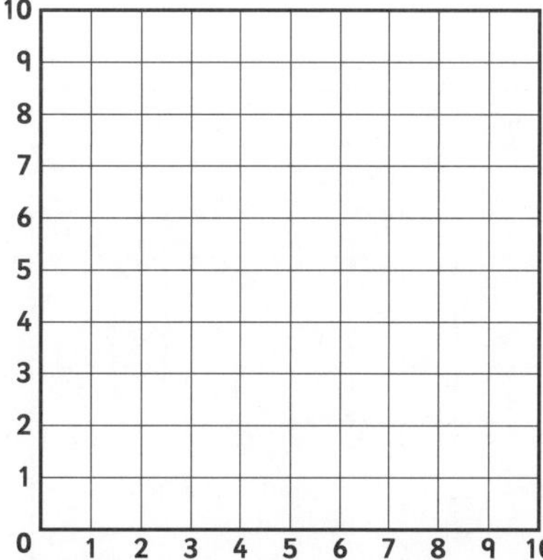

Make a right angled triangle. Use (1,1) to start. Write its co-ordinates here.

____

Co-ordinates: translation

1

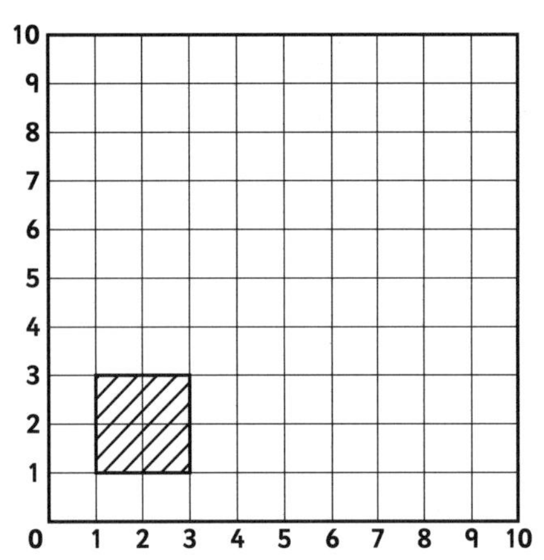

The co-ordinates of this square are (1,1) (1,3) (3,1) (3,3).
Add 4 to the co-ordinates like this (1,1) (5,5). Draw the new square.

2

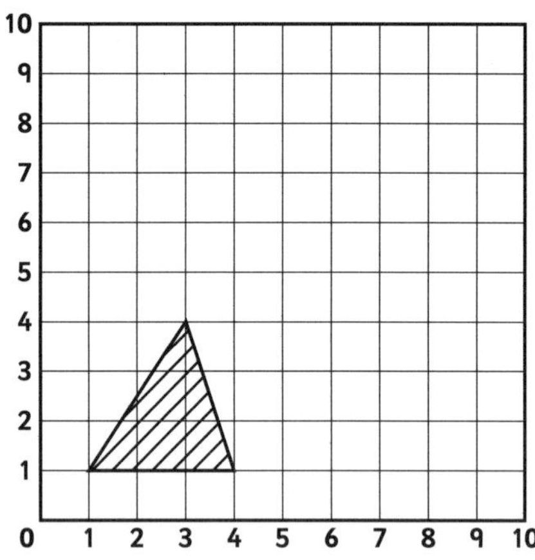

What are the co-ordinates of this triangle? Add 3 to every co-ordinate and draw the new triangle.

3

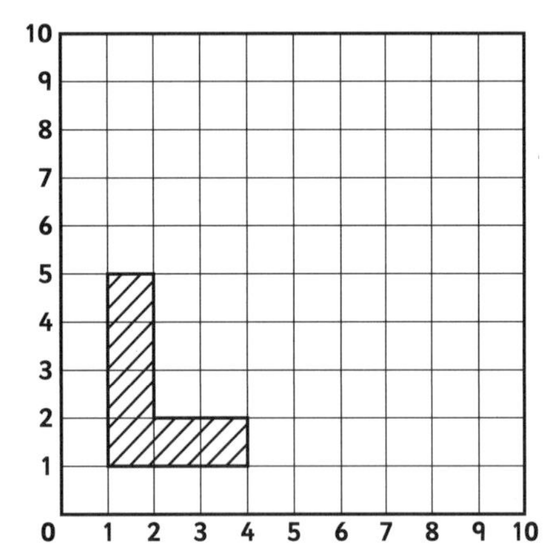

Add 5 to only the x values of these co-ordinates to make a new 'L'.

4

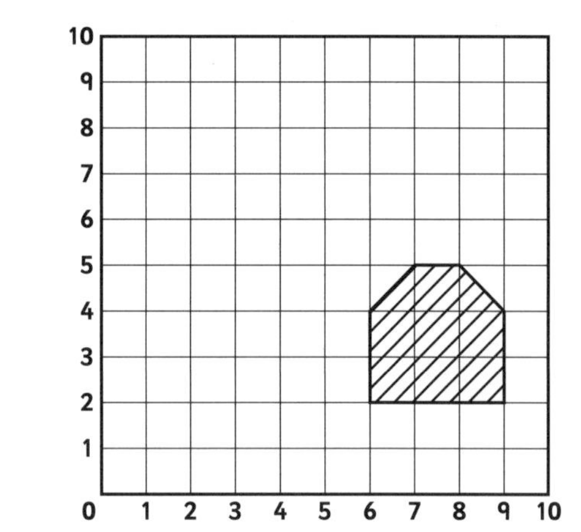

Subtract 4 from the x value. Where is the new shape?

5

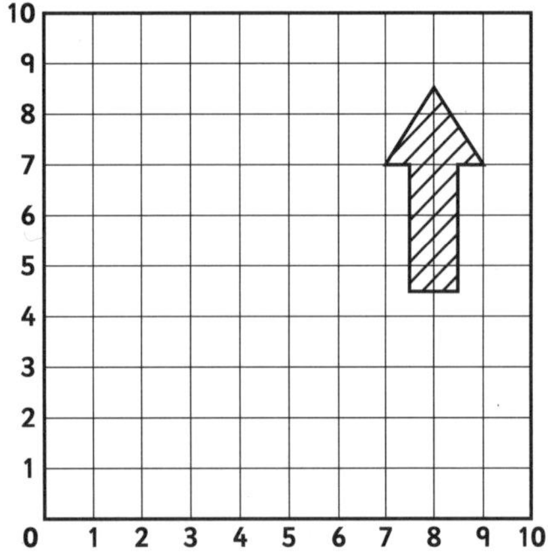

Subtract 3 from both the x and y values and plot the new arrow.

6

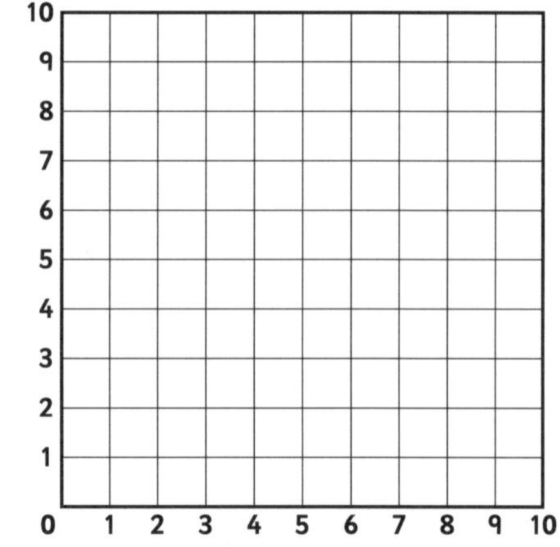

Now make up one translation for your friend.

Co-ordinates: enlargement and reduction

Make a square with sides twice as long as the one below.

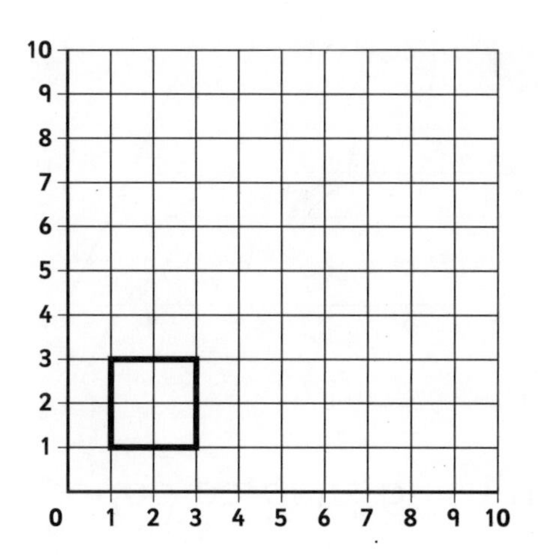

Make a triangle with sides three times the size of the one below.

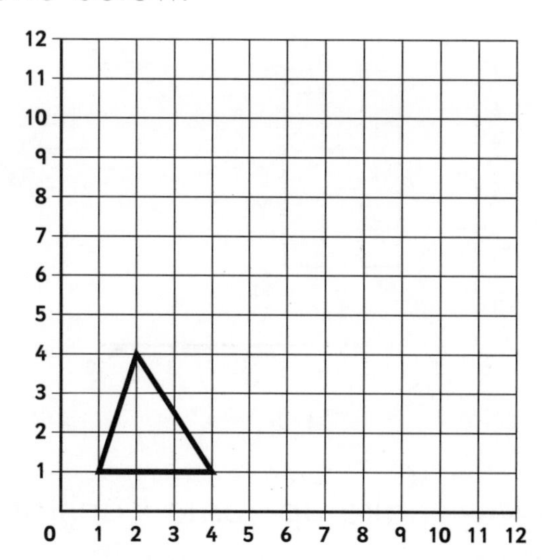

Make an arrow with sides twice as long as the one below. Then make one half the size of the one below.

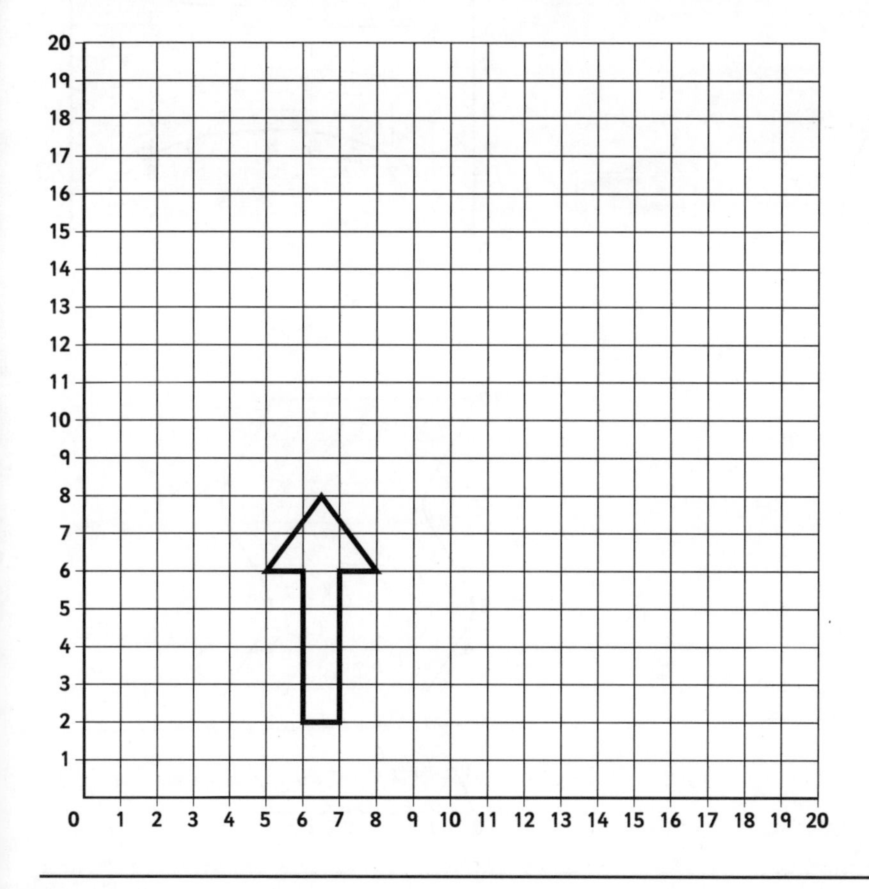

Make a trapezium with sides half as long as the one below.

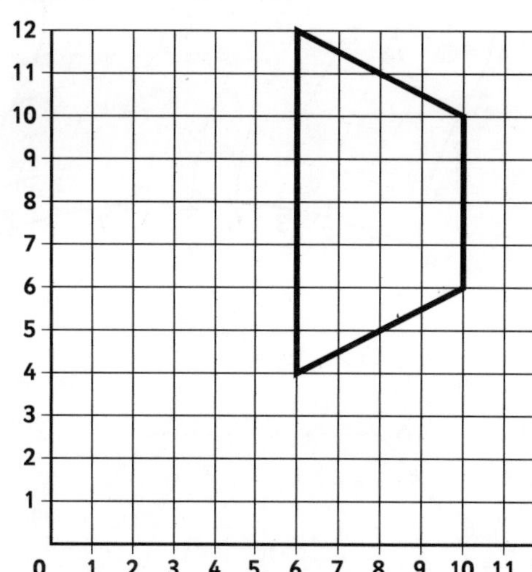

24 Co-ordinates: transformations

Transform this letter H.

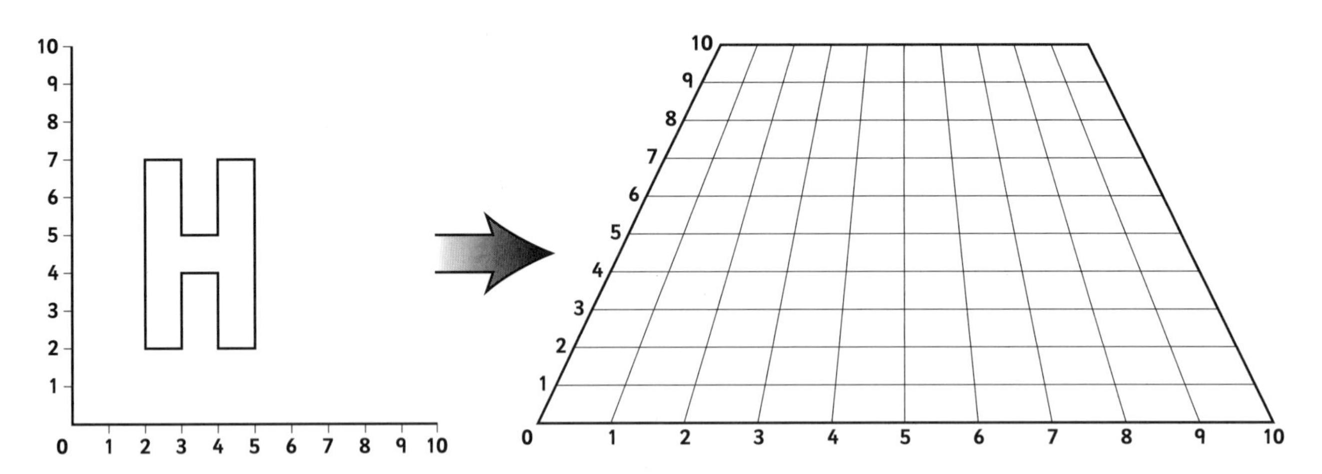

Now make up some transformations of your own using squared paper and transformer grids like these.

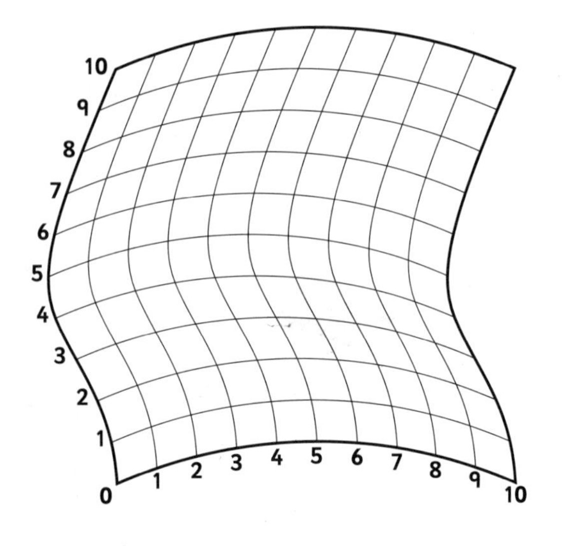

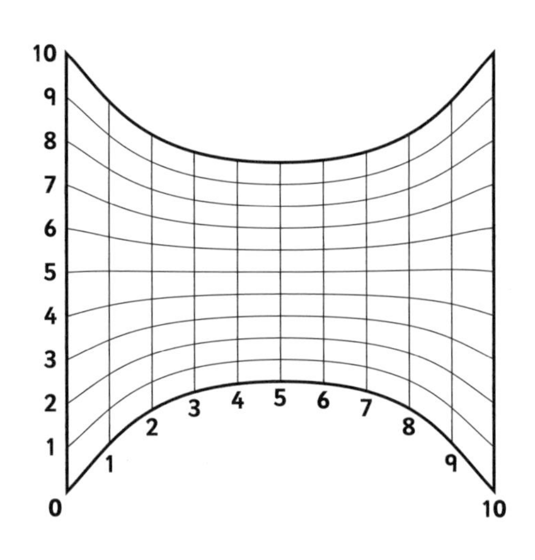

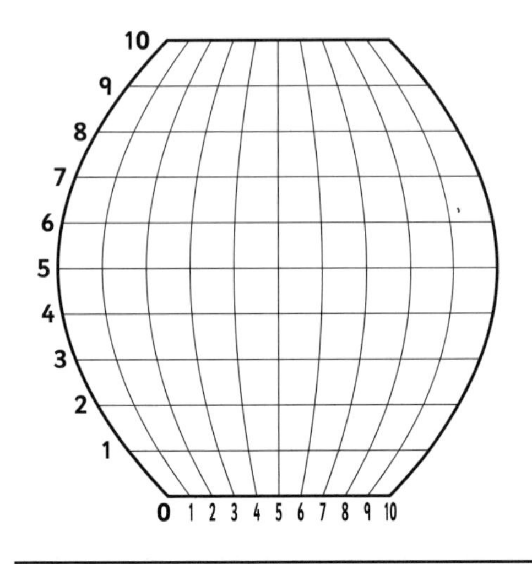

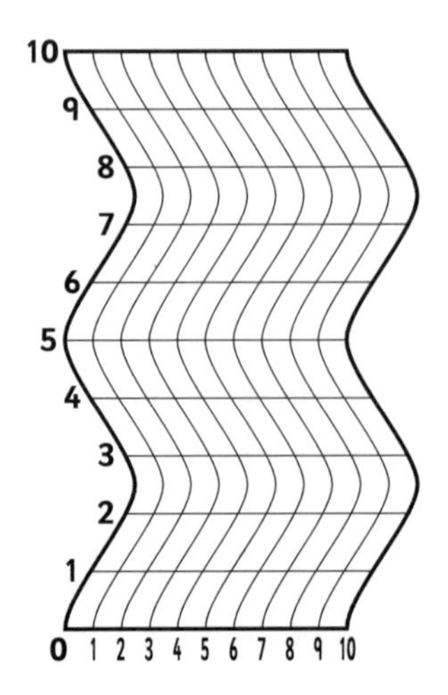

Compass directions

Journey around the UK. Visit a city in England, Scotland, Wales and Northern Ireland at least once. Write down the places you visit and the compass directions for each part of your journey.

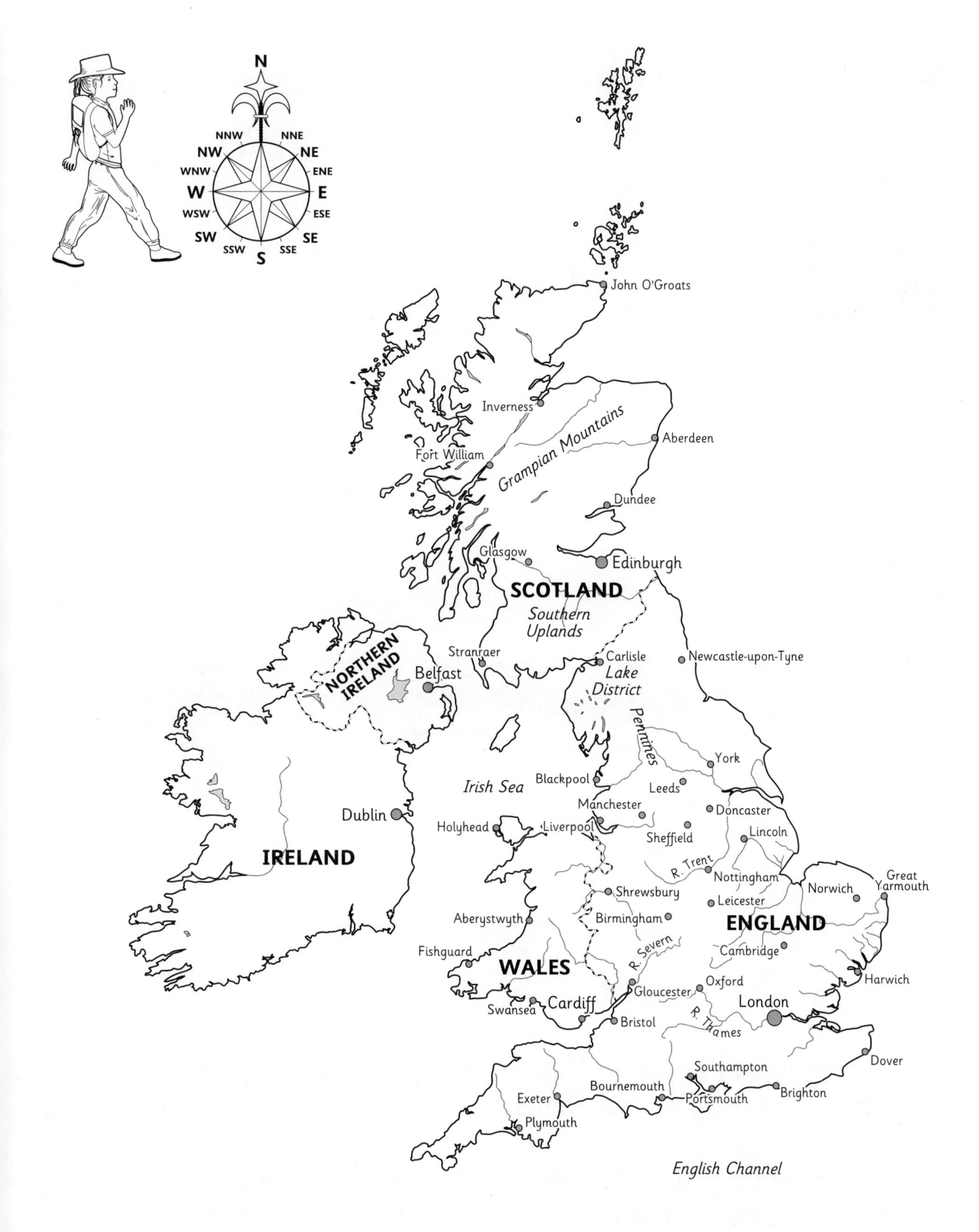

Bearings

Can you find your bearings?

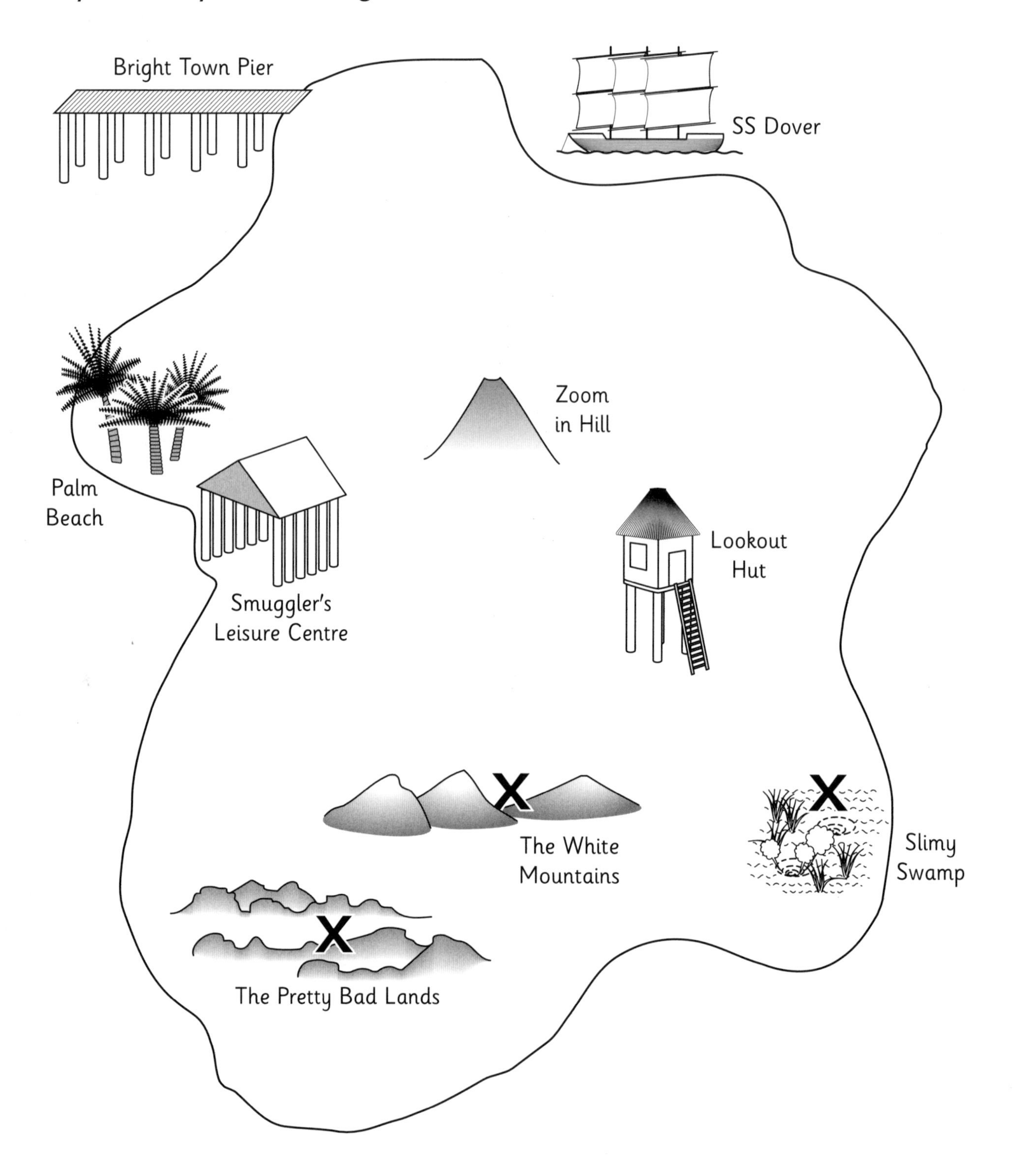

1 You are on top of Zoom in Hill. What are the bearings from you of the places marked X? Draw lines on the map and put in the bearings.

2 If you went aboard the SS Dover, what would be the bearings of Smuggler's Leisure Centre and Lookout Hut from there?

Estimating length

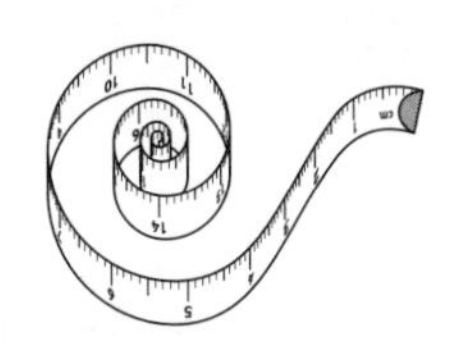

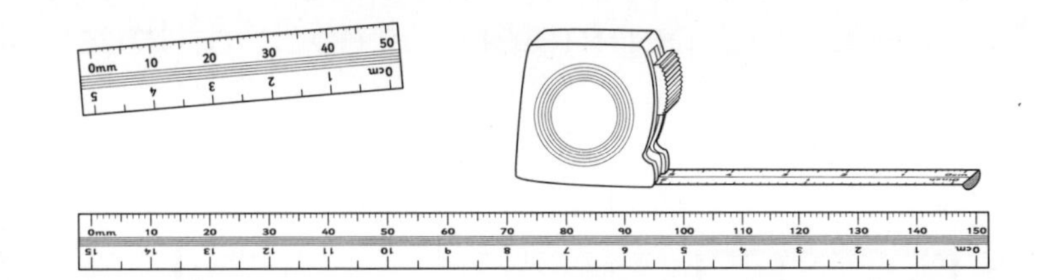

Work with your partner to fill in the table. Remember to estimate before you measure. Write down the measurement then work out how close you were each time.

Name of object	Estimate	Actual measurement	Difference between my estimate and the actual measurement

Don't forget that **metre** can be written as **m** and **centimetre** as **cm**.

Finding areas and perimeters

Find the areas and perimeters of each of these shapes.

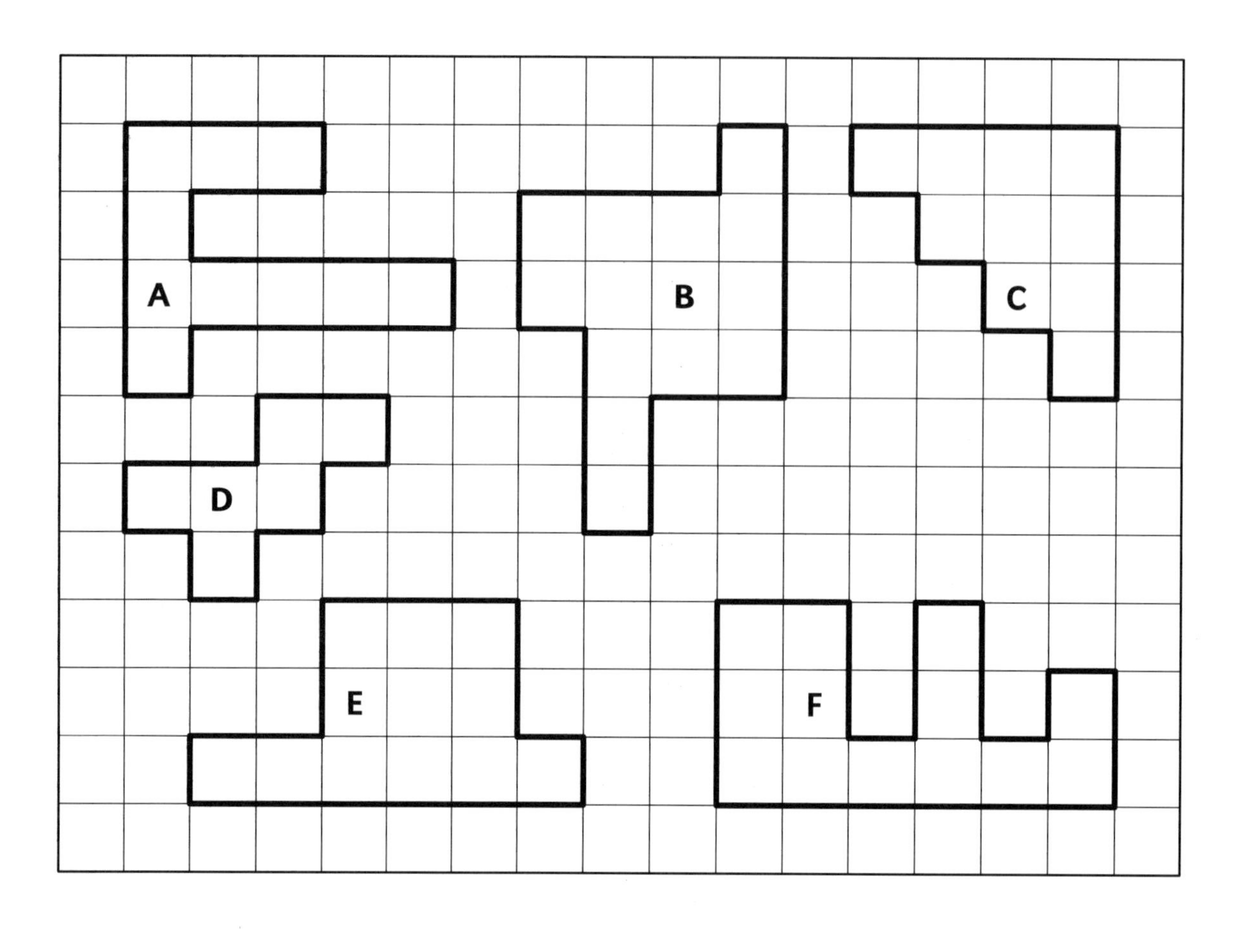

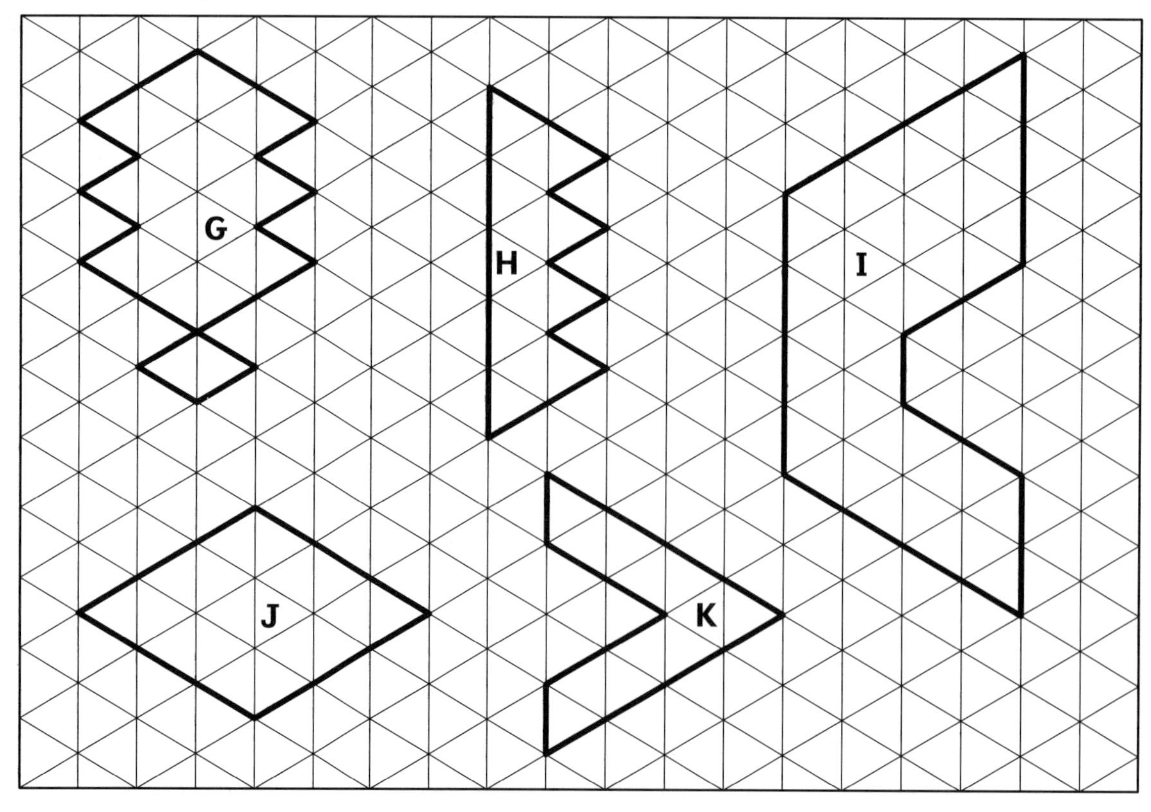

29 Constructing triangles

Follow these instructions to make a right angled triangle.

• make mark with pencil – place compass point here
)(arcs made with compass pencil

a) 

b) 

c) 

d) 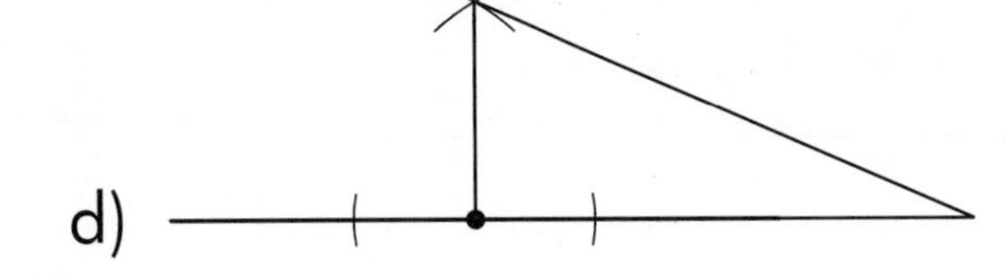

Now you try.

Here is how to draw an equilateral triangle.

a)

b) 

c)

Now you try.

30 Constructing a square/rectangle

Remember how to make a right angle like this:

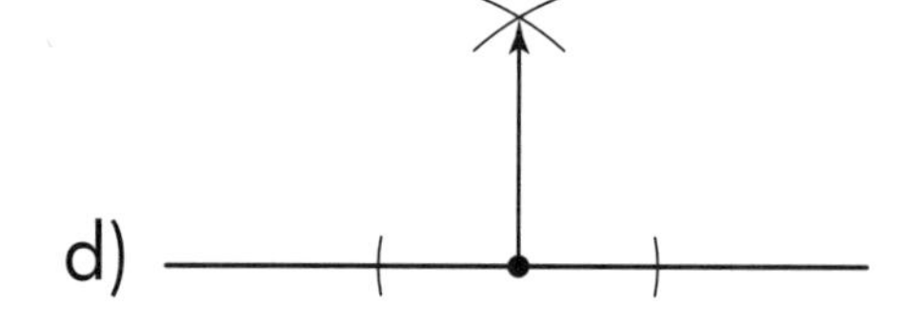

• make mark with pencil – place compass point here

)(arcs made with compass pencil

Now try to make a square, then a rectangle.

Constructing regular polygons

Try to make these regular polygons:

- pentagon – angle at centre 72°
- hexagon – angle at centre 60°
- octagon – angle at centre 45°

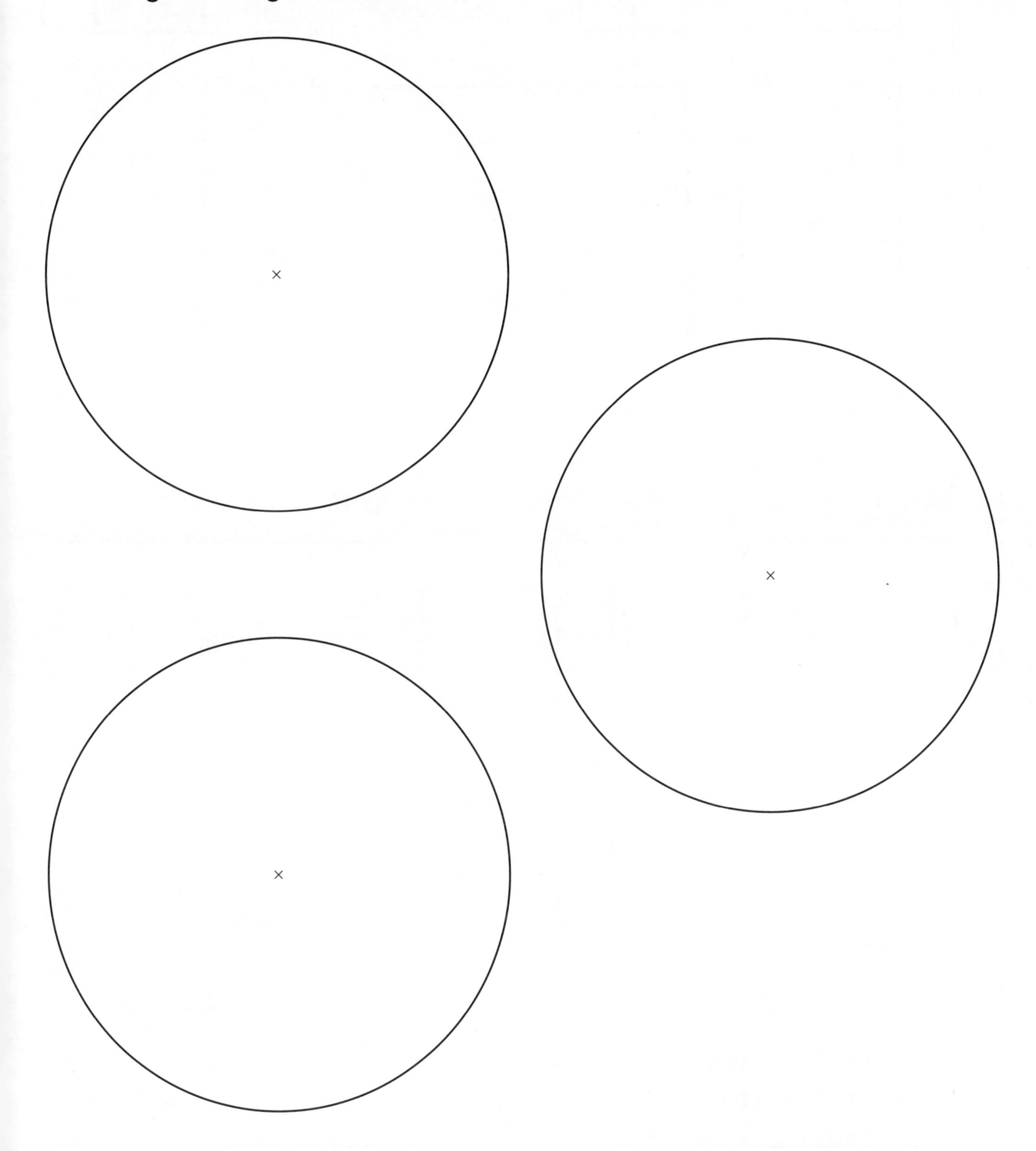

32 Areas and perimeters: rectangles

1 Work out the area and perimeter of each rectangle.

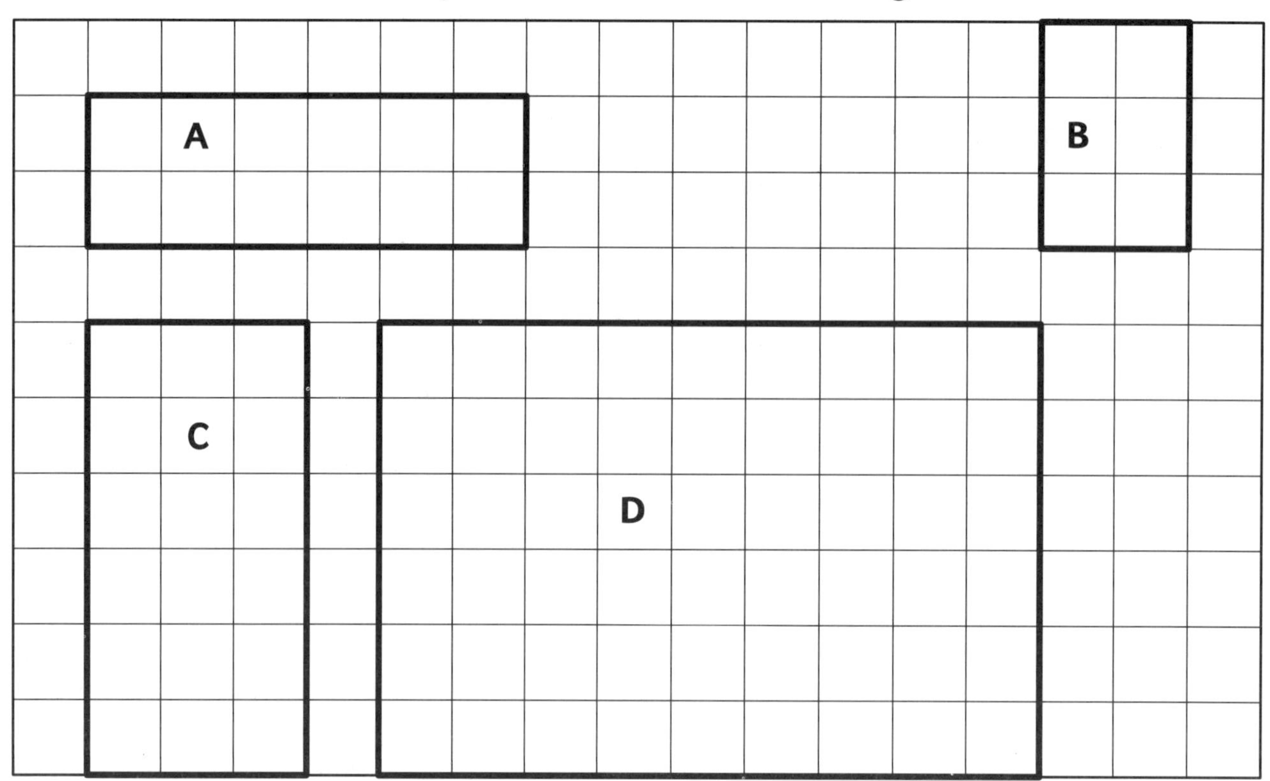

2 Now try these. Remember, the perimeter can be calculated by length × 2 plus breadth × 2, and the area by length × breadth.

A

B

C

D

E

Areas and perimeters: rectangles and triangles

1 Work out the area and perimeter of each rectangle or triangle.

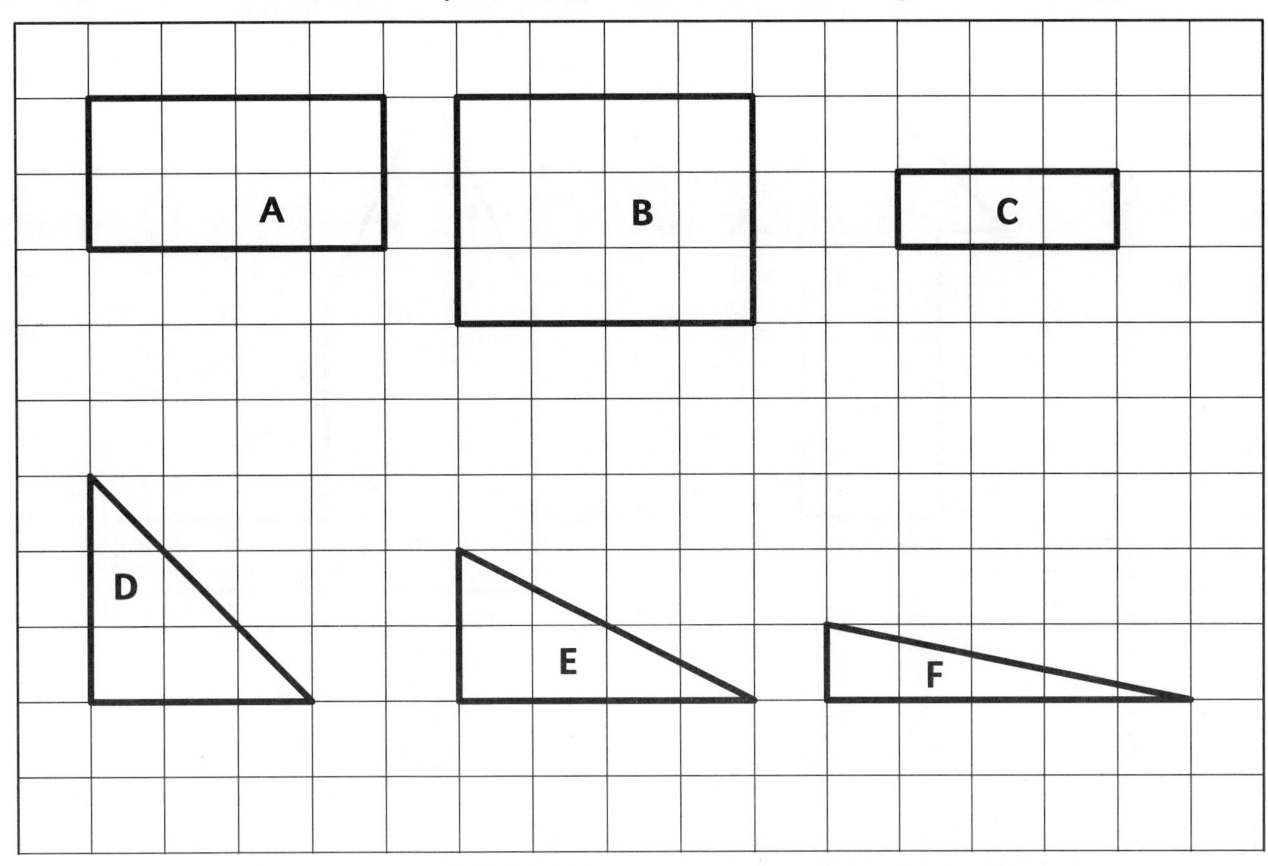

2 Now try these. Work out the area and perimeter of each triangle.

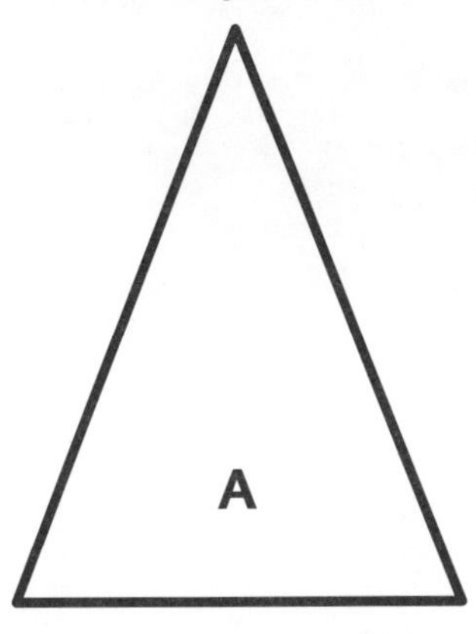

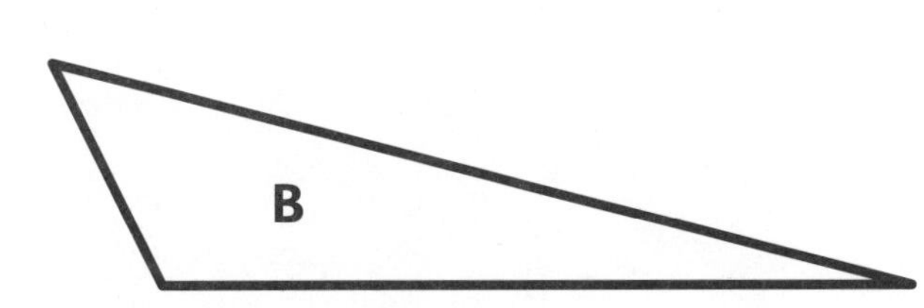

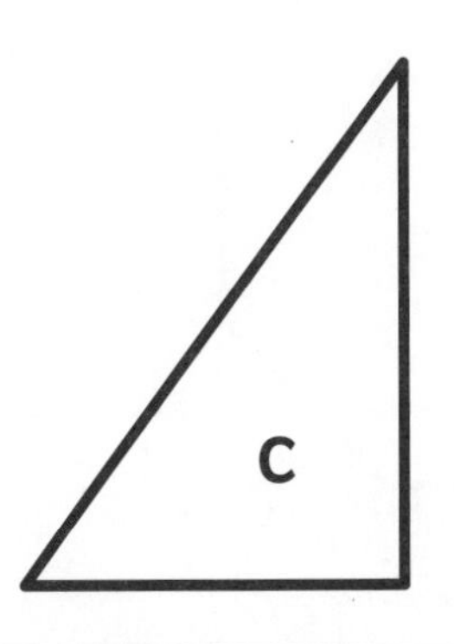

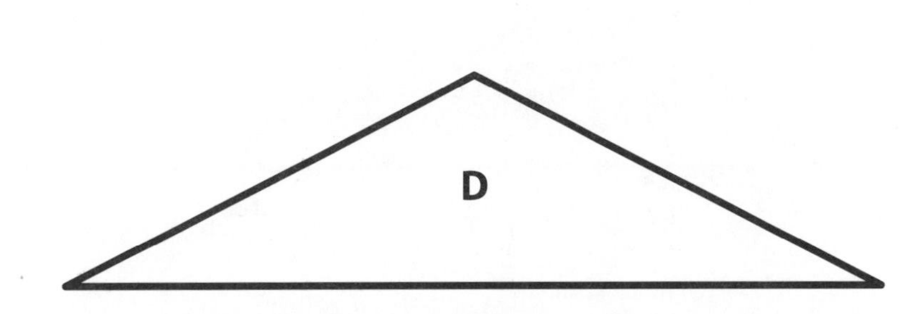

Areas and perimeters: irregular shapes

Try to work out the area and perimeter of each shape.

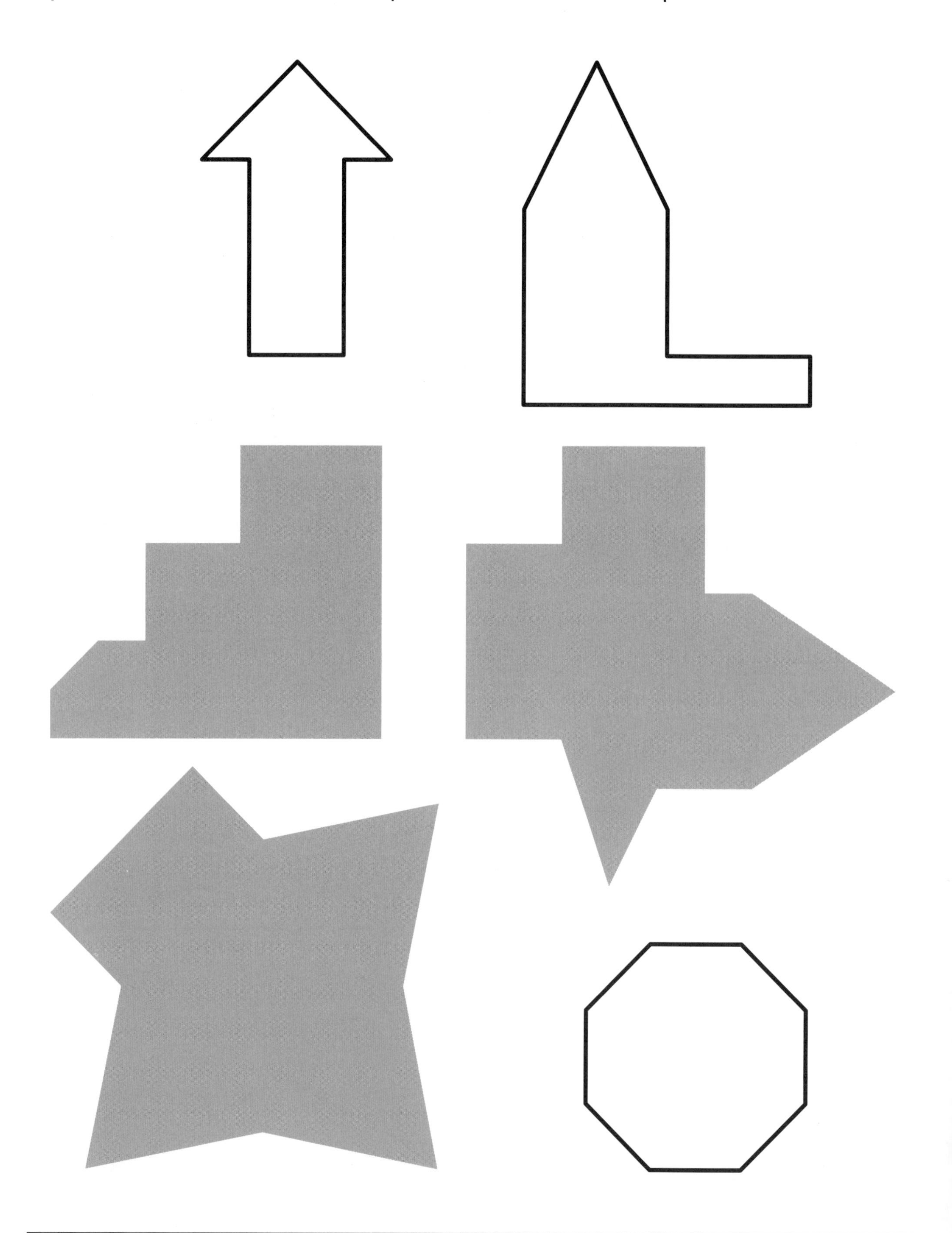

Height at a distance

Remember what you need to work out the height of an object.

Keep a record of three measurements.

- Your height.
- Your distance from the object.
- The angle of your view of the top of the object.

Here is a picture to help with this.

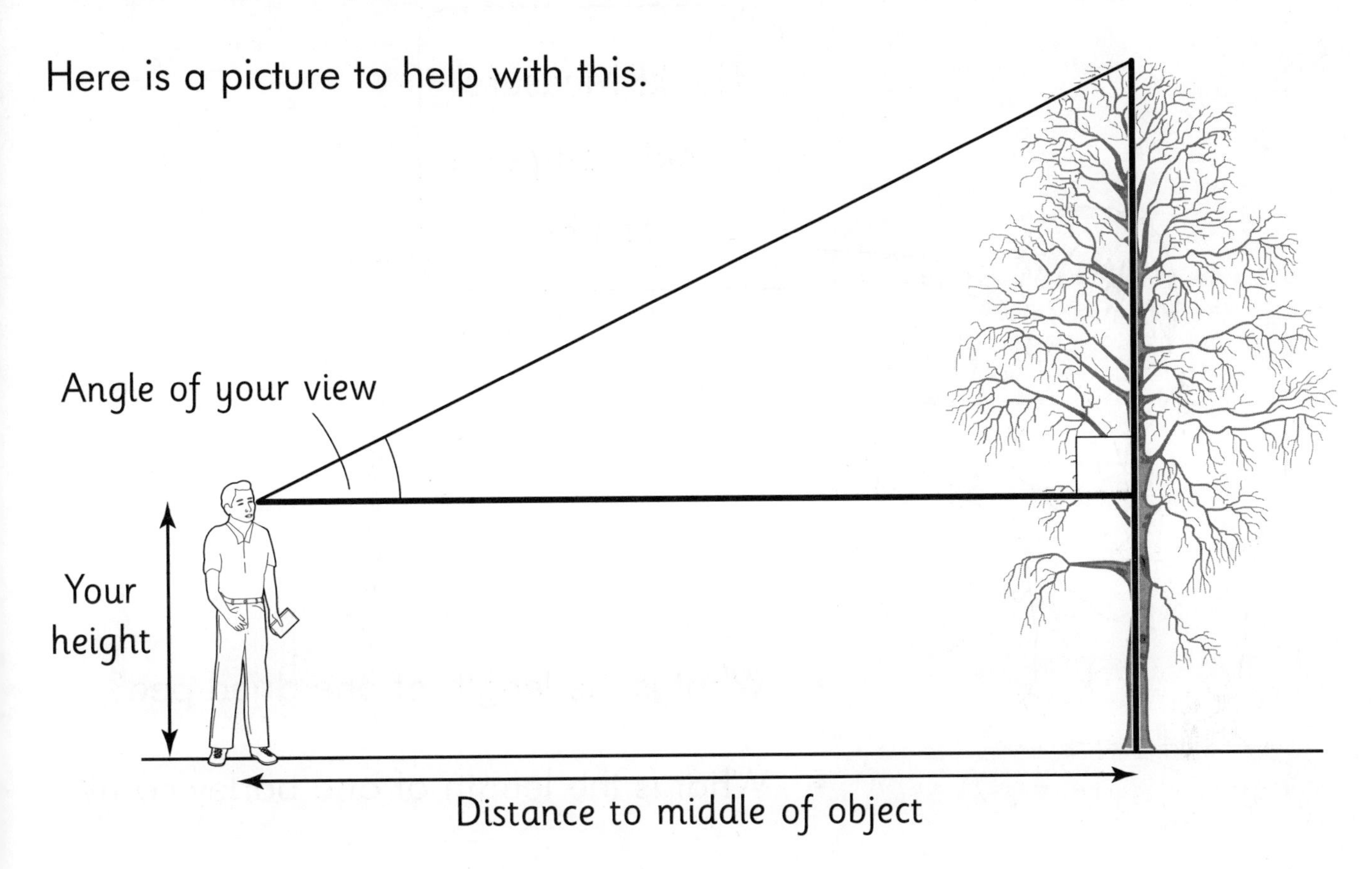

Write the three measurements here.

My height
The distance
The angle

Now make a scale drawing.

Measuring small objects

Here are some challenges for you to try.

- How many pin-heads fit in a square centimetre?
- If 100 peas were placed touching side by side in a row how long would the row be?

- What is the length of one dried pea?
- What is the length of one barley corn?
- How wide is the eye of a needle?
- How many cocktail sticks would fit end to end along your table top?
- How thick is a sheet of paper?
- How thick is a page of your reading book?

Measuring large objects

Can you answer these challenges?

- How long and wide is a brick or breeze block?
- How high is your classroom?
- How high is the school?
- How many cocktail sticks would fit the length of the hall?
- How many bricks would cover the playground?
- How many PE benches would cover the floor of the school hall?
- How high are 1,000 bricks; 10,000 bricks; 1,000,000 bricks?

Capacity: arbitrary units

Draw the measure you used.

Write inside each container how many of your measures filled it.

39 Capacity in ml and cc

What amounts are these? Give your answers in ml.

1 $\frac{1}{2}$ l + $\frac{1}{2}$ l =

2 $\frac{3}{4}$ of a litre + 55ml =

3 75ml + half a litre =

4 125ml + 503ml + 99ml =

5 275ml + 275ml + 125ml =

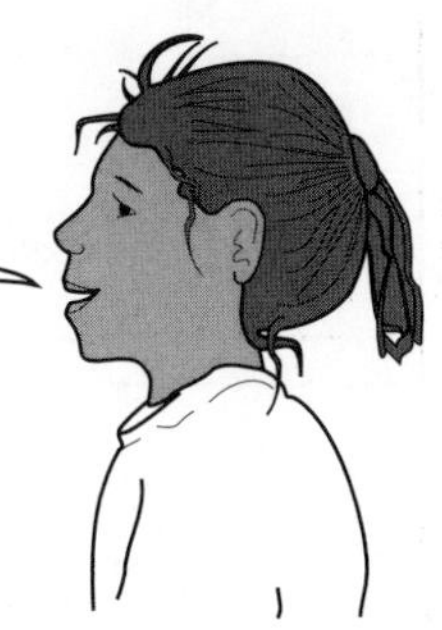

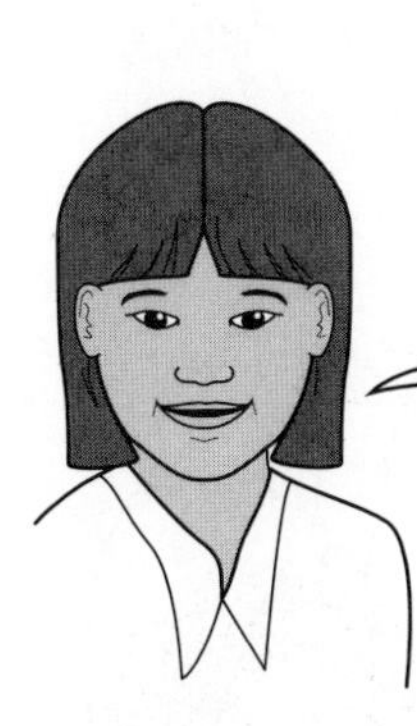

Choose three boxes. Estimate the capacity of each one. Write your answers here.

Box 1 ☐ cc Box 2  cc Box 3 ☐ cc

Shape and volume

Look at some packages and complete this table.

Draw the shape of the package if that is easier.

Product	Volume/ capacity	Shape of package	Any questions or ideas

Wow! Some packs hold a lot more than I thought!

41 Volume in cc

Work out the volume of each shape.

1

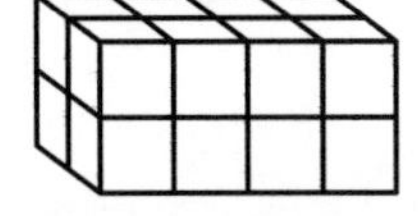

2

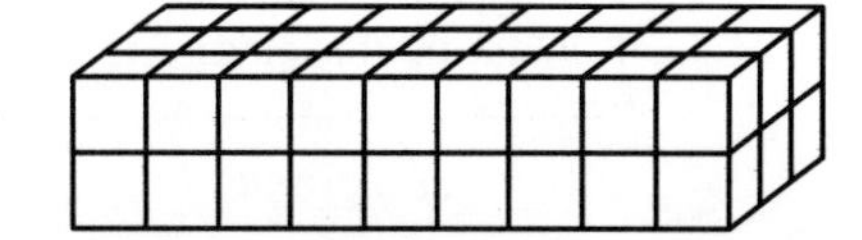

3

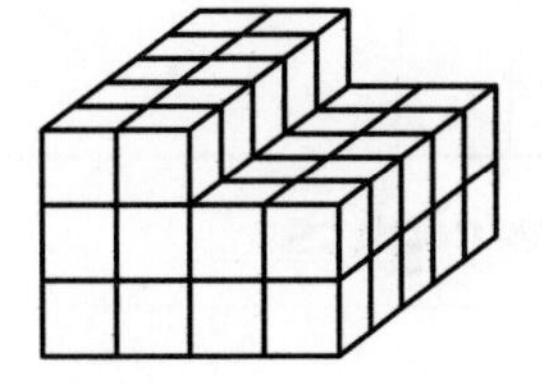

4

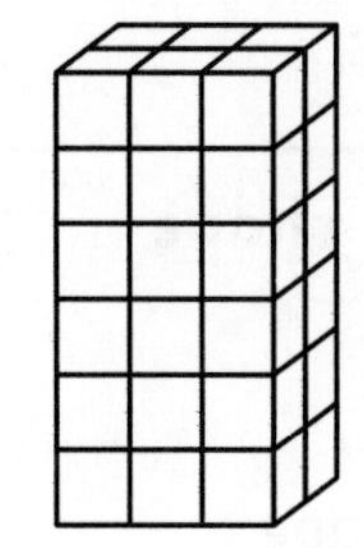

Here are some measurements in centimetres.
Can you work out the volume of each shape?

1

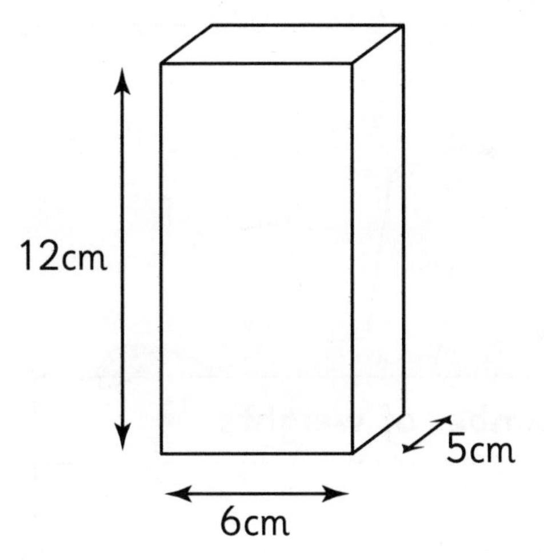

2

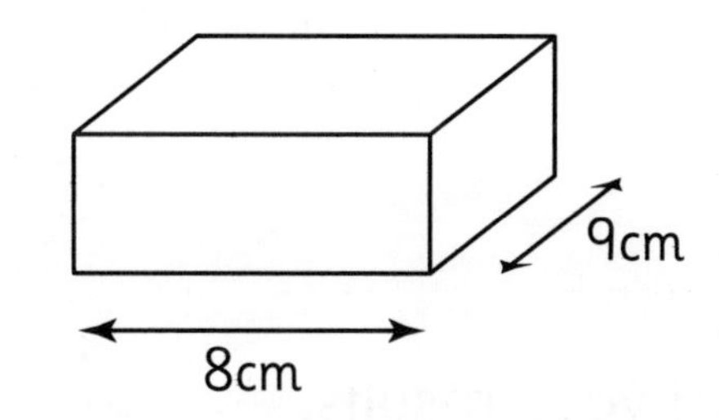

3

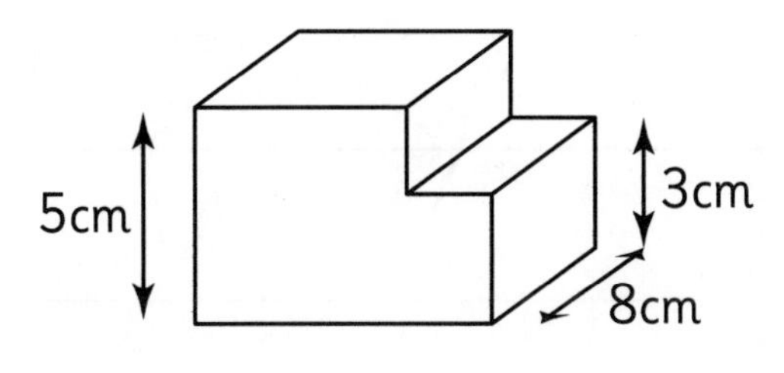

(Not drawn to scale)

4 If the net below was folded, what would be the capacity of the container?

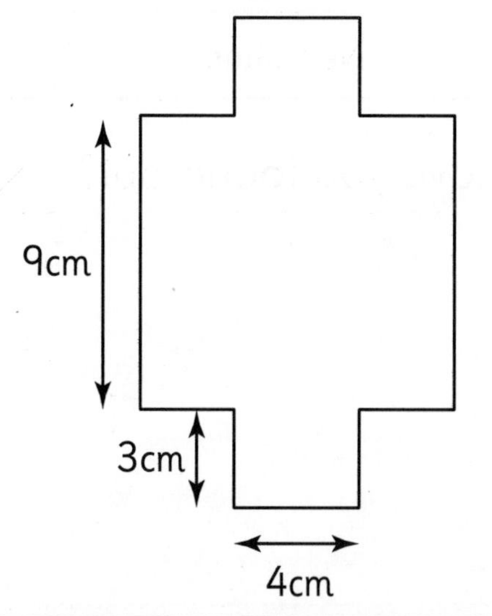

Shape and "weight"

Record your results.

Plasticine shape	Number of weights
Ball	
New shape	
New shape	

Record your results.

Multilink shape	Number of weights
First shape	
New shape	
New shape	

What have you found out?

Estimating "weight"

Complete the table.

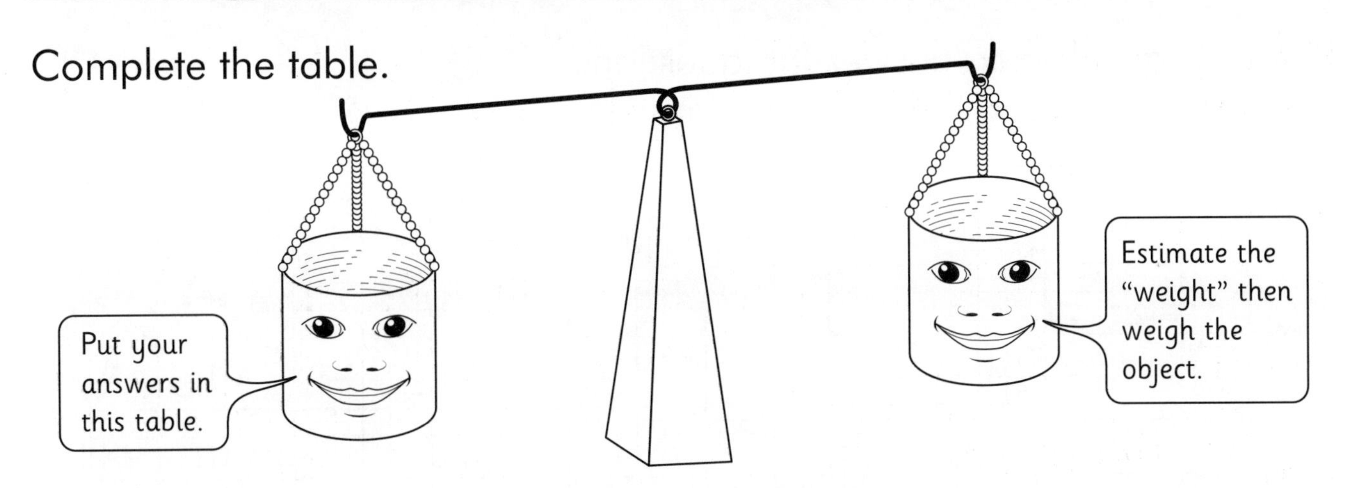

Object name	My estimate	The actual "weight"	The difference between my estimate and the actual "weight"

Conversion graph: g and oz

Plot your graph then answer the questions.
Don't forget, 1kg = 2.2lb (approximately 2lb 3oz)

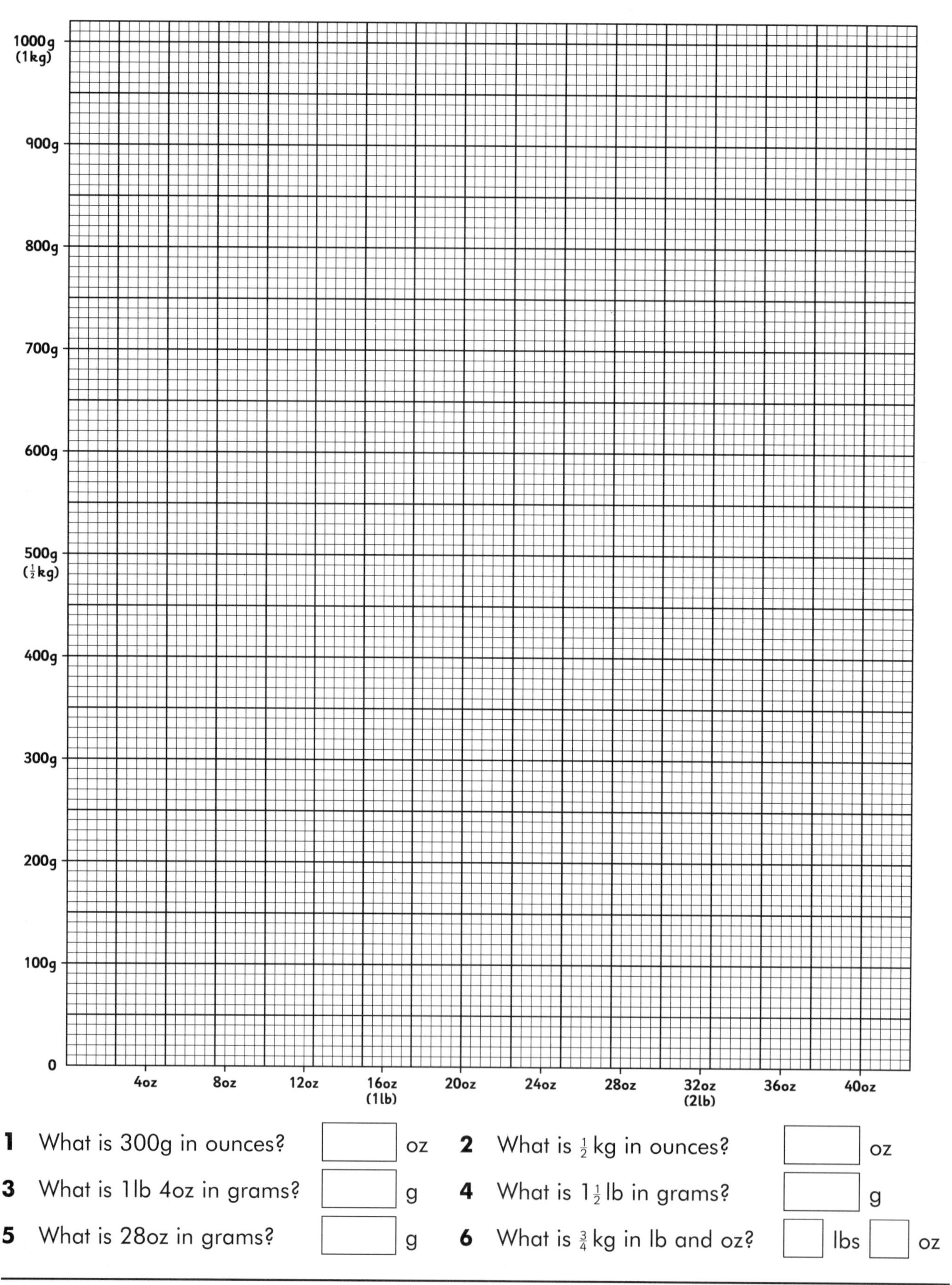

1 What is 300g in ounces? ☐ oz

2 What is $\frac{1}{2}$ kg in ounces? ☐ oz

3 What is 1lb 4oz in grams? ☐ g

4 What is $1\frac{1}{2}$ lb in grams? ☐ g

5 What is 28oz in grams? ☐ g

6 What is $\frac{3}{4}$ kg in lb and oz? ☐ lbs ☐ oz

Weighing light objects

Complete the table. Then answer the questions.

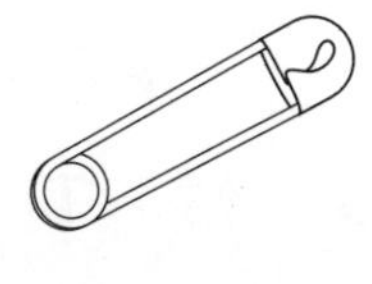

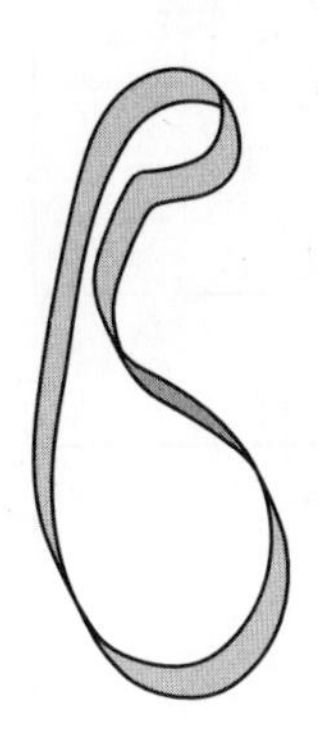

Object to be weighed	How many did you weigh?	What is the "weight" of them?	What is the average "weight" of one object?

Which is your lightest object? ______________________

Which is your heaviest object? ______________________

Put the objects in order from heaviest to lightest. ______________________

____

Calendar puzzle

Find the patterns.

DECEMBER

S	M	T	W	T	F	S
1	2	3	4	5	6	7
8	9	10	11	12	13	14
15	16	17	18	19	20	21
22	23	24	25	26	27	28
29	30	31				

FEBRUARY

S	M	T	W	T	F	S
						1
2	3	4	5	6	7	8
9	10	11	12	13	14	15
16	17	18	19	20	21	22
23	24	25	26	27	28	

AUGUST

S	M	T	W	T	F	S
					1	2
3	4	5	6	7	8	9
10	11	12	13	14	15	16
17	18	19	20	21	22	23
24	25	26	27	28	29	30
31						

OCTOBER

S	M	T	W	T	F	S
			1	2	3	4
5	6	7	8	9	10	11
12	13	14	15	16	17	18
19	20	21	22	23	24	25
26	27	28	29	30	31	

- Draw a box around any 2 × 2 numbers. One has been done for you in the first month. Can you find patterns in the numbers in the box? Do the patterns always work – no matter which dates are in the box?

- Draw a box around any 3 × 3 numbers. Are there patterns here? Do they always work?

- Can you find more patterns in these calendar months?

Line graph

Draw two line graphs. Use one colour for sunrise and another for sunset. The table below gives you the times to use.

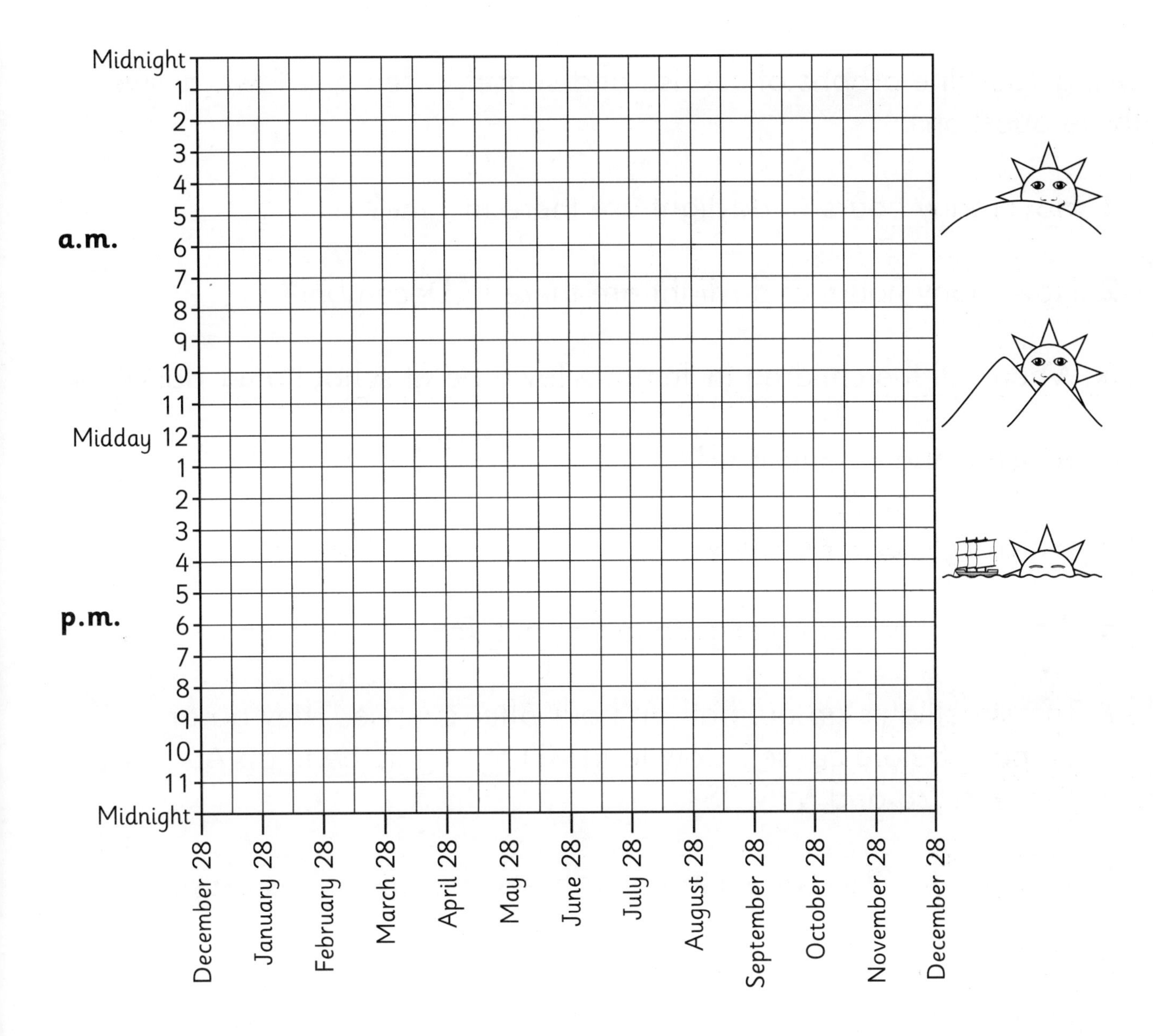

Sunrise and sunset times in Tempus Town												
	JAN	FEB	MAR	APRIL	MAY	JUNE	JULY	AUG	SEPT	OCT	NOV	DEC
Sunrise (a.m.)	8	7	6	5	4	3	4	5	6	7	8	9
Sunset (p.m.)	5	6	7	8	9	10	9	8	7	6	5	4

48 Line graph challenge

Using your line graphs of sunrise and sunset in Tempus Town answer these questions.

1 How many hours of daylight are there in June?

2 How many hours of daylight are there in December?

3 When will the children in Tempus Town be at school after dark?

4 Which is the longest day?

5 Which is the shortest day?

6 When is it the spring season in Tempus Town?

7 The streetlights go out half an hour after sunrise. They go on half an hour before sunset. How long will the lights be lit on August 28, February 28 and May 28?

8 Why has the 28th of each month been chosen for this graph?

9 Which two days of the year might Tempus Town choose to change the clocks?

10 Now can you think of some teasers to ask your friend about Tempus Town's days and nights?

Timing puzzle

Work out the order for cooking a meal that is to be eaten at 1.00 p.m. Here is a list of cooking times for the food that has to be prepared.

Food	Cooking times
Apple pie	1 hour 10 minutes
Roast chicken	2 hours (needs 20 minutes to rest after cooking)
Custard	Heat milk 3 minutes, make custard 3 minutes (may be kept warm until required)
Gravy (instant)	5 minutes (may be kept warm until required)
Peas (frozen)	10 minutes after water boils (serve immediately)
Roast potatoes	$1\frac{1}{2}$ hours (serve immediately)
Celery soup	Reheat 12 minutes (must not be kept warm)

Write out the cooking order for the meal.

Cooking order

Then write out the menu.

Menu

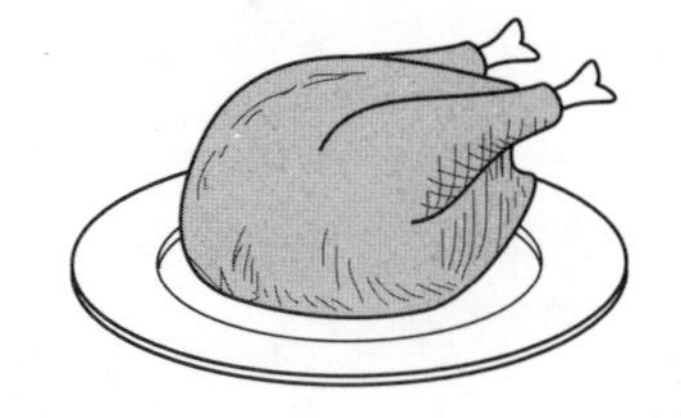

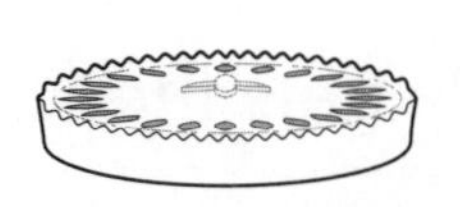

Timetable

Use your timetable to complete the table below.

Activity	Time spent each week (in hours and minutes)
Mathematics	
English	
Science	
Technology	
R.E.	
P.E.	
History	
Geography	
Art	
Music	
Play time	
Lunch time	
Assembly	
Other	
Total time	

1 How much time is spent on Mathematics, English and Science altogether each week?

2 How much play and lunch time is there each week?

3 Which activity gets the most time?

4 Which activity gets the least time?

51 Telling the time

Write the time for each clock.

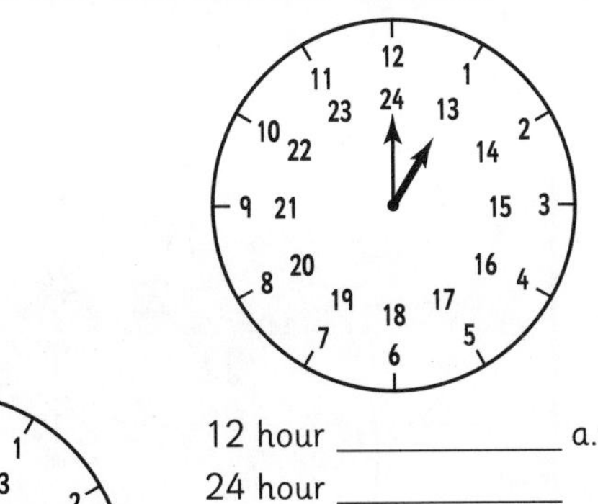

12 hour ____________ a.m.
24 hour ____________

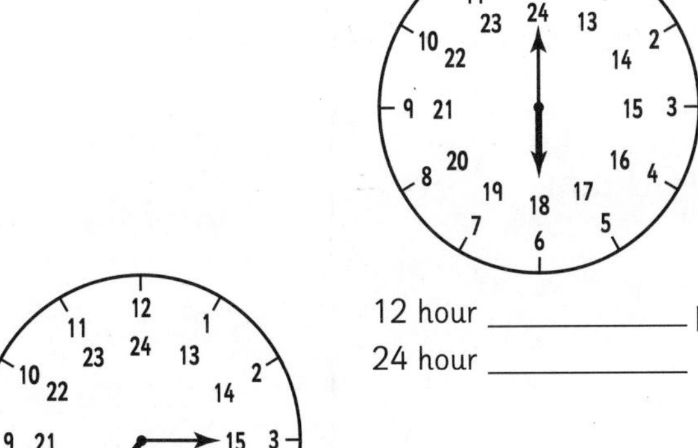

12 hour ____________ p.m.
24 hour ____________

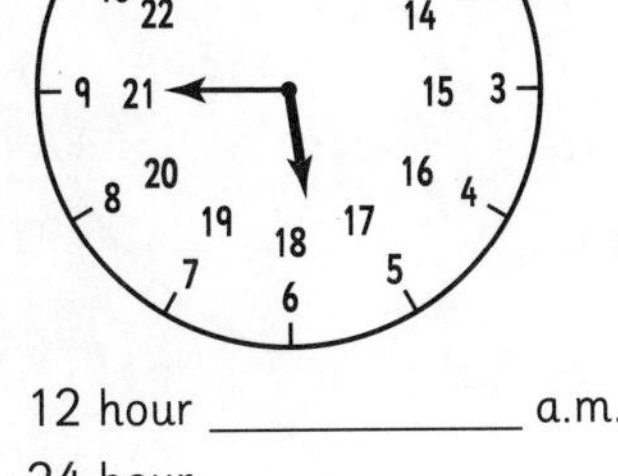

12 hour ____________ a.m.
24 hour ____________

12 hour ____________ p.m.
24 hour ____________

Using this time strip, answer the questions.

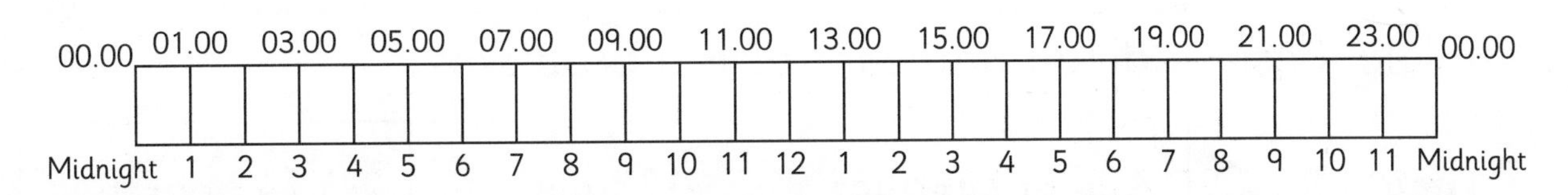

1 What time does school start and finish?

Start 12 hour ____________ 24 hour ____________

Finish 12 hour ____________ 24 hour ____________

2 The TV programme I want to see starts at 5.00 p.m. and lasts for $1\frac{1}{2}$ hours. What time does it finish? ____________

What are the start and finish times on a 24 hour clock?

Start ____________ Finish ____________

3 What time is your bedtime?

12 hour ____________ 24 hour ____________

4 Amy's Mum works all Friday night at a local superstore. She starts at 8.00 p.m. and finishes at 6.00 a.m. What are these times in the 24 hour system? ____________ , ____________

How long does she work? ____________

12 and 24 hour clocks

Complete this table.

12 hour system	24 hour system
10.00 a.m.	
	15.30 hours
Half past midnight	
3.25 p.m.	
	22.35 hours

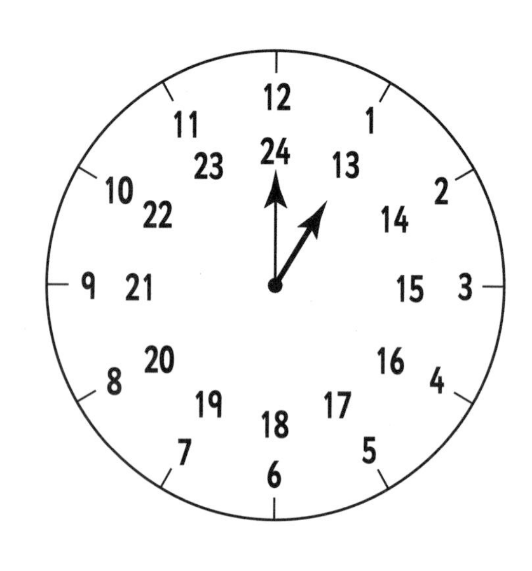

Complete these addition and subtraction problems.

Time	Add or subtract	12 hour	24 hour
3.45 p.m.	+ 20 minutes		
8.55 a.m.	+ 15 minutes		
9.20 p.m.	– 45 minutes		
7.59 a.m.	+ 18 minutes		
10.05 p.m.	– 38 minutes		

Write out the timings of a school day using a 24 hour clock.

Write out a day you remember on holiday or at a weekend, from getting up to going to bed, using the 24 hour system.

Railway timetable

	Train 1	Train 2	Train 3	Train 4
Edinburgh		08.10		08.50
York		10.42		
Preston				12.59
Derby	07.39	12.37		
Crewe			11.48	13.52
Birmingham	08.28	13.28		14.58
Bristol	09.54		14.34	16.30
Exeter		15.46	15.49	17.38
Plymouth	11.48	16.43	17.08	18.44
Penzance		18.49	19.06	20.45

1 What is the length of time taken by the quicker train from Edinburgh to Penzance?

2 How quickly can you travel from Crewe to Plymouth?

3 I live in Derby and want to have a meeting in Birmingham before I travel to Exeter. What train could I catch and how long would I spend in Birmingham?

4 Which train is quickest between Plymouth and Penzance and what is its journey time?

5 How long does it take to get from York to Bristol?

Sundial

Make a sundial.

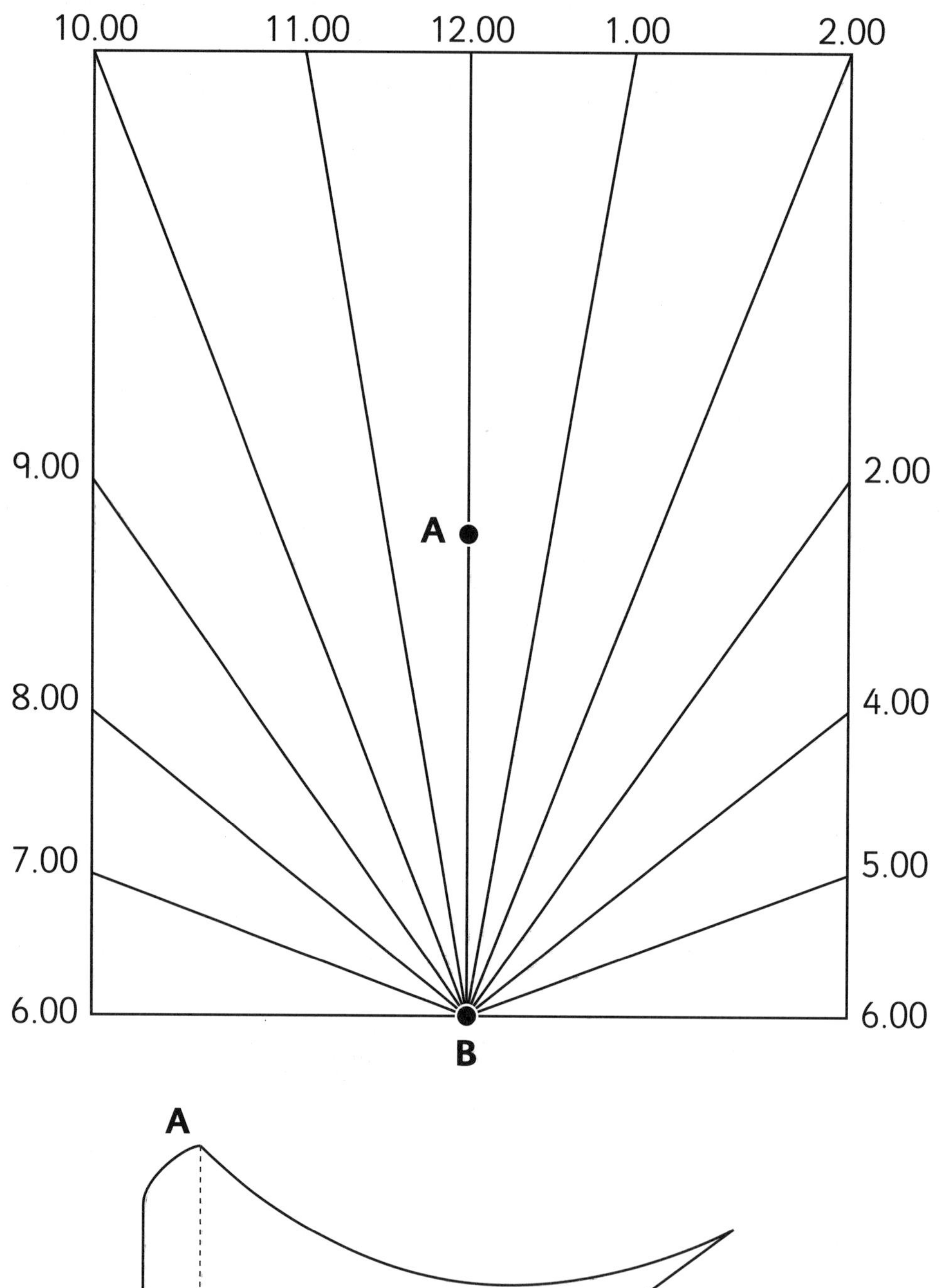

A
fold line
B

55 Pendulum

Make a pendulum. Try different "weights" for the bob.

"Weight"	What did you find?

Now alter the angle you let it swing from.

Swing	What did you find?

Now try different lengths of string

Length	What did you find?

56

Scale map

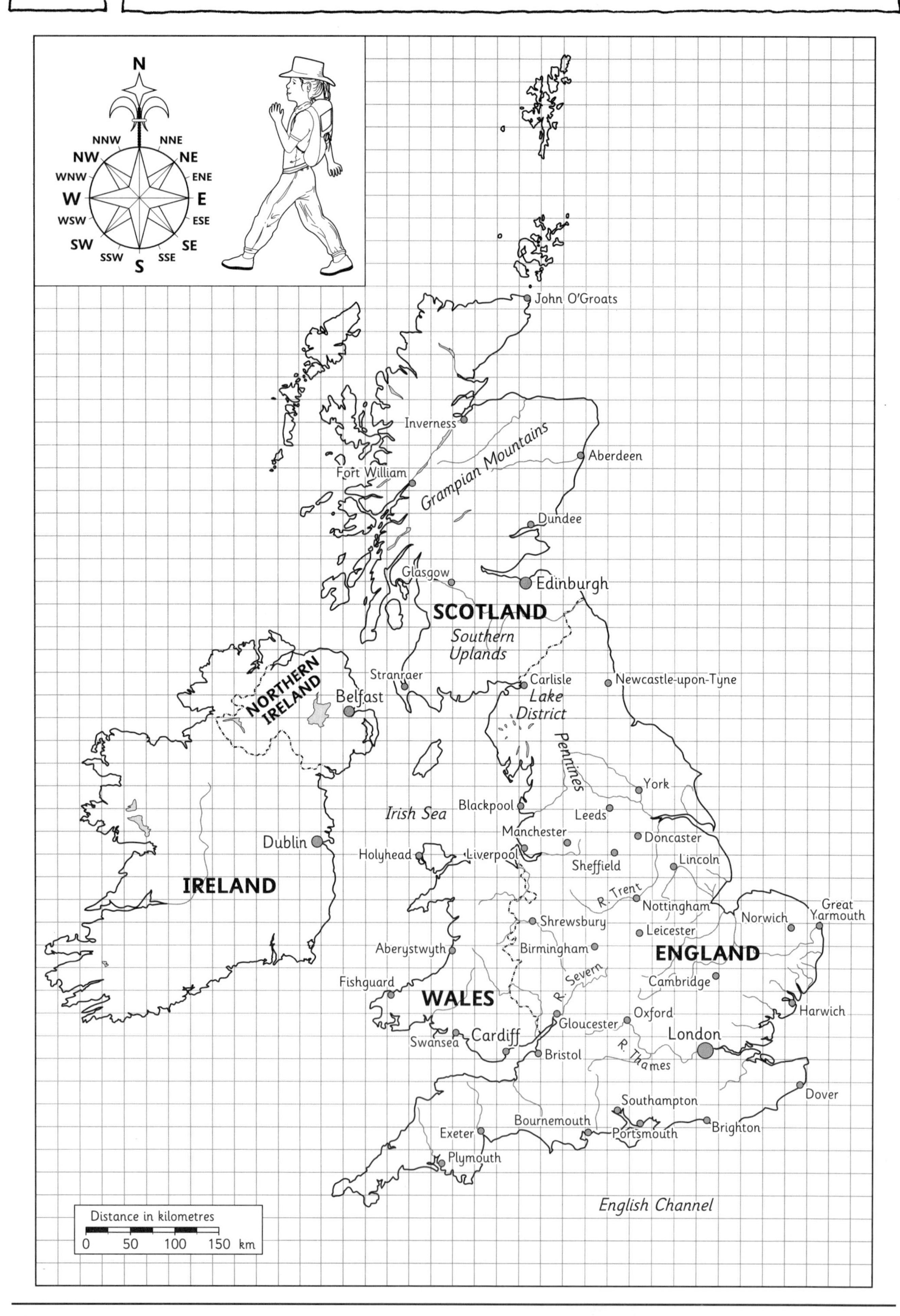
N
NNW
NNE
NW
NE
WNW
ENE
W
E
WSW
ESE
SW
SE
SSW
SSE
S
John O'Groats
Inverness
Aberdeen
Fort William
Grampian Mountains
Dundee
Glasgow
Edinburgh
SCOTLAND
Southern Uplands
NORTHERN IRELAND
Stranraer
Carlisle
Newcastle-upon-Tyne
Belfast
Lake District
Pennines
York
Irish Sea
Blackpool
Leeds
Dublin
Manchester
Doncaster
Holyhead
Liverpool
Sheffield
Lincoln
IRELAND
R. Trent
Nottingham
Great Yarmouth
Norwich
Shrewsbury
Leicester
Aberystwyth
Birmingham
ENGLAND
R. Severn
Cambridge
Fishguard
WALES
Oxford
Harwich
Gloucester
Swansea
Cardiff
London
R. Thames
Bristol
Dover
Southampton
Bournemouth
Brighton
Exeter
Portsmouth
Plymouth
English Channel
Distance in kilometres
0 50 100 150 km

Speed-distance-time graph

Plot the results of the walk.

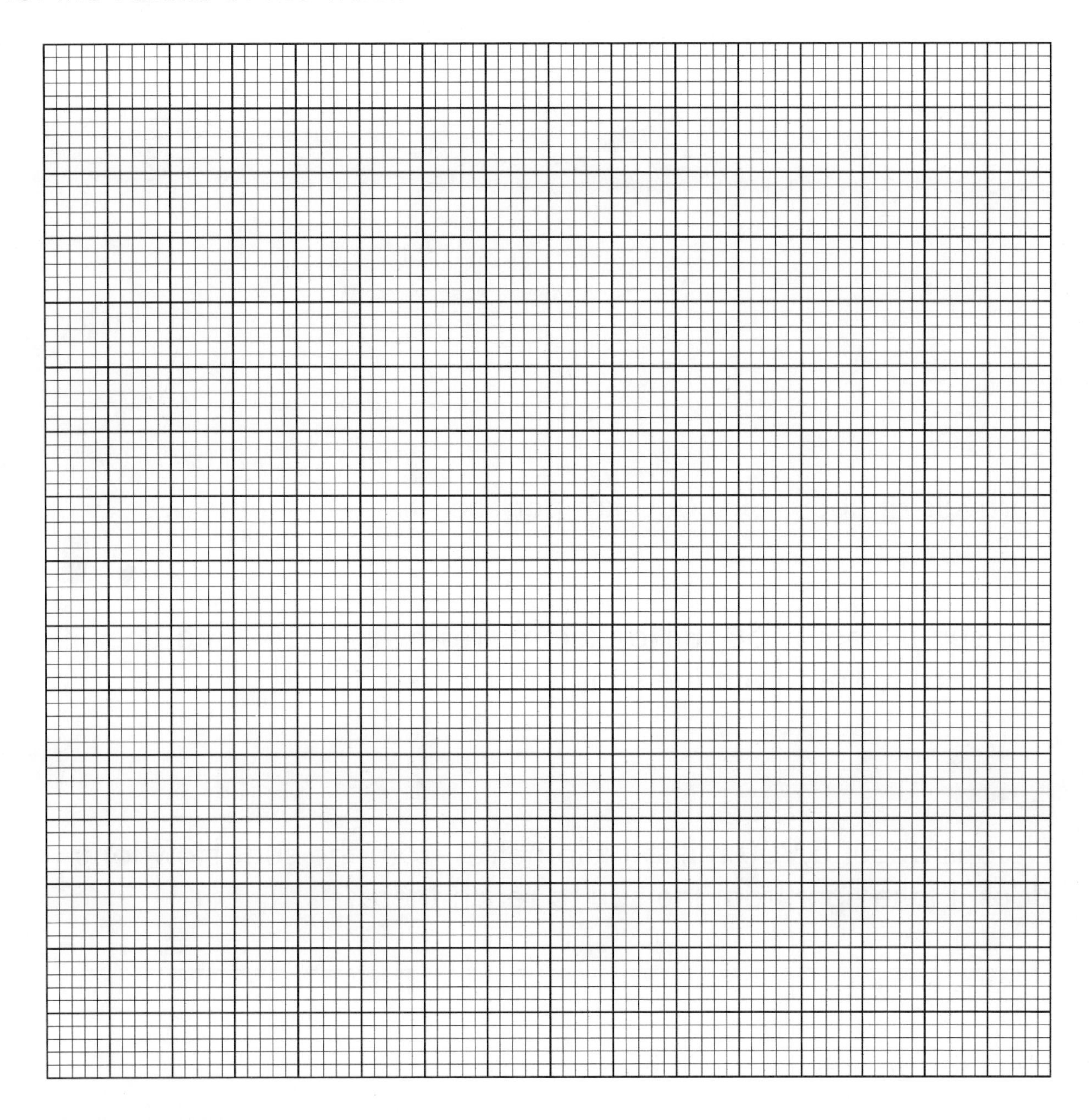

1 Who was the quickest? ________________

2 Who was the slowest? ________________

3 What do you notice about the lines on your graph? ________________

____

4 How long did it take each person to travel:
half the distance? ________________
a quarter of the distance? ________________
a fifth of the distance? ________________

5 How could we work out the average speed of each of the walkers?

____

Speed of light

Answer these questions about the speed of light.

Light travels at about 300,000 km per sec.

1 The sun is about 150 million kilometres away. How long does it take for the light from the sun to reach us?

____

2 Pluto is about 5,900 million kilometres from the sun. How long does it take light from the sun to reach there?

____

3 How far does light travel in an hour?

____

4 How far does light travel in a day?

____

5 A light-year is the distance light travels in a year. How far is that?

____

Dotted paper

Dotted paper

1 cm squared paper

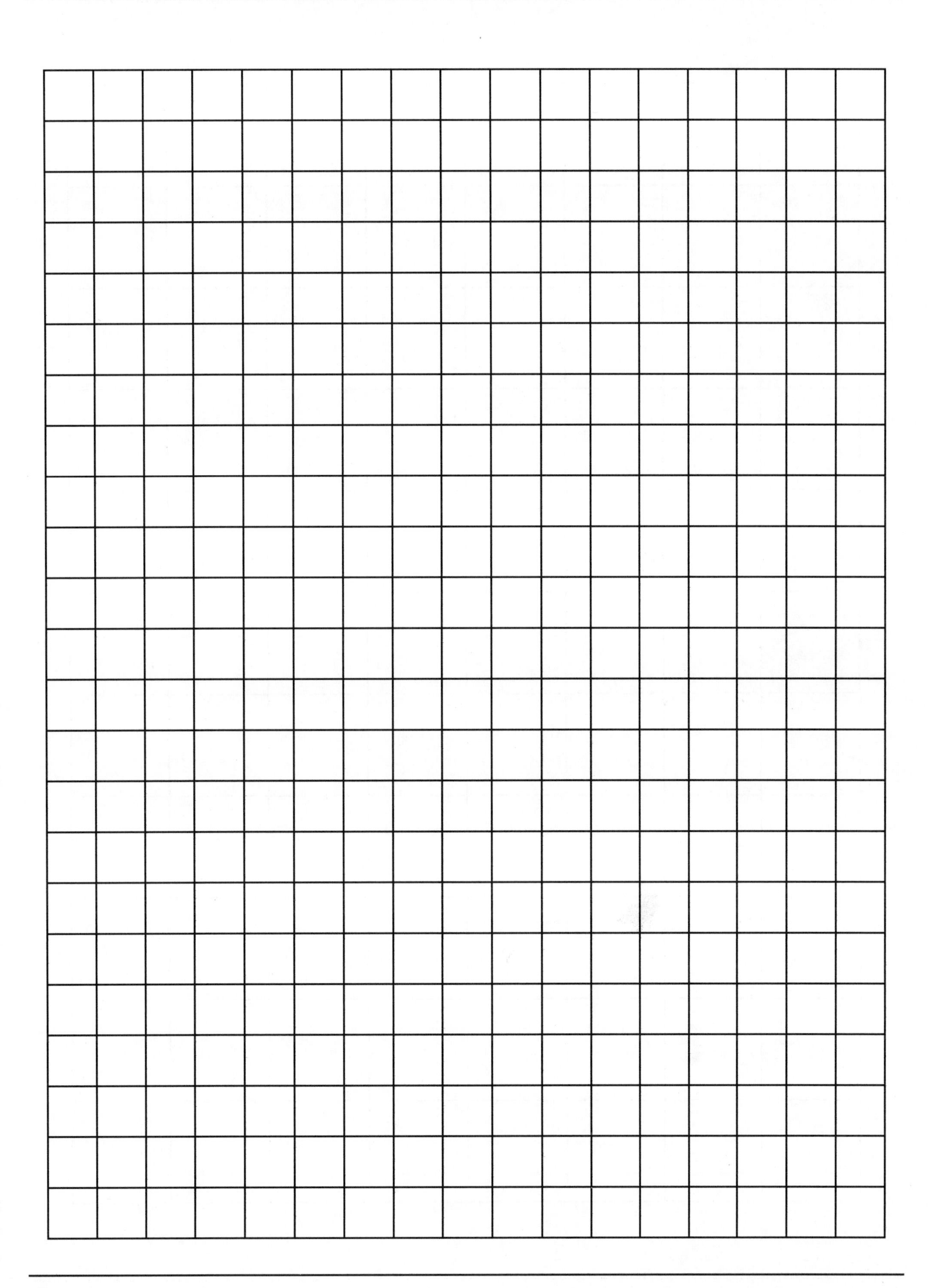

2 cm squared paper

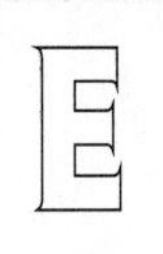

Isometric paper

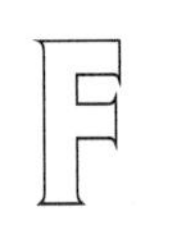

5 mm squared paper

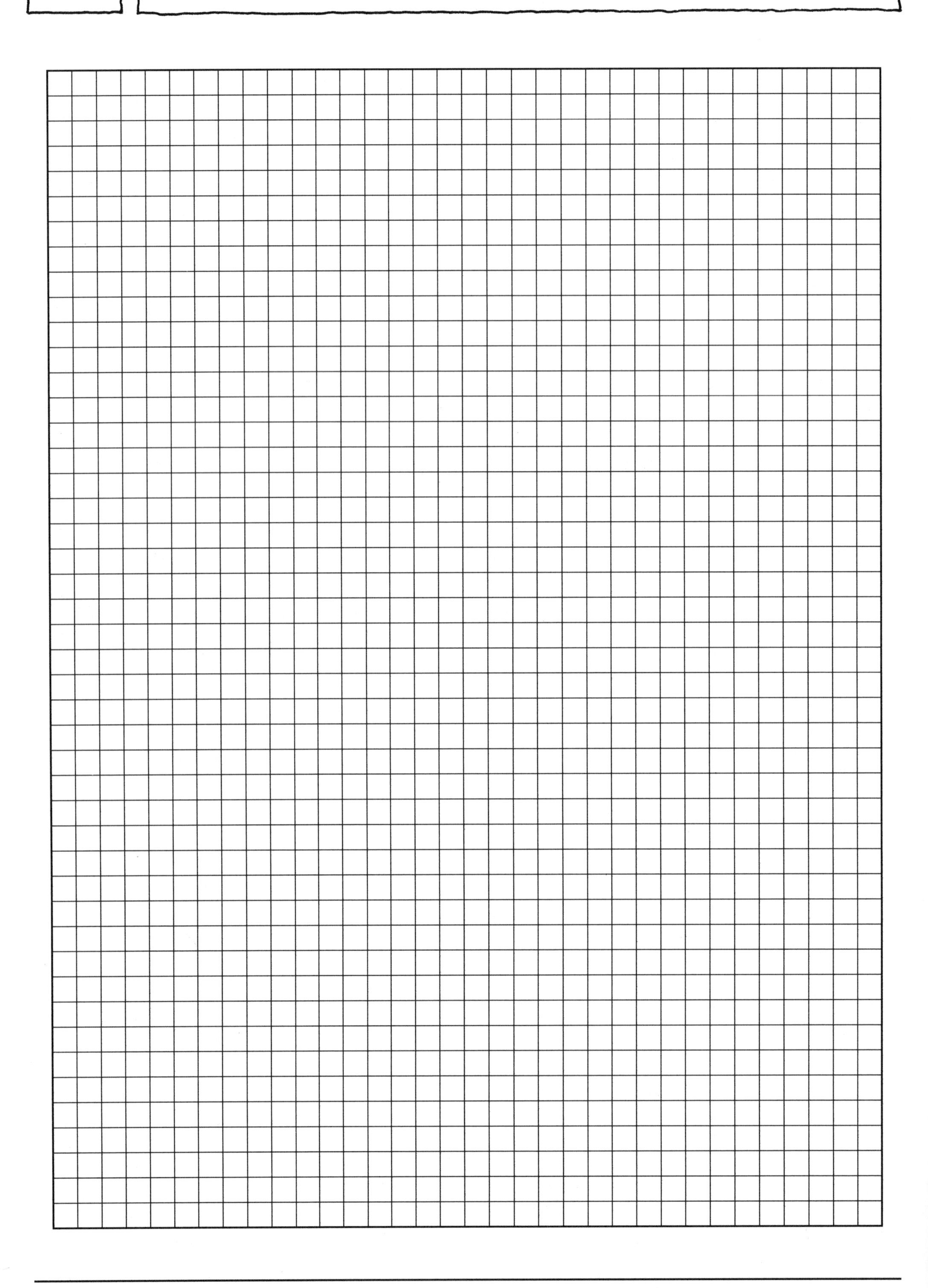

Graph paper (2 mm/10 mm/20 mm)

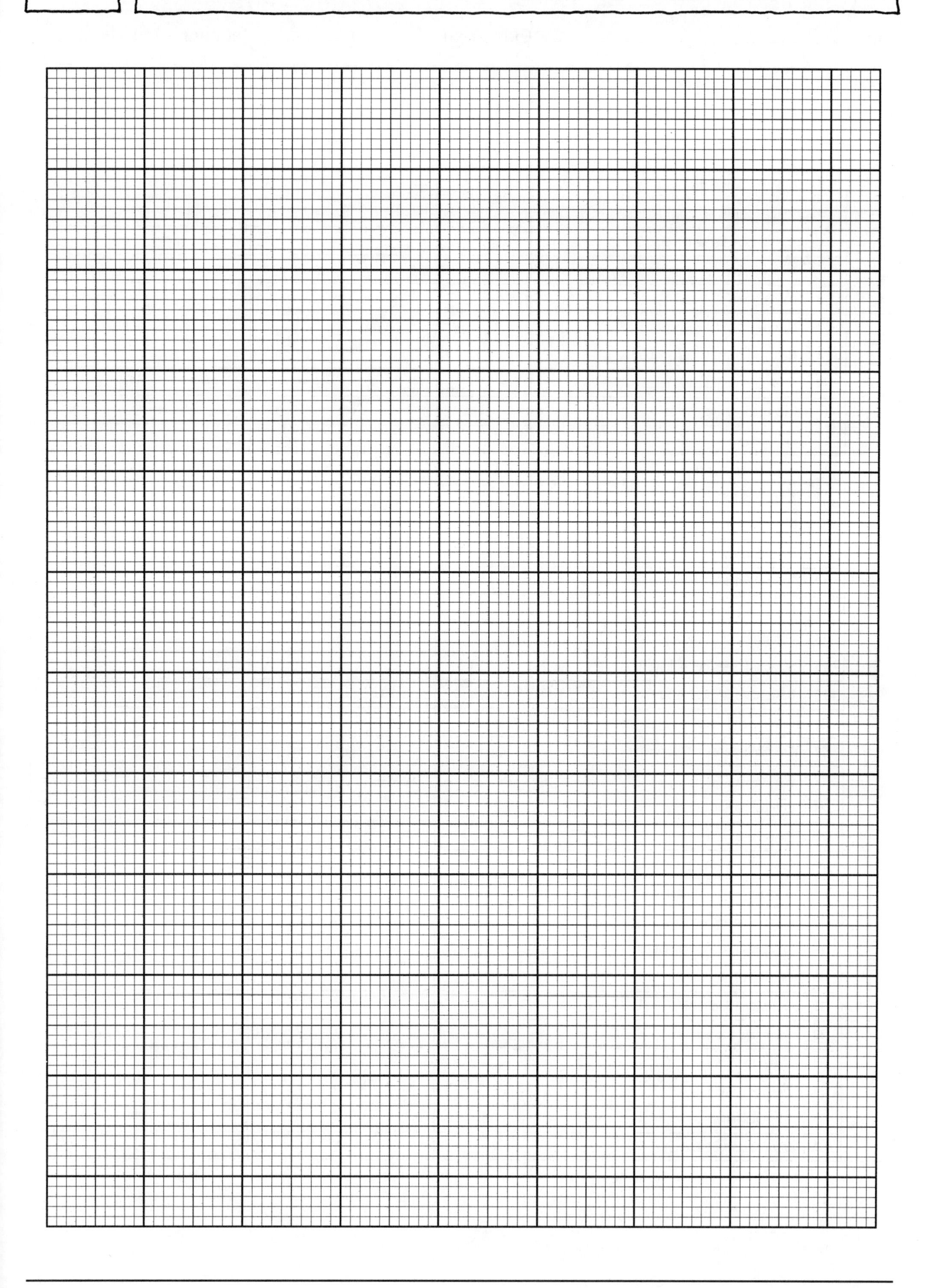

Learning Targets: Shape, Space and Measures Key Stage 2

RECORD SHEET

Name ____________________ Class/Year ____________________ Teacher's initials ________

Section	*Theme*	*Performance in relation to learning targets*			*Summative remarks*
		1	2	3	
2-D Shapes	1 Name, make and sort 2-D shapes				
	2 Reflective symmetry				
	3 Shape families and their names				
	4 The characteristics of some 2-D shapes				
	5 Tessellation				
	6 Polyominoes				
3-D Shapes	7 Name and sort 3-D shapes				
	8 Nets and constructing shapes				
	9 More nets and the five regular solids				
	10 Faces, edges and planes				
Angles and Co-ordinates	11 Right angles				
	12 Grids and position				
	13 Angle and rotation				
	14 Measuring and constructing angles				
	15 Co-ordinates				
	16 Translation and transformation				
	17 Compass points and bearings				
Length, Area and Perimeter	18 Comparing and ordering				
	19 Standard measures of length				
	20 Basic ideas in area and perimeter				
	21 Drawing and constructing shapes				
	22 Calculating area and perimeter				
	23 Problem-solving				
Capacity and Volume	24 Comparing and ordering				
	25 Measurement				
	26 Calculating capacity and volume				
	27 Displacement, area, mass and volume				
Mass and Weight	28 Comparing and ordering				
	29 Conservation and estimation				
	30 Families of measures				
	31 Estimating and testing				
Time	32 Calendars and seasons				
	33 Check the time				
	34 24-hour system				
	35 Time machines				
	36 Distance, speed and time				